ELECTRONICS
FOR
EVERYONE

Second revised edition

ELECTRONIC

THE STORY OF ELECTRICIT

TELEVISION, RADIO, RADAR, HI I

WHAT THEY ARE AN

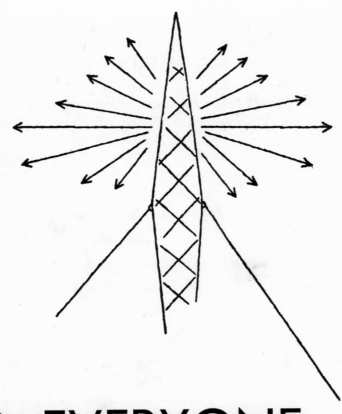

OR EVERYONE

ACTION: TRANSISTORS,
EO TAPE, SPACE ELECTRONICS—
W THEY WORK

MONROE UPTON

THE DEVIN-ADAIR COMPANY

New York 1960

Manufactured in the United States of America

Designed by Lewis F. White.

Library of Congress Catalog Card Number: 54–9298

Canadian agent: Thomas Nelson & Son, Toronto

First printing, August 1954
Second printing, July 1955
First revised edition, May 1957
Second revised edition, January 1959
Fifth printing, May 1959
Sixth printing, May 1960

TO EMERITA AND JONIKA

CONTENTS

FOREWORD

What is electricity? Benjamin Franklin, who experimented in the days of the spectaculaɪ friction machine and the glass-jar condenser, guessed that it was a fluid. Electricians still call it *juice;* and we still use *flow* to describe the movement of electricity in a circuit.

In school they gave me the impression that man hardly dared hope ever to find an answer to the question; he could only profit by observing the effects of electricity. As to its true nature, why speculate about something so perilously close to nothing at all that it drifted like the wind through a length of solid copper wire? But in spite of this pessimistic view, electricity has finally been tracked to its lair—inside the atom; and its unmasking is at the bottom of those recent triumphs of science that come under the head of electronics.

Electricity, it seems now, is composed of particles we call electrons. Electrons come from atoms. We discovered this by means of experiments in which electricity was passed through a gas. At the same time the foundation was laid for a much more subtle *control* of electricity, from which electronics evolved. This control takes place in a tube, such as the common radio tube, or in a transistor.

Because electricity's home is in the atom, and all matter is composed of atoms, our book opens with a sort of worm's-eye view of matter, followed by a brief survey of its atomic structure. This should make more understandable the romantic story of electricity that follows, starting in the year 1600 and continuing on down to the present.

I have not written in outline, textbook style. No dust gets in your eyes as you turn the pages. Electricity has been close to my heart ever since the midnight in 1913 when the first dots and dashes from my home-built receiver gave me what still stands as probably the grandest thrill of my life, and writing about it has made me fully appreciative of Aristotle's dictum: learning is the greatest of pleasures. My approach is both informal and personal. Progress in electricity is joined to the lives and struggles of the scientists and inventors who have given us such things as the condenser, the electric battery and generator, FM, radar, the proximity fuse, and the transistor.

You will need no wide knowledge of physics and mathematics to discover how a radio or TV set works, or to learn how to assemble a radio and make simple television adjustments. And because I have stressed *basic principles,* the merchant, salesman, legislator, journalist, professional man, or anyone whose work touches upon electronics at some point (and whose work doesn't, these days?) should get from these pages a satisfying grasp of electronic theory. However, after you've polished off the final chapter, I don't recommend that you start scanning the Help Wanted columns for a job as electronics engineer, television technician, or radio officer on ship or plane. Though if you decide to consult more technical treatises with an eye to one of these jobs, your time spent here will not have been wasted. Most of the essential theory, plus much of the simple basic mathematics, is included.

Because electronics is playing such a vital role in our expanding industrial plant, in defense, medicine, entertainment, and many other fields, it is our fastest-growing industry. The present second revised edition, coming four years after the first edition, contains extensive changes which cover latest developments as far as possible. New material on such subjects as transistors, computers, hi-fi, and aviation electronics has been added.

A complete new chapter on the role played by electronics in missiles and satellites completes what I think is a pretty helpful up-dating. It goes without saying that we could never have put the satellites up there without the help of the mighty electron. The role played by electronics in connection with missiles and satellites, as well as with all types of aircraft, has become enormous. Our aim has been to clarify some of the principles involved in such phases as testing, guidance, and communications.

M. U.

Tucson
December 1958

ELECTRONICS
FOR
EVERYONE

1

NEW ATOMS FOR OLD

Today we have a neat theory which says that electricity consists of particles from the atoms of matter. Let's dig deeper by asking: what is matter?

Common sense takes the answer to this question for granted: matter is anything that is evident to at least one of the five senses. The classical physicist tries to be a little more explicit: matter is whatever has mass (weight) and occupies space. But what is space? Space, he replies, is *absence* of matter. Which should fill us with tolerance for the dog chasing its tail.

The scientist (and philosopher) might also fend us off with this definition: matter is whatever is extended in space and persistent in time. This leaves him wide open for another counterpunch. What is *time?* In some mysterious way, time, space, and matter seem to be all of a piece. Einstein assures us that we can't conceive of one without help from the other two.

3

Until recently, at least, science and common sense have always shared some faith in the *reality* of matter. For, if matter is not real there is no point in seeking truth by weighing and measuring it, after the fashion of the physicist. Philosophy hasn't always sanctioned this agreement. Though some philosophers have argued that all our knowledge must derive from sense experience, most of them have denied the importance of the material world, granting it at best a secondary role: because for them the only true reality comes from an inner sense of the ideal, the spiritual, and the eternal.

The Western World's first approach to matter in the common-sense, scientific way was made by philosophers of Greek Ionia, a strip along the coast of Asia Minor that is now part of Turkey. Some of the roots of their philosophy were nourished by the arts of invention, such as weaving, ceramics, and metallurgy. First among them, and first among the Seven Wise Men of Greece, was Thales, Father of Science. He was born about 640 B.C. in the booming mercantile city of Miletus. Thales was a versatile man with a wide variety of interests. Once he turned businessman and made a fortune by cornering all the olive presses, just to prove to the skeptical that a philosopher could be a practical man too, if he chose. Without any instruments, he calculated that there are 365 days in a year. (Correct figure: 365 days, 5 hours, 48 minutes, 44 seconds.) Thales devised the first geometry, basing it upon Egyptian land measurement. However, his debt to the past stopped short of the cosmology of the popular mysteries. To him, the earth was a flat disc floating on water; there was water above our heads and all around us; the sun, moon, and stars were vapor in a state of incandescence.

The second great Ionian, Anaximander, also from Miletus, doubted Thales' theory that everything is water. Why not earth, he asked, or fire, or mist, since they all change into one another? He concluded that all four are merely forms of a fifth substance, an indeterminate substance common to them all.

Anaximander was followed by Anaximenes, who argued for mist as the basic substance of the universe. Xenophanes, a still later Ionian, said that all things are made from earth and water. And Heraclitus, from Ionian Ephesus, whose basic philosophical belief was that "all things flow, nothing abides," saw everything either coming from or returning to ever-changing, everlasting, divine fire.

Note the emergence from all this speculation of a total of four (basic?) elements, water, fire, earth, and mist. Empedocles, the eccentric eclectic of Acragas, Sicily, around 450 B.C., embraced all four. But he made an important change: for mist he substituted air.

Empedocles *discovered* air, which, before his time, had not been distinguished from empty space. He discovered it by means of a clepsydra, a small household device, cone shaped, with a hole in its tip. By holding his finger over the tip when he thrust the large end in water, he prevented the water from entering readily. Empedocles was impressed. Today we say that air pressure keeps the water out, though the Greeks weren't quite equal to this concept. Empedocles had proved that something *invisible*, air, both occupies space and exerts power.

Empedocles' demonstration that matter can exist in a form too fine to be seen by the eye was very significant: it revealed that it is possible to discover truth *indirectly*, by a process of inference based upon observation. Modern physical science has always used this method; by means of it we know the atom, the electron, and all the other particles. Empedocles' proof that an "unseen body" was at work in nature was a healthy stride toward the atomic theory of Democritus, as we shall see in a moment.

The Greek four-element theory was not even challenged until the Mohammedan alchemists set out to find the Philosopher's Stone and transmute base metals into gold. And it was not finally upset until our own age. One of the first of the modern scientists to realize that common substances are usually a combination of several substances was Robert Boyle.

Boyle's epitaph describes him as "The Father of Chemistry and the Uncle of the Earl of Cork." In 1661 he defined elements as "certain primitive and simple bodies which, not being of any other bodies or of one another, are the ingredients of which all those called perfectly mixed bodies are immediately resolved."

Take alcohol as an example of one of his "perfectly mixed bodies." From alcohol the chemist can obtain carbon, hydrogen, and oxygen. However, he can't get anything out of carbon but carbon. Hence, carbon is an element. So are oxygen and hydrogen elements. The physical scientist has been busy for nearly 300 years searching for new ones; and though he has looked throughout the entire universe, as far as his giant telescopes will reach, and as deep as he has been able to dig, he has found a total of only 92 natural elements. Elements 93, 94, 95, 96, 97, 98, 99, 100, and 101, all discovered since 1940, are man made, no longer present in nature.

Many elements, such as hydrogen, nitrogen, oxygen, iron, copper, zinc, silver, tin, lead, gold, are familiar to all. Others have strange names that could have been lifted from the sides of old Pullman cars: krypton, palladium, ruthenium, tellurium, thallium. Most common substances, such as rubber, wood, paper, glass, sugar, and salt, are, like alcohol, combinations of two or more of the 92 elements, so we call them *compounds*. All but a very few of the elements combine with one another so readily that the chemists are familiar with 500,000 natural compounds.

Thanks to a Quaker schoolteacher of Manchester, England, John Dalton, we can think of the combining elements as made up of particles called atoms. All matter, said Dalton in 1803, is composed of atoms. Each atom is so small that it can't be divided further. In Greek, atom means indivisible. The atoms of each of the 20 (then known) elements are all different from one another—for the simple reason that no two of them have the same weight.

Here's an experiment. Take a razor blade and cut in two a tiny speck of clay. Do the same to one of the halves, then one of the quarters. Continue—but you've lost it? Never mind, continue subdividing in your imagination. You'll be curious about this point: could you go on, indefinitely, halving specks, or would you find yourself, sometime in the distant future, with an *indivisible* particle on your hands?

The ancient Greeks pondered a good deal about this. Plato, when he condescended to look down at matter, favored an indivisible-particle theory, an atomic theory. Later, Aristotle pointed out that it is only logical to assume that if a large particle can be divided, so can a small one, regardless of how small it might be. Thus the Greeks have money on both entries and stand to collect no matter which theory triumphs; providing, of course, the issue is ever decided.

The best early atomic theory comes from Democritus (about 420 B.C.), a native of Abdera, Thrace. Democritus got its outline, at least, from his teacher Leucippus, said to have founded the school of Abdera. The theory follows in the tradition of naturalism that began with Thales of Miletus and continued through Anaximander, Anaximenes, Xenophanes, Empedocles, and others. These material-minded philosophers, you remember, tried to explain the universe in terms of simple elements. Thales took water as the first principle, Anaximenes took mist, etc. Empedocles proved that empty space is not empty at all, but is filled with a corporeal substance, air. This revelation of a material world beyond the reach of the senses was a very important step toward the atomic theory. It caused Empedocles to think that different substances can be explained by combinations of the four basic elements in different proportions (under the influence of love and hatred, by the way). Leucippus and Democritus went one step further and plumped for a single element in the form of indivisible atoms. Democritus wrote: "According to convention there is a sweet and a sour, a hot and a cold, and according to convention there is color. In truth there are atoms and a void."

By convention, Democritus meant our senses: without our sense of taste, for example, there would *be* no sweet and sour. But the *primary* things, such as matter itself, and even man's soul, are composed of atoms. The atoms differ mainly in size and shape, though they have movement and may also combine. The soul's atoms are perfectly round. Apparently Dalton's simple matter of weight wasn't important; in fact, the Democritus atoms may not have had any weight at all.

Aristotle's objection to an indivisible atom on logical grounds failed to dismay Democritus; he took care of the matter by means of an "end around." In his universe of atoms and a void, the void is *nothing,* an absolute vacuum (a slightly more than difficult conception in itself). The atoms are indivisible because *there is no void within them;* they are completely impenetrable.

Pretty hard and tight little particles, the atoms of Democritus!

Since Dalton revived the atomic theory of Democritus, it has been given a solid foundation on what we fondly call facts, facts obtained by means of laboratory experiments. In one of these experiments a current of electricity is passed through water. Hydrogen bubbles up at the point where the current leaves the water, oxygen where it enters the water. After a while the water disappears: it has been converted into two gases, hydrogen and oxygen. If we measure their volume, there will always be just twice as much hydrogen as oxygen. Water, then, is composed of two parts hydrogen and one part oxygen, by *volume.* Assuming that the water is composed of atoms, and that equal volumes of the gases contain an equal number of atoms (Avogadro's Law), there must be two atoms of hydrogen to one atom of oxygen. And as all the oxygen weighs eight times as much as all the hydrogen, each oxygen atom must weigh 16 times as much as each hydrogen atom.

Dalton's theory was later extended as follows. When elements combine to form a compound, the atoms come together in identical little "groups." Each "group" of atoms is as orderly as the figure formed by a drill team. It is called a *molecule*.

Chemistry has a symbol for each of the elements in a molecule. Two atoms of hydrogen is H_2, a single atom of oxygen is O. Put them together and we get the familiar symbol for water, H_2O.

A compound is more than a mere *mixture* of elements. Neither sodium nor chlorine would taste very good on your breakfast eggs; the first would combine violently with the moisture in them, the second might kill you. And yet, their *chemical combination* in the molecule of salt (NaCl) gives us a stable molecule that is essential to life.

Down through the years the atomic theory has been the Gibraltar of chemistry. From chemistry's viewpoint, there is still an atom of a different atomic weight for each of the 92 elements, and these atoms group themselves in molecules to form compounds. But, in spite of this, Democritus, Dalton & Co. were fundamentally mistaken: the atom is not indivisible. Atoms must divide before we can have either an electric charge or a current flow.

2

MEET THE ELECTRON

O NCE upon a time we believed that electricity was some kind of strange, weightless fluid, a fluid so fine that it passed through the densest materials. The theory was finally flushed down the laboratory drain by a type of experiment used very early by Michael Faraday. I shall mention Faraday's name more often than any other in this book, and he had been dead for 30 years before the electron was discovered. Nevertheless, this self-taught blacksmith's son, who became one of the world's greatest scientists. probably contributed more to the electrical sciences than any other man. Faraday was 12 years old in 1803, the year of Dalton's atomic theory.

Faraday sealed metal stoppers into the two ends of a glass tube. The stoppers, or *electrodes,* he connected to a battery. Nothing happened until a pump had removed most of the air from the tube; then it would pass electricity. The current flow through the small amount of gas remaining, mostly oxygen and nitrogen, caused the tube to glow with pretty colors.

Some years later a German glass blower, Heinrich Geissler, became an expert at making tubes of this sort for the experimenters, mostly in odd, twisted shapes. The trick was to get an air-tight joint between metal electrode and glass. Geissler later took to experimenting with the tubes himself, rounding out his career as a distinguished physicist.

In England, well-to-do businessman William Crookes, son of a tailor, became interested in the strangely fascinating colored electric lights. The work of this famous amateur experimenter with the tube gave it its name, and also helped to win him a knighthood.

The Crookes tube is shown in Fig. 1. Examine it carefully. It is the daddy of the X-ray tube, neon sign, and fluorescent lamp; it is the granddaddy of television's camera tube, and

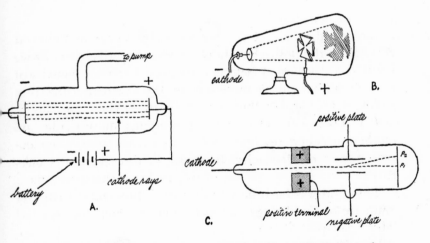

FIG. 1. The Crookes tube. (A) Tube lights up when applied voltage forces a current through the partial vacuum. (B) Sharp shadow on glass behind cross indicates electricity must consist of particles. (C) The beam of particles can be controlled by voltages on plates. This is basic to television, radar, and other applications.

the picture tube of your television receiver. It is also a blood relative of the Geiger counter, the device that detects radioactivity.

Connect a Crookes tube to the voltage from a battery or a generator, as in Fig. 1A; pump out the gas until current starts to flow, and you will see first a blue glow at one end of the tube, the negative, the rest of the tube being pink; as more and more gas is removed from the tube, the pink glow slowly retreats before the blue until the blue fills the tube except for two narrow dark spaces. Sometimes an old radio tube will turn blue in this fashion, when it is said to be *gassy*. Other gases produce different colors.

What was the true nature of this electricity that, leaving a solid conductor, produced such gay colors as it streamed through gas in a tube? Was it matter itself, or something separate from matter that passed through it? Was it in wave form, or did it consist of separate particles?

Goldstein, a German physicist, called the new bottled electricity *cathode rays,* simply because it came in through the negative end of the tube, the cathode, and proceeded straight through to the positive end. The name stuck. To this day we say that a discharge of electricity through a tube consists of cathode rays; and your television set's picture tube is a *cathode ray tube.*

J. J. Thomson is credited with divesting the cathode rays of their mystery, revealing what we now believe to be the true nature of electricity. In short, he discovered the electron.

Thomson was born near Manchester, England, in 1856. A graduate of Cambridge, he became an instructor there, and later head professor at the Cavendish Laboratory. He contributed greatly to the development of this great laboratory, both directly through his achievements and indirectly through his personality and his encouragement of others. Author of many books on electricity and allied subjects, he lectured frequently in the United States. "J. J.," as he was known among his intimates, received many awards and honors, among them a Nobel prize in 1906 and a knighthood in 1908. He died in 1940.

German experimenters had managed to attract or repel the cathode rays by means of a magnetic force; but they failed to deflect them by means of a voltage. A voltage has no effect upon a wave, and from this they concluded that the electricity in the tube must consist of waves. They described the cathode rays as a "flexible electric current flowing in the ether." The majority of the British scientists, on the other hand, felt that the cathode rays must consist of negative atoms or molecules. Neither view proved correct in the light of Thomson's experiments.

Thomson suspected that no one had been able to deflect the cathode rays by means of a voltage, because there was too much gas left in the tube, pumping techniques not being highly developed in those days. After months of patient effort, he managed to get a better vacuum than ever before; though he didn't come close enough to the "void" of Democritus to cause any rumblings in that atomic Greek's grave. With less gas he also got a much purer stream of cathode rays: a *beam* of cathode rays, which he readily deflected by means of voltages on plates inside the tube.

The positive voltage attracted the beam, the negative voltage repelled it, revealing not only that the current flow is composed of particles but that the particles are negative. (Positive and negative charges are explained on pages 16-18.)

Next, Thomson determined how fast the negative particles were traveling; for knowing their velocity was a necessary step toward finding out the mass or weight of each particle. He accomplished this by moving the electron beam, first by means of a magnetic force (current through a coil) and then an equal distance by an electrostatic force (voltage on plates). The magnetic force required for this is always less than the electrostatic force, and the faster the electrons are moving the greater the difference; thus, dividing the electrostatic force by the magnetic force gave him a figure for velocity. Why the difference? Because the electron beam is itself surrounded by a magnetic field, one that pushes against the coil's; and the beam's magnetic field is more intense the faster the electrons are traveling.

Once he knew the velocity of the particles, another simple experiment with the magnetic field alone gave him some more valuable information: the *relationship* between each particle's charge and mass. So, if he knew the charge on each particle, he could fit it into this relationship (written e/m) and learn the mass. Thomson took a chance that the charge was the smallest known: the one carried by the atom of hydrogen in solution, estimated years before by Faraday. A charge of this size in e/m gave the particle a mass only about 1/1,000th as great as the mass of the whole hydrogen atom, the *lightest* of all the atoms. (The correct figure was later found to be 1/1846th as great.)

No matter what kind of gas was in the tube, or what kind of metal in the electrodes, Thomson always got the same relationship of charge to mass. He concluded, therefore, (1) *that all the negatively charged particles always carry the same charge and have the same mass;* (2) *that the particles are all torn from the atoms of gas or metal.*

In short, the indivisible atoms of Dalton, as well as of Democritus, described by Lord Kelvin as "indestructible, eternal in nature," had been knocked apart. Thomson called the new negative particle a corpuscle, a name that was later changed to *electron*.

German physicists interpreted Thomson's experiments differently. The fact that any kind of gas or metal produced the same negative particles of mass so much lighter than hydrogen seemed to them to prove that the particles came from neither the gas nor the metal; that electricity, therefore.

was separate from matter. But Thomson's theory was confirmed by experiments with the new radium discovered by the Curies in Paris. As radium releases its energy it slowly disintegrates—changes to lead, which is lighter. Part of radium's radiation consists of the more familiar forms of energy, which we call light and heat; but it was also found that another part is a stream of electrons: for it can be deflected by means of either a magnet or a voltage in the same way as Thomson's beam of cathode rays (Fig. 3). The electrons, then, must have been part and parcel of the disintegrating atoms.

Mortal man can no more visualize an electron (.00000000-00000000000000000009 of a gram) than he can see a ping-pong ball in Los Angeles from a rooftop in New York. And yet, these incredibly tiny particles light our homes and run our factories, streetcars, and trains. The same particles, delicately controlled by means of a tube, such as the common radio tube, give us what we call electronics.

It isn't the electricity itself that we see in a Crookes tube, a neon sign, or a sodium highway lamp: it is only the light produced by the speeding electrons when they bump into the molecules of gas. Today's television picture tube has a much higher vacuum than Thomson obtained; a much more abundant supply of electrons comes from a *heated filament,* one very similar to a light-globe filament. The tube is funnel shaped to provide a large, round or rectangular, almost flat end for the picture screen. Voltages on plates (or currents in coils) rise and fall rapidly to keep the electron beam moving back and forth while its tip "brushes" a series of pictures on the screen with light. The electron brush moves so fast that one complete picture follows another even more rapidly than on a movie screen. Thus, the light that partially filled the gaseous Crookes tube or completely fills today's neon-sign tube, is concentrated in the picture tube at the point where the beam tip touches the screen: because with so few molecules of gas left to impede the speeding electrons, no light is released until they crash into the molecules of the glass. The glass has been coated with a chemical that enables the electrons to release more light.

2

It was only natural for Thomson and his fellow experimenters of the time to assume that there are two kinds of electricity, positive and negative, for the idea was old even then. About the middle of the 18th century, Du Fay in France, and later Benjamin Franklin in America, had offered proof of this. Perhaps we should examine this proof before we continue on our trip into the atom.

It's hardly front-page news that after you have passed a comb through your hair it will attract a tiny piece of paper. Not only the comb but also your hair becomes charged with electricity, as evidenced by its effort to stand up straight in defiance of gravity. This method of generating electricity by means of friction was noted by the Greeks. They believed, however, that it could only be generated in a single substance, amber, which is a fossil resin from an extinct variety of pine tree. (That the Roman, Pliny the Elder [A.D. 23-79], mentions the black, coallike mineral, jet, as having the same property seems to have long been overlooked.) The Greek word for amber is *elektron;* the Latin word is *electrum.* William Gilbert in 1600 earned for himself the honorary title of Father of Electricity for a book he wrote in which he used the word *electrics* to describe all the many materials which, he had discovered, could be electrified by friction. Gilbert was the first to show that amber isn't unique in this respect. Today we realize that there are no exceptions.

Franklin found that when he rubbed a glass rod on silk, the glass was charged with one kind of electricity; and when he rubbed a stick of sealing wax on a cat's back, the sealing wax was charged with another kind. A simple experiment convinced him the two electricities were different; and you will be convinced too, if you care to carry out the experiment of Fig. 2A,B, though you may prefer to take Franklin's word for it.

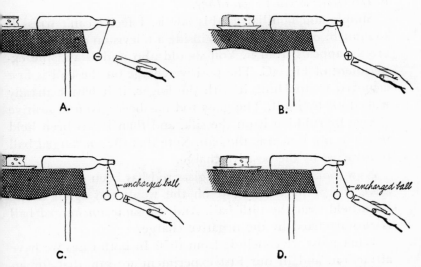

Fig. 2. The fundamental laws of electricity. (A) Like charges repel. (B) Unlike charges attract. (C), (D) Electrostatic induction. Either a positive or a negative charge attracts an uncharged body.

Charge one end of the glass rod by rubbing it briskly on a piece of silk. Touch the part of the rod that contacted the silk to the pith ball for an instant. This permits some of the rod's charge to escape to the ball.

Next, rub the rod on the silk again to renew the charge; then merely hold it near the pith ball. The ball will be repelled by the rod. This proves that like charges repel each other.

As a substitute for Franklin's sealing wax and cat's back, in case you do carry out the experiment and your cat is away, the same glass rod and a piece of woolen cloth will serve.

Charge the rod again by rubbing it on the wool; then hold it near the pith ball. This time the charged ball will be attracted by the rod, proving that unlike charges attract each other.

Like charges of electricity repel each other; unlike charges of electricity attract each other.

Simple and familiar as this law is, I feel I can't stress it too much; on a cat's back or inside a television camera there are no appeals from it. You should also understand the experiment of Fig. 2C. The positive charge on the ball is first removed by touching it with the finger, if it hasn't already leaked off by itself. The glass rod has been given a positive charge by rubbing it on the silk, and then it has been held near but not touching the ball. Note that the *uncharged* ball is attracted by the positive charge.

Now look at Fig. 2D. The glass rod has been given a negative charge by rubbing it on the wool, and again it has been held near the pith ball. And the same *uncharged* ball is also attracted by the negative charge.

What must we conclude from this? In both cases we have attraction, and in our first experiment we saw that for attraction the charges must be unlike or opposite. Therefore, in both Figs. 2C and 2D it must be that the ball, when the rod is merely held near it, somehow acquires a charge opposite to the rod's charge. This acquired charge must also be temporary—for it disappears when the rod is removed.

Communication of a temporary charge to a body in this way, with no physical contact, is technically known as *induction*. Induction is a good word to remember. We say that the charge on the rod *induces* an opposite charge on the pith ball.

The Greeks, in their own way, tried to solve the mystery of electrical attraction, which involves induction. To a piece of amber, electrified by friction, they attributed a soul and so explained its lifelike actions on the basis of sympathy and antipathy. The theory is attributed to Thales, who felt that mind was also a substance of some sort. The next chapter explains induction in terms of the particles of electricity in the atom. Among these particles is the negatively charged electron, with which we already have better than a bowing acquaintance.

3

JOURNEY INTO THE ATOM

THE physicist, at one stage of his experiments, arrived at a theory of atomic structure which has proved very useful ever since, and it is still considered the "basic" structure. This concept was a rung in the ladder that led to the tremendous explosion, precisely on schedule, that fateful morning in July 1945 at Alamogordo, New Mexico; and it remains invaluable for an understanding of electricity and electronics. I refer to the solar-system atom, with its positively charged central sun and revolving planetary electrons negatively charged. You would have to go pretty far back in the woods today to find an adult not at least superficially familiar with this delightfully simple, all-electric affair.

Rutherford, Mosely, and Bohr were the three atomic explorers chiefly responsible for the solar-system atom. They arrived at the concept by inference, just as Empedocles did when he demonstrated that "empty space" is filled with particles of matter.

The central, guiding figure in the activity from which the new atom evolved was Ernest Rutherford. Rutherford is one of the giants of modern science, in the Galileo, Newton, Faraday, Maxwell, Einstein class. Eddington said of him that he introduced the greatest change in our idea of matter since the time of Democritus. He was born on August 30, 1871, in the tiny settlement of Spring Grove, later called Brightwater, 13 miles from the town of Nelson, New Zealand. His mother, a former schoolteacher, was also something of a musician. His father, son of immigrants from Perth, Scotland, was a wheelwright, farmer, bridge builder, and miller. Ernest went from Nelson college to the University of New Zealand to Cambridge on scholarships. At the New Zealand school he made his first foray into science when he began some research on "magnetization of iron by high-frequency discharge." This may sound forbidding, but it later had a practical application: the reception of electromagnetic waves. (These, of course, create a high-frequency current in the receiver.) Hertz had recently sent and received the waves in his laboratory, and Marconi was just beginning his outdoor experiments, trying to make them useful. Marconi was using the Hertz transmitter and the Braun receiver, though his company later came around to Rutherford's type of receiver.

Young Rutherford came to the Cavendish Laboratory, Cambridge, in September 1895, as a research student under J. J. Thomson, still busy with his Crookes tubes. He continued with the magnetic detector of electromagnetic waves and was soon sending messages from his rooms to the laboratory, a distance of about three-quarters of a mile. He even thought some about the commercial possibilities of a telegraph without wires; it occurred to him that if he could make it work over a distance of 10 miles it could be installed on lightships or lighthouses for communicating with the shore. But in

1895 Becquerel discovered radioactivity, and in 1897 Thomson took his promising young research student off his wireless project and put him to work on radium. In later years Thomson voiced some misgivings about having switched Rutherford from wireless to pure science. After all, Marconi made quite a name for himself, and how many people have heard of Rutherford?

In 1898 Rutherford went to Montreal's McGill University as professor of physics; while there, he unraveled the mystery of the radiation given off by radium. Nine years later he transferred to Manchester University to head the physics department. Already a famous scientist—a Nobel prize came to him a year later—at Manchester he discovered the nucleus of the atom.

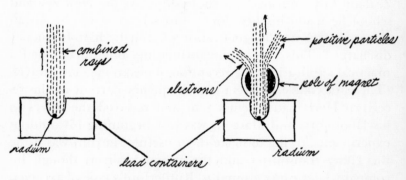

FIG. 3. The field of a magnet divides the electrical radiation from a spot of radium.

Radium's electrical radiation is by no means confined to the electrons mentioned in Chapter 2. Radium pours out a constant stream of *positively* charged particles as well. In the drawing of Fig. 3, a speck of radium is on the bottom of the lead container, which concentrates the radiation in a beam, like a flashlight. Directed at a plate covered with zinc sulphide, the radiation makes a circular spot that glows in the dark. (Zinc sulphide is a type of chemical known as

fluorescent: it releases light when bombarded with particles
or rays.) A magnet placed near the radium beam divides it
as shown; part of the energy (the negative electrons) is deflected in one direction; another part is deflected in the opposite direction, proving that it is composed of positive particles. Each positive particle was found to carry just twice
the charge of an electron, and to be several thousand times
heavier.

At Manchester, Rutherford began a series of experiments
in which he used radium's positive particles to bombard various elements. One of his first targets was a piece of gold
leaf (Fig. 4). By surrounding the leaf with zinc-sulphide-
coated screens, he could note (in the dark) the direction
taken by his radium bullets.

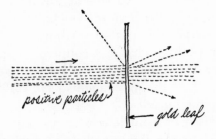

FIG. 4. Most of Rutherford's positive particles passed straight through the
gold leaf.

Most of them sailed right through the gold leaf, like the
stream from a hose through a wire fence. But there was some
scattering. A few of the particles were deflected at various
angles; and a very few, perhaps 20 in a million, even bounded
straight back.

Rutherford knew that the electrons in the gold leaf
couldn't have interfered with the flight of his bullets; the
bullets were much too massive and, being positively charged,
would have been attracted rather than repelled by the negative electrons. It followed that the gold atoms must contain

a positive charge of considerable mass. To account for the few bullets that bounced straight back, he was forced to assume that the gold's positive charge was very much heavier; and in addition carried a charge many times greater than the charge on a single electron.

But why so few direct hits? All but 20 in a million of the positive particle bullets couldn't have passed *between* the atoms, because the atoms of a solid such as gold are packed too closely together. There was only one explanation: the bullets went *through* the atoms. The positive charge inside the atom, despite its great mass, relative to the electron, must be very small in size compared with the over-all dimensions of the atom. Indeed, the atom must consist almost entirely of empty space!

After a long series of experiments, using many different elements for targets, Rutherford concluded that each atom contains a heavy positive charge surrounded by lightweight electrons. The positive charge accounted for practically all the atom's mass or weight. (This was Dalton's atomic weight, different for each of the 92 elements.) He called the atom's positive charge the *nucleus*.

Unable to discover a nucleus with a charge smaller than the one carried by the lightest element, hydrogen, Rutherford reasoned that the hydrogen nucleus is a basic particle, found in all the other elements. The heavier nuclei must be made up of "clusters" of hydrogen nuclei. In 1920 he named the hydrogen nucleus the *proton*. The positive-particle radium bullets he used have in them two protons.

In 1910 H. G. J. Mosely, one of Rutherford's assistants at Manchester, had discovered *atomic number*. Atomic number says that the number of positive particles (protons) in each atom is always equal to the number of negative particles (electrons). And as proton and electron charges are always equal, the atom is balanced electrically.

A third atomic explorer, Niels Bohr of Denmark, who had

also worked under Rutherford at Manchester, gave order
and arrangement to the electrons. Bohr placed the electrons
in rings, or shells. The first ring, closest to the nucleus, is
only big enough for two electrons. So this ring holds hydrogen's single electron or helium's pair of electrons (Fig. 5);

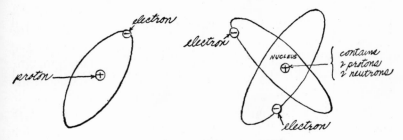

FIG. 5. Atoms of hydrogen and helium.

though lithium, which has three electrons, needs a second
ring, which holds a *total* of 8 electrons. Neon, with 10 electrons, completely fills first and second rings. Third, fourth,
and fifth rings hold 8 or 18 electrons each. Elements like
neon, with full outer rings, are chemically stable. Copper (29)
and silver (47) make good conductors because their single,
outer-ring electron is loosely held, as we shall soon see.

The Rutherford-Mosely-Bohr concept of the atom just
described has, however, a rather serious flaw. The lightest
atom, hydrogen, consists of one electron and one proton, and
so has an atomic number of one, an atomic weight of one. So
far, so good. But helium's atom, with two electrons and two
protons, has an atomic number of two, but an atomic weight
of four. Uranium's atomic number is 92, its atomic weight
238. How to account for this extra mass in the nucleus?
The only solution seemed to be to concede extra protons to
the nucleus—which meant they had to be joined by an equal
number of electrons to neutralize them; otherwise the atom
would lose its electrical balance. But this left the scientists
feeling a bit uneasy.

Several big-particle hunters noted some odd results when firing radium bullets into beryllium, a rare metal now useful as an alloy in steel for jet-engine parts that must withstand high temperatures. In 1932 James Chadwick, who was working under Rutherford at the Cambridge Cavendish Laboratory, discovered that the hunters were blasting a brand-new particle out of the beryllium nucleus, a particle he called the *neutron.*

The neutron, as its name implies, lacks any electrical charge, so it doesn't unbalance the atom electrically; and its mass, being almost identical with that of the proton, accounts very nicely for the atom's extra nuclear weight. The helium nucleus consists of two protons and two neutrons, adding up to an atomic weight of four; the uranium nucleus has 92 protons and 146 neutrons, which add up to 238.

In 1919, Rutherford replaced his old chief, electron-discoverer J. J. Thomson, as head of the Cavendish Laboratory at Cambridge. While there, he was the first to transmute one element into another. The King knighted him in 1914, made him a baron in 1931. He died in 1937, at the age of 66, as the result of an operation for hernia when he was otherwise in very good health. He is buried in Westminster Abbey, appropriately just to the west of Sir Isaac Newton, for Rutherford was the Newton of the atom.

The protons, "clustered" together in the nucleus (with the neutrons), should logically repel each other because of their positive charges. Then why doesn't the nucleus explode? The physicist doesn't know for certain. He still finds the atomic nucleus almost as much of a mystery as what lies behind the Mona Lisa smile. However, electronics is concerned only with the perfect balance of the atom—the electrical balance between the positive nucleus and its revolving negative electrons. The normal atom is said to be *neutral;* it doesn't reveal its electrical properties until it loses (or gains) one or more electrons. We find plenty of unbalanced electrons in our Crookes tube of Fig. 1A, once we pump out some of the air and switch on the battery.

The battery functions in this fashion: a *chemical* process, which we shall look into later, removes electrons from the positive terminal and piles them up on the negative terminal. Our tube is thus caught between one battery terminal that is hungry for electrons (positive), and one that has a surplus and is eager to be rid of them (negative). This is one way of saying that the tube is subjected to an electrical pressure or *potential difference,* a voltage. If the gas in the Crookes tube doesn't offer too much opposition (isn't too dense) the battery voltage will move electrons through it from the negative to the positive terminal. But the electrons in this current movement do not all come from the battery's negative terminal. Its positive terminal has only to attract a few of the lightweight electrons in the tube, which speeds them up so that when they strike atoms of gas they knock out other electrons. These released electrons are also pulled along by the positive battery voltage at a high rate of speed, perhaps destined for further atomic crashes that release still more electrons, etc., and the tube is quickly filled with freed electrons, all banging their way through the tube toward the positive terminal. The electrons knocked free are all from the gas atoms' outer orbits. And, of course, an atom with one or more of its outer-orbit electrons missing is no longer electrically balanced; it is no longer *neutral;* it has become *positively charged.* If an atom's outer orbit should *acquire* one or more extra electrons, as can happen under certain conditions, the atom becomes *negatively charged.*

The unbalanced atom, whether positive or negative, is called an *ion.* Ion is a Greek word that means "wanderer" or "goer." It isn't new in our language. Faraday used it first to designate the charge on each molecule when a current flow passes through a conducting liquid. Thomson's use of the size of this charge led to the discovery of the electron (page 14). Now let's see what else goes on behind the ion curtain.

When a gas-filled cathode ray tube is passing current, collisions between electrons and atoms produce a tremendous number of positive ions. The ions are attracted to the tube's negative terminal. Thus they move through the tube in an opposite direction to the electrons, which seek the positive terminal. The ions, being weighted with protons, and except in the case of hydrogen with neutrons also, naturally move much more slowly than the lightweight electrons. The ions may be goers, but they're regular stay-at-homes compared with electrons. (In most television picture tubes, a magnet is used to trap heavy negative ions in the electron beam, preventing them from striking the screen.)

The positive ions and the electrons, being oppositely charged, are also attracted to each other, and so are caused to recombine. (It is mostly as a result of this recombination that light and heat are generated.) But when a gas-filled tube is conducting, there is always much less recombination than separation. In fact, it may take only an instant for the number of free electrons to build up to the point where the tube offers such little opposition to the battery voltage that we have what is called a "direct short" across the battery.

When current passes through a solid, such as a length of copper wire, there is little or no movement of the positive ions in an opposite direction to the electrons. Current flow in a solid is even more important for us, and we shall now examine it in some detail.

Though the molecules (or atoms) of a solid are quiet, compared with the molecules of a gas or even of a liquid, they do move around some, like a horse tethered to a peg in a clover patch. The scientist says they "move around positions of equilibrium," which is fair enough. At the same time, the electrons are carrying on business as usual, whirling in their orbits far from their nuclei—thousands of times farther, relative to their size, than the moon is from the earth. In some of the *metals*, the attraction between nucleus and outer electrons isn't very strong. As a result, these electrons shift about some from atom to atom. And lucky for us!—if it weren't for this "wanderlust" on the part of a few of the electrons in some of the metals, such as copper, we'd still be carrying candles up to bed; for without such a *conductor* we could neither generate nor transport an electron current.

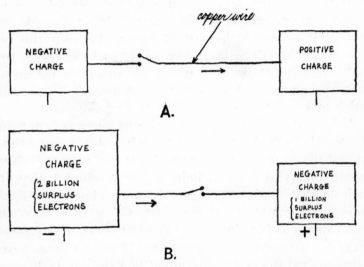

FIG. 6. Electrical charges and current flow. (A) Equal positive and negative charges completely neutralize each other. (B) The smaller of two negative electrical charges is positive *with respect to* the larger.

Fig. 6A shows a positive and a negative charge connected by a copper wire. The wire itself is neutral; it contains equal numbers of protons and electrons, even though some of its outer-orbit electrons are jumping about from atom to atom, temporarily unbalancing the atoms. With this situation firmly in mind, we can picture the following action taking place when we close the switch and the wire starts to *conduct*.

The surplus electrons of the negative charge exert such a pressure that some of them are forced into the wire; but how, when the wire is *neutral?* Because at almost the same instant the wire starts losing free electrons to the positive charge at its other terminal. So the positive charge drains off electrons at the same rate that the negative charge moves in replacements, and the net result is electrons moving through the wire in one direction: an *electron current.*

Substitute some material such as rubber, mica, glass, quartz, or waxed paper for the copper wire of Fig. 6A, and there will be some electron movement between the two charges, but it will be very, very small. These materials lack the travel-minded electrons which are present in the metals in varying numbers. We say that they have a *high resistance,* which makes them valuable as insulating materials.

Radio and television waves travel from antenna to antenna at a speed of 186,000 miles per second; which is seven times around the earth while your watch ticks off a second. (New measurements in Great Britain and at Stanford University indicate that the correct figure is much closer to 186,282 miles per second.) Even the current flow in a wire can travel almost as fast, despite the fact that the *electrons themselves* are never in much of a hurry. Think of them gravitating toward the positive terminal like clearance-sale shoppers impelled toward an exit by the clang of a closing bell. There is no contradiction in this. I said, remember, that when we close the switch some of the electrons leave the positive terminal at almost the same instant that others enter the negative terminal (Fig. 6A). The wire is something like Junior's bean shooter completely filled with beans. One more pushed into the shooter will cause a single bean to emerge from the opposite end; thus the effect of the extra bean is felt almost immediately the full length of the shooter, even though no single bean moves very far.

The electron current in the wire of Fig. 6A doesn't last

long; only an instant is needed to neutralize the two charges. If the two charges are equal in size, neutralization will be complete. But suppose, instead of positive and negative charges, we have two charges of the *same kind,* what happens? If they are also equal in size (have the same voltage) nothing happens; it's a stand-off, like two football teams so evenly matched neither one can gain on the other. But say the two like charges are of unequal size. Take two unequal *negative* voltages (Fig. 6B). Close the switch, and current flows between them—just enough current to equalize the two voltages. What we really have, then, for all practical purposes, is a positive and a negative voltage, even though each voltage by itself is negative. But one, being *less negative* than the other, is really positive with respect to it, which is what counts. It's a matter of comparison. You may think your sister is fat till you take her to the circus side show, where she looks positively skinny next to the fat lady.

The electrical charges we have been talking about are called *static electricity.* (Static means at rest.) They are the same charges as those of our experiments in the preceding chapter. With the Rutherford-Mosely-Bohr "roomy" planetary atom in mind, we should now be able to clear away the mystery about those experiments that intrigued the Greeks.

We rub the glass rod on silk and get a positive charge, leaving a negative charge on the silk. Rubbing two materials together this way generates unlike charges simply because one material acquires some of the other's electrons. When the two planetary systems are crowded together, some of the electrons in the outer orbits of one material go over to the other material. All electrons being negative charges, both materials become electrically unbalanced: the one losing electrons acquires a positive charge, the one gaining them acquires a negative charge.

Rubbing gives us a much more intimate contact between the two materials than can be had by merely pressing them together. Charges of electricity can always be generated in this fashion because no two kinds of material cling to their electrons with the same degree of tenacity; one of them will always give up electrons to the other.

Why do unlike charges attract? When our positively charged pith ball swung toward the negatively charged glass rod, it was trying to get back its missing electrons from the rod's surplus, in order to return to a normal, neutral state; its movement toward the rod was just as natural as water flowing downhill. The explanation of why like charges repel may not be so convincing. Let's look at it this way.

Both charges are suffering from the same kind of unbalance. If both charges are positive they are both seeking electrons. Obviously they can't get them from each other; in fact, they have a better chance of getting them from any neutral object in some other direction. This causes them to move apart, which looks as if they are repelling each other.

In our second experiment, the charged rod *induced* a charge on the uncharged pith ball, a positively charged rod giving the ball a negative charge, a negatively charged rod giving it a positive charge. The electron theory takes electrostatic induction in stride. Some of the ball's electrons leave their outer orbits and move toward the positive rod, anxious to remedy its electron deficiency. (In the case of an insulator, not many electrons actually desert their atoms, though they shift toward the rod, distending the atoms till they are shaped more like lemons and less like oranges.) The side of the ball nearest the rod, then, gets some extra electrons; and as these are pulled from the far side, the far side is left with a deficiency. So the near side is charged negatively, the far side positively. But there will naturally be more attraction between the rod and the ball's near side than there will be repulsion between the rod and the ball's far side. Net effect: attraction. And when the rod is negative, it makes the uncharged ball's near side positive, leaving its far side negative.

This type of induction, because it involves static charges of electricity, is called *electrostatic* induction. In the chapter that follows we shall see how it is put to work in radio, television, and other electronic circuits through the medium of a device older than our country: the condenser. There is one other kind of induction, involving currents of electricity, which was the basic discovery of both Faraday and Henry.

4

THE ELECTRON RESERVOIR

Our early electrical experimenters happily busied themselves with a ball of sulphur. The great German scientist, inventor of the air pump, Otto von Guericke (1602-1686), mounted one of these balls, "about the size of the head of an infant," on an iron shaft so it could be turned by a crank while one hand was held against it. The friction between hand and sulphur built up a pretty potent charge on the ball. (On the hand, too, by the way.) Glass globes and cylinders were next. Newton built machines of this type. Instead of the hand, pads or cushions pressed against the glass. Then came the big glass-disc machines, some of which were capable of building up charges of hundreds of thousands of volts, enough to produce lightning-like sparks several feet long. This awesome display was a prime source of wonder to the poor layman of the day: "What will they think up next!" One friction-type generator in Holland had two large glass discs, eight rubbing pads, two cranks to spin the discs, and is said to have generated a charge big enough to attract a bit of thread 38 feet away.

Watching the charged sulphur ball snatch floating bits of thread, straw, or paper out of the air, even slivers of wood, the early experimenter pondered at length. How was the force exerted through space? He concluded that something *material* must pass between the ball and the floating bits. He called it *effluvium*. There were other names for it too, *humor* and *unctuous stream*. Composed of particles small enough to penetrate solid bodies, it spread out equally in all directions from the charged ball—like the fragrance from a piece of ripe cheese. The general idea seemed to be that the effluvium was somehow capable of latching on to any small, light object and darting back to the sulphur with it.

But an object, after it had come in contact with the charged ball of sulphur, was then *repulsed* by it. This put quite a strain upon the effluvium theory, for it seemed as though the stuff was capable of changing its mind. Von Guericke said, "When it does not want it does not attract." There must have been many a yearning backward glance to the Greek soul theory.

Newton felt that there must be something between the sun and the planets to transmit his force of gravitation— some *medium*. However, the necessity for thinking in this fashion gradually disappeared, and after a time they tried to tailor electrical to gravitational forces: no medium need exist between two charges, just as none need exist between a falling apple and the earth. Action-at-a-distance became the theme. Electrical and gravitational attraction do have something in common: the force diminishes with the square of the distance between the two bodies. (Twice the distance away means a force only one quarter as great, etc. This was demonstrated in France by Coulomb, late in the 18th century.) But until Einstein's latest theory proves otherwise, the similarity goes no further. Much later, Faraday gave us his *lines of force* to explain electrical attraction and repulsion. Lines of force are no more logical nor believable than effluvium, but they proved practical.

The 18th-century French and English academies of science were very much interested in its practical aspects; though nobody seemed to see much promise in electricity. This pleased the "electricians," who were more intent on prying a secret loose from Mother Nature than in putting it to work. Neither friction nor electrostatic induction is a practical method for generating electricity. The 300-year-old friction machine and its successor, the 95-year-old electrostatic induction machine, are seen today only in museum or school laboratory. At one time they were featured in doctors' offices, though whatever help they were to the sick came from the faith, not the electricity, they generated.

The electricians were mostly amateurs (called virtuosos) like Franklin. Before 1746 the electrical secrets they had succeeded in prying loose from Mother Nature were these: 1. There is repulsion as well as attraction between charged bodies (Von Guericke). 2. A body merely held close to a charged body also becomes electrified (Von Guericke) (Fig. 2C, D). 3. Electrical attraction is mutual (Robert Boyle). 4. Electrical attraction operates through a vacuum (Robert Boyle). 5. Some materials can be classified as conductors of electricity, others are nonconductors (Stephan Gray, 1696-1736). 6. There are two kinds of electricity. Unlike charges attract, like charges repel (Charles du Fay, 1698-1739). This fact was later demonstrated, independently, by Franklin, who called them plus and minus charges, or positive and negative.

At this point the scientists were stalled on a dead-end street: All they were getting out of their friction machines were bigger and better sparks, unless you want to count the fun they were having. Then, in 1746, a new device came to their rescue: the *Leyden jar*. It acted on the scientific world like

Vitamin C on scurvy. The jar could be charged up by means of an electrical (friction) machine, and it would retain the charge for a short time; in other words, act as a temporary "reservoir" of electricity. This was fruitful in itself. Franklin charged the jar with electricity from the air, just as easily as with an electrical machine, thereby proving the identity of lightning and frictional electricity. But even more important, the current flow from the charged-up jar was larger than could be had from the friction machine direct. And this current was more easily handled because its pressure (voltage) was lower for the same *amount* of electricity.

Today's version of the Leyden jar is called a *condenser,* or *capacitor*.

The Leyden jar condenser was first discovered by Von Kleist, at Kammin, Germany, in 1745. However, Von Kleist was not a scientist, and his story of what took place is rather vague. So credit usually goes to Professor Musschenbroek, of Leyden, Holland, who independently made the same discovery (accidentally) the following year. The Dutchman sensed its scientific possibilities and began experimenting with it right away.

The professor's discovery was made in this fashion. One day, as he was charging the water in a glass jar held in his hand, he reached over and touched the conductor between the water and the charging machine with his other hand. From this careless bit of fingering he got a shock, and no ordinary shock. He wrote afterward that it was of such violence that his whole body was shaken as if by a lightning stroke, and he thought he was done for.

Despite its age, the condenser is far from being a museum piece like its progenitor, the friction machine. Your radio has at least a dozen condensers of various shapes and sizes, all essentially the same as the first Leyden jar. A vital part of one television-camera tube is made up of millions of tiny condensers on a small plate. An electronic circuit without at least one lineal descendant of Professor Musschenbroek's jar of water is as rare today as a Western without six-guns.

In Fig. 7A two metal plates are shown connected to the terminals of an ordinary six-volt battery. The plates are merely extensions of the battery terminals, so one of them will have a negative charge, the other one a positive charge. If we open the two switches, disconnecting the plates from the battery, the plates will retain their charges. However, these charges will be very small.

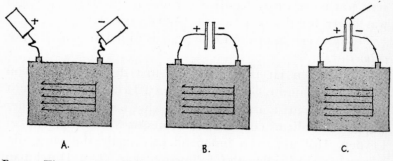

FIG. 7. The principle of the condenser. (B) The closer together the plates the larger the charge received from the battery. (C) Discharging the condenser.

Next (Fig. 7B), we bend the wires until the metal plates face each other, close together. Now, if we open the switches, the charges left on the plates will be very much larger than before. The plates, separated by an insulator, in this case air, constitute a simple condenser. A condenser stores a charge. All the time we were moving the two plates closer together, electrons were flowing from the battery up into the negative plate to make it *more* negative, and electrons were flowing from the positive plate down into the battery, leaving this plate *more* positive. (In the first condenser, the professor's hand was one conductor, water the other, and the glass between was the insulator.)

Why should moving the two plates—mere extensions of the battery terminals—closer together increase the charges on them? We find an answer in electrostatic induction (pages 16-18). Either a positive or a negative charge induces an opposite (unlike) charge on an uncharged body (Fig. 2C, D). But in the case of the condenser, what do we have? *Two unlike charges brought close together!* As a result of the proximity, the inductive reaction between them is greatly increased. In other words, the whole becomes greater than the simple sum of the two parts, a principle that is common to the arts.

The positive and negative charges together are known as the condenser's charge. The charge stays put because its two halves attract each other through the insulation that separates them, while at the same time the insulation prevents much electron flow (there is always a little) between the plates to cause neutralization. Neutralization, or discharge, is obtained by means of an external path or circuit (Fig. 7C).

Experimenters were soon building large, compact condensers put together as in Fig. 10A. The bulky jars, however, were favorites for a century and a half. Marconi used them in his early wireless transmitters, and I saw them in the wireless shacks of British tramp steamers as late as 1920.

We are indebted to Faraday for many of our technical terms in electricity. The insulation between the conducting plates of a condenser, he named the *dielectric*. The next time your radio needs a new condenser—and quite often a serious malady can be traced to a "ruptured" dielectric—don't argue with your radio man if he says that the "condenser is shot." He means the same thing—unless the condenser has opened up, stopping the current flow, which can also happen.

2

The early experimenters believed that the electrical "fluid" was *condensed* in the Leyden jar; thus its name. They charged up their jars by means of a friction machine to obtain current for their experiments, suggesting my term "reservoir" of electricity. And many of our electronic circuits use the condenser as a temporary storage tank. In the photographer's speedlight, current for the big flash accumulates in a large condenser. Radar and television circuits use condensers to hold charges of electricity for brief periods.

It is apparent from a glance at Fig. 7 that after the direct current from the battery has charged up the condenser, current flow stops; for the electrons can't get through the insulation between the plates. For this reason, students of electricity are often puzzled as to how current flows in a circuit with a condenser in it.

A condenser blocks only a direct, steady current flow. If a direct current is constantly *changing,* that is, rising and falling, it keeps the condenser charging and discharging, and there must be some current in the circuit at all times. The current's passage *through the insulation* is explained by electrostatic induction as described above and illustrated in Fig. 2C, D.

Electronics uses condensers both with a changing direct current and with an alternating current. Our introduction to alternating current is a little early here: but it is one that is constantly reversing its *direction* of flow, perhaps many

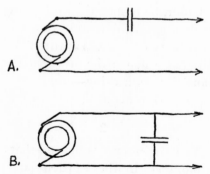

Fig. 8. (A) Circuit with series-connected condenser opposes low frequencies more than high. (B) Circuit with condenser connected across line opposes high frequencies more than low. Note similarity of *symbol* for condenser to the two plates of Fig. 7.

millions of times each second. The number of reversals per second is called its *frequency*. Thus it is constantly attacking the condenser, first from one direction then from the opposite direction, charging it (oppositely) with each reversal.

The condenser offers some *resistance* to such an attack; and this resistance is greater the lower the frequency. A circuit with a condenser in one side of the line opposes the lower frequencies more than the higher ones (Fig. 8A). Connected *across* the line (Fig. 8B), the circuit has the opposite effect: the higher frequencies fall into the condenser, as it were, and the lower ones tend to stay in the line. The larger the condenser the less its resistance to *any* frequency; therefore the range of frequencies to be suppressed determines its size. Encouraging some frequencies at the expense of others is called *filtering*. Filtering is as essential to electronics as Band-aids to a Sunday School picnic.

Connect a condenser to a coil of wire and you have a *tuner*,

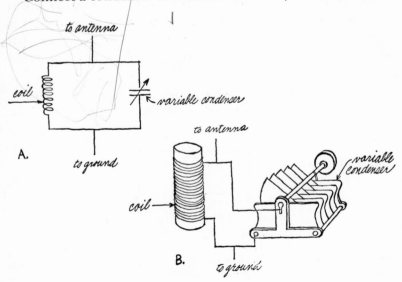

FIG. 9. (A) Diagram for simple tuner. (B) Circuit's coil and variable condenser.

which is a kind of superfilter (Fig. 9). A condenser alone, or a coil alone, offers a certain amount of resistance to *any* frequency: but hook them together and the two frequency-opposing forces *turn against each other* (are opposed in phase; see Fig. 41). At one particular frequency the forces are directly opposed and completely eliminate each other, letting that frequency through without opposition. This is the *resonant frequency*. All other frequencies meet some opposition from either coil or condenser.

3

When I speak of the size of a condenser I mean its electrical size, called *capacitance* or *capacity*. C is the symbol for capacitance.

The greater a condenser's capacitance, the larger the charge (the more electricity) it will hold. The size of the charge it takes, however, depends upon the pressure of the charging current, the voltage. In this respect it is like the pneumatic tire. The service-station man inflates your tires with air from a tank. If the tank's pressure is 40 pounds, your tires get a maximum of 40 pounds of air, not an ounce more; though they would take 50 pounds from a 50-pound tank. This is true for a tire of any size, from child's bike to transcontinental truck. And with the condenser, too, a higher voltage will always give it more charge, regardless of capacitance. The amount of charge on the condenser of Fig. 7B could be doubled by replacing the 6-volt battery with a 12-volt unit.

Of course, at 40 pounds pressure the truck tire holds *much more air* than the bicycle tire. And so it is with the condenser; the greater its capacitance the more charge it takes from any given voltage. Substituting for the condenser of Fig. 7B one with double its capacitance would enable the six volts to give it twice the charge.

There are three things that govern a condenser's capacitance. Two of these have already become evident. The closer together its plates the greater the capacitance, because of the larger mutual reaction between the positive and negative charges. The larger the area of the plates facing each other the greater the capacitance.

The third governing factor derives from the nature of the insulation (dielectric) between the plates. Any solid insulation commonly used, such as mica, glass, or paper, provides more capacitance than air. In Fig. 7B the capacitance can be multiplied about six times by placing a sheet of glass between the plates.

Radio and television sets employ from two to four variable condensers, each for a separate tuner. When you twist the knob of your radio, you change the capacitance of these condensers, which are mounted on the same shaft so they turn in unison. A tuning condenser has two *sets* of plates, as shown in Fig. 9B. One of the sets moves in and out of the other, stationary, set. Insulation between them is air. Fully meshed, the condenser provides maximum capacitance.

Most of the other condensers in your radio or television set are not variable, which classifies them as *fixed condensers*. Insulation between the conducting plates is usually either mica or waxed paper (Fig. 10). Just as too great an air pressure will cause a tire to burst, too high a voltage will *puncture* one of these condensers. Some of the current flow is also lost, mostly by conversion to heat in the dielectric. Mica stays coolest and so has the lowest loss.

The unit of capacitance is called the *farad*, for Michael Faraday. It is far too large a unit for handy use in electronics, so we use the *microfarad*, which is one millionth of a farad. Even the microfarad is pretty large: your radio tuning condenser, for instance, may have a maximum capacitance when fully meshed of only .00035 microfarad, abbreviated mfd or μf; mmfd or μμf for micro-microfarad is also used.

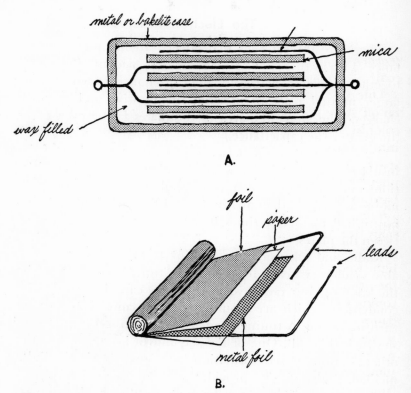

FIG. 10. Fixed condensers. (A) Mica. (B) Paper.

4

The loud, crackling spark from his giant friction machine should have told the electrical experimenter that he was merely duplicating, on a small scale, nature's miles-long streak of lightning. He did, no doubt, suspect this, but at the same time he was reluctant to abandon the generally accepted theory that the flashes of sky fire, warning the creatures below of the cannonade to follow, were explosions of gases. He called the gases "inflammable exhalations." They rose to the sky from vegetable and animal matter and contained such things as sulphur and saltpeter. Wasn't *gun-*

powder made from sulphur and saltpeter—plus a little char-coal?

One who scorned the explosion theory was a printer in far-off America, Benjamin Franklin by name. This upstart colonist argued in some letters he had written, since made into a book, that a bolt of lightning was a colossal electric spark. A few of the less conservative of Europe's philoso-phers were soon putting the theory to a test. Thomas d'Ali-bard of Paris, on May 10, 1752, had the first proof.

Following Franklin's suggestion, D'Alibard used, as a snare for any electricity that might be loose in the atmos-phere, a pointed metal rod 40 feet high, supported by a light wooden tower. He took pains to *insulate* the rod from the wood, so that any electricity picked up by the rod couldn't elude him by sneaking off to the earth through the damp wood. And during the first spell of inclement weather it was found that when a loop of wire was held close to the rod (insulated from the hand), occasional *sparks* would jump the gap. The sparks looked and sounded just like those from a friction machine. They even smelled the same.

Others in Europe also had proof of the theory before Franklin, ignorant of the rumpus he had started across the sea, finally got around to his own test. He had ordered a metal rod; but he believed that it had to be placed on top of a high building (he had recommended this in his letters), and he was awaiting the completion of Christ Church, in Philadelphia, with its high spire. Meanwhile an alternative occurred to him: a kite.

The kite had a length of pointed wire projecting beyond its wooden frame to which a string was tied. Franklin be-lieved that after rain had wet the string it would conduct the "electric fire" down to the earth. He was right.

He described his triumph in these words: "The phial may be charged; and spirits may be kindled and all the other electrical experiments performed which are usually done by the help of a rubbed globe or tube, and thereby the sameness of the electrical matter with that of lightning completely demonstrated." (The phial was a Leyden jar condenser.)

The ingenious Franklin, as he stood in the cow pasture near Philadelphia grasping his kite string, had *eternity* by the tail: for his new international sport of drawing current from the heavens was a dangerous one. In the same year, George William Richman, a Swedish professor at St. Petersburg, was killed when a spark almost a foot long jumped from the metal rod to his head. However, Franklin was the last person in the world to let a little mortal danger stand in the way of satisfying his lively curiosity.

Lightning, then, was finally tagged as electricity, the same electricity generated by friction. Many years later, its sameness with the electricity from Volta's battery, and later still from Faraday's coil, also had to be determined.

A flash of lightning involves the same process as the one that fills a Crookes tube with light. The atmosphere's atoms of oxygen and nitrogen often lose their outer electrons to become positive ions. The electrons are knocked loose by fast-moving particles from the sun or outer space, the *cosmic rays*. (The cosmic-ray disrupters are neutrons, traveling at speeds very close to the speed of light.) So the atmosphere always contains a number of charged particles, positive ions and negative electrons; it is, in a word, *ionized*. But where does the high voltage for the lightning flash come from? What does Mother Nature use for battery or generator? She moves up a thundercloud or two.

A cloud is an aggregation of tiny drops of moisture, soupy enough for the wind to blow it around. To become a thundercloud, it must accumulate a charge of electricity from the ionized atmosphere. How? There are theories, but they're too involved to go into here. Usually the cloud collects a surplus of electrons to become negatively charged. A thundercloud may carry a charge of hundreds of millions of volts.

Drifting close to another cloud (or to the earth) it charges it by induction (see page 32). Once the positive charge starts speeding up some of the free electrons between, it isn't long, less than a second in fact, before the big flash comes, moving at a speed of about 28,000 miles per second.

Flash of lightning, Crookes tube, neon sign, fluorescent lamp—in all of them we have free electrons smashing their way through the orbital electrons of atoms of gas, releasing light and heat as they go. And I have told how (page 15), in the high-vacuum television-picture tube, an abundant supply of electrons from a hot filament is focused into a narrow pointed beam that releases light only from the fluorescent glass screen.

If you don't see how a picture can be "brushed on" by a dot of light in this fashion, think of a light globe mounted on the rim of a wheel; turn the wheel slowly, and your eyes follow the light all the way around the circle: but turn it fast enough, and all you see is a solid ring of light. Similarly, it is possible for the tiny dot of light released from the screen by the beam tip, if it sweeps back and forth across the glass fast enough, each line a little lower than the preceding one, to cover it with a solid block of light. (You may still see the lines.) And the lights and shadows of the picture? how are they formed? By regulating the number of electrons in the beam to alter the *intensity* of the dot of light as it covers the screen. The number of electrons in the beam is regulated by means of a rapidly changing voltage. Just how the television camera obtains this changing voltage from the picture, how the voltage is then sent through space, and finally the way it is received and applied to the beam to re-create the picture, is the business of this book to explain—in easy stages.

5

VOLTA MAKES ELECTRONS FLOW

The 18th-century experimenter's Leyden jar wasn't a very deep reservoir of electricity. The discharge lasted for a very short period, perhaps less than a minute, before recharging by the friction machine was necessary. Even so, this was enough to start a rash of new experiments all over Europe and Philadelphia. Franklin used current from the jar to kill a 14-pound turkey.

Another very notable experiment was performed near Paris by the natural philosopher Abbé Nollet, using enough Carthusian monks to form a circle a mile around (Fig. 11). The monks made contact with each other through pieces of wire held in their outstretched hands. Several charged Leyden jars were inserted in this circuit of metal and human flesh. When contact was made, it was plain for all to see that the electricity traveled the full circular mile in practically nothing flat: for didn't each and every monk jump at precisely the same instant?

FIG. 11. The Abbé Nollet sends a current flow through a circle of monks.

The Abbé noted also that all the monks felt the shock equally. (He must have measured the leap of each monk, making allowance for his normal agility.) It is related that the invited audience of French nobles and their ladies were much impressed by the demonstration. The common people enjoyed similar demonstrations of smaller proportions staged by traveling shows of the time.

Current from Leyden jars was heavy enough to heat up pieces of gold and lengths of wire, and this fact also provoked a multitude of experiments. Du Fay, the Frenchman who had anticipated Franklin in discovering that there are two kinds of electricity, now succeeded in sending some of the charge from a friction machine along a wet thread for about one thousand feet. But Dr. William Watson, an Englishman, sent the discharge current from a Leyden jar a distance of 12,276 feet "along" a wire.

This long-distance record of almost two and one-half miles was possible because of the condenser's lower voltage. The condenser can provide much more electricity (more electrons) than the friction machine *for the same voltage*. (The difference between current and voltage is explained in the next section.) But even so, the current capacity was still too low and the voltage still too high. Experimenters who tried to build a telegraph system with the jars were doomed to failure. The small amounts of electricity they were able to transmit for any distance made the received signal too much of a problem. They tried tiny sparks, swinging pith balls, the attraction of a charged wire for a bit of gold leaf, but to no avail. What they needed was a steadily maintained current flow of much lower voltage; in other words, a steady supply of fewer electrons. The first device to provide this was the combination of chemical cells, or battery, invented in Italy in 1800 by the man after whom the unit of electrical pressure was later named, Alessandro Volta.

Alessandro Giuseppe Antonio Anastasio Volta was born in 1755 in what is now a popular resort town, Como, in Lombardy. During his school years, Volta seemed destined to become a poet, but for some reason, when he was 24, he switched to science. He never had reason to regret it, for his long life, aside from the historic controversy with fellow scientists over what made his battery go, ran smoothly and was filled with honors, fame, and fortune. The Royal Society of London, in 1794, awarded Volta the Copley Medal for his work on the condenser. Marrying late in life, at 49, he had three small children to divert him when he retired at the age of 60, after a lifetime of teaching and research, first in Como and later at the University of Pavia. His final years were spent with wife and children, and two brothers who were in the church. He never completely abandoned research, spending much of his time and energy aiding the nearby farmers, particularly in combating crop diseases. A modest fortune and a pension from the government relieved him of money worries. He died in 1837, aged 82.

Volta's most famous invention was his famous pile, or *pila,* the first battery. He had an assist from his countryman, Luigi Galvani, Professor of Anatomy at the University of Bologna. Galvani's discovery was another of those lucky accidents so common in science. The story is told that while dissecting a frog on a table near an electric (friction) machine, he was struck by a strange occurrence. When he touched the nerves of the frog with his scalpel at the same time that a spark was being drawn from the nearby machine, the frog's legs were violently convulsed.

Puzzled, Galvani made many experiments trying to solve the mystery. One day, six years later, he noted the same effect in the frog when a thunderstorm was raging in the vicinity. Then he discovered that he could also cause the frog's leg to contract suddenly by means of two metals—a short length of copper or brass in the frog's spinal cord and an iron plate attached to its feet. The spasm occurred when he completed the circuit through the metals and the frog by touching the copper to the iron. It seemed obvious enough that with the electric machine or lightning the frog merely picked up or detected the electricity; but with the metals, where did it originate? In the metals or in the frog?

Galvani was convinced he had made the marvelous discovery that the electricity was generated by the nerve of the frog; which led him to believe that the electric fluid explains *vitality* in the animal organism. So he called it *animal electricity*.

After repeating Galvani's experiments, Volta accepted his vital-fluid theory. But soon he became skeptical. To Galvani, the copper wire and iron plate were merely conductors of the electricity; but Volta proved, at least to his own satisfaction, that the metals had more than that to do with the frog's convulsions, for he used two pieces of the same metal and got no reaction.

Volta had previously generated minute charges on two different metals, such as copper and zinc, merely by bringing them together. He called it *contact electricity*. In our experiments of Chapter 2, we called it frictional electricity. Volta detected the charges by means of an *electroscope*. And so, said Volta in 1792, the electricity in the frog was merely contact electricity. This stung the Bologna anatomist into further activity, for he thought he had settled the matter; and soon he was getting a very slight twitch of the frog's muscle by means of two pieces of the *same metal*. Volta verified this, but he also pointed out that one of the metals had to be slightly different from the other one in some fashion: had to be clean and bright while the other was discolored (by oxidation), or had to be hot while the other was cold.

And then a follower of Galvani actually succeeded in causing a slight twitch of the frog's muscle without the use of any metal at all. He merely bent the nerve around until it touched the muscle at the other end. So there it was, all sealed up and delivered: Galvani's diagnosis of animal electricity was correct.

But Volta was stubborn—fortunately. He said that the nerve and the muscle merely took the place of different metals, or of the same metal if the two were in some way dissimilar. And the next victory was his. He obtained a current flow by using copper and zinc plates that were separated not by a moist frog but by moist *paper*.

The controversy was soon blazing again among Europe's scientists as to whether the electricity was animal in its origin, as Galvani had contended (he died in 1798), or was generated by contact, as Volta's latest experiment seemed to prove. Volta was way ahead in the argument when another Italian scientist, Giovanni Gabroni, fanned the flames once more with his theory of the *chemical* origin of the electricity. Finally, in 1806, Sir Humphry Davy, the English scientist, got the fire under control, at least, with some satisfaction to both contact and chemical advocates. Sir Humphry had completed, for the first time, the electrolysis experiment described on page 8. This indicated the action was chemical, though he acknowledged that contact itself might still have something to do with the current flow. The argument smoldered on for years. As late as 1839 Faraday was still trying to convince the "contact men," as he called them, that chemical action was the answer.

But Galvani, with his animal electricity, was on the right track too: electricity *is* closely related to life. Not only will electricity stimulate a nerve, but it works the other way 'round: each time a nerve is stimulated, or each time a muscle contracts, a surge of electricity is generated. By means of modern radio tubes we can magnify (amplify) the electricity millions of times. The doctor is finding these tiny nerve and muscle voltages increasingly useful in diagnosis.

Almost from the beginning Volta combined a number of units of his "pairs of metals" to make his famous pile. The order was: copper plate, moist paper, zinc plate, moist paper, copper plate, moist paper, etc. (Fig. 12). Arago, French

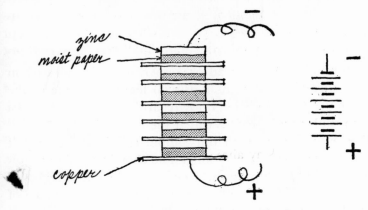

FIG. 12. Volta's pile, the first battery.

physicist and astronomer, said that in his opinion Volta's pile was "the most marvelous instrument that human intelligence had ever created." But Arago was notorious for extravagant eulogy.

Volta wasn't long in discovering that, if the paper discs were moistened with a dilute salt or acid solution, he got more electricity. (The plain water contained enough impurities to function feebly.) From this it was but a short step to his *crown of cups*. Each *goblet,* or *cell,* was half filled with salt-water solution. His electrodes were strips of zinc and silver. Two or more of such units made up a *battery* of cells.

Zinc and copper electrodes in a glass jar of a sulphuric-acid solution make a simple experimental cell (Fig. 13).

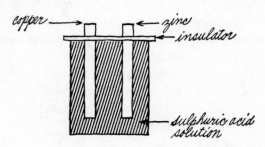

Fig. 13.   Simple experimental cell.

Carbon may be used instead of copper, even though carbon is not a metal. And we might as well learn the name of the between-the-plates solution now: regardless of whether it is a salt, an acid, or a base, it is called the *electrolyte.*

The only trouble with our simple cell is that it won't generate electricity for very long. The chemical action causes oxygen to bubble up at the zinc electrode (negative) and hydrogen to rise at the copper electrode (positive). Some of the hydrogen-gas bubbles cling to the surface of the copper. Now, hydrogen is an insulator, and as the bubbles accumulate they remove more and more of the copper's surface from contact with the electrolyte. This reduces cell efficiency by lowering the generated voltage. Ways were soon found to correct this "bubble trouble," or *polarization,* as it is technically known.

The development of Volta's battery to its present level of efficiency has been largely a matter of finding better materials to use between the conducting plates: from Galvani's frog to Volta's moist paper to salt solutions, and finally to acid solutions. Some day when you are having a New England boiled dinner, you might try converting it to an electric cell by inserting an electrode of a metal different from that of the pot. A silver spoon, say, inserted in the pot (insulated from it) would provide a cell à la Volta. It will work better if the cook has added salt. And as you eat the dinner it may merely be traveling from one battery to another; for the human mouth, if the teeth have fillings of dissimilar metals, such as gold and silver, is also a chemical cell. Saliva is a good electrolyte. Half a volt may be generated.

A superior between-the-plates material was provided in 1868 by a Frenchman, Georges Leclanché. The Leclanché cell was the first of today's ubiquitous "dry" cells. His electrodes were carbon and zinc; and between them he used crushed carbon, moistened with two chemicals. (One, sal ammoniac, was the electrolyte for the current flow; the other, manganese dioxide, was the *depolarizer*.)

Note that, in Volta's pile, copper is next to zinc, zinc next to copper, etc., like black and white beads on a string. This is what is known as a *series* connection. With a series connection the total voltage is the sum of all the individual cell voltages. The two or three cells in a flashlight battery are connected in series. Radio's standard 45-volt B battery has 30 series-connected cells, each cell providing about a volt and a half. (Still necessary in portable radios; a miniature version is used in hearing aids.) As early as 1809, Sir Humphry Davy, in London, was using a battery of 2,000 cells, providing close to 3,000 volts. Sir Humphry could have connected all 2,000 cells in *parallel,* like horses harnessed abreast, and gotten only a volt and a half from them, though the total volume of *current* available from the battery would have been 2,000 times greater than from a single cell.

So far we have learned that we can generate a voltage by

placing a pair of dissimilar metals in any kind of salt or acid solution. The same is true of a *base* solution. But what happens in the solution to give us the voltage? How is *chemical* energy transformed to *electrical* energy? Electron theory, front and center!

You remember how we caused ionization in the gas of a Crookes tube or a neon sign by applying a voltage to it. But when we add a salt, an acid, or a base to water, no voltage is needed for ionization. *The act of solution itself breaks up the molecules into positive and negative ions.*

Consider the solution in the simple cell of Fig. 13. The sulphuric-acid molecule is written H_2SO_4, which means it contains two hydrogen atoms, one sulphur atom, and four oxygen atoms (page 9). In solution, this molecule breaks up into three parts: two separate hydrogen atoms and what is left of the molecule SO_4. In addition, each of the three parts acquires a charge: both hydrogen atoms lose an electron, which converts them to positive ions; the lost electrons stay with the SO_4 group, which converts it to a negative ion— a double-negative ion, actually, written SO_4^{--}. Each positive hydrogen ion is written H^+.

Placing the pair of dissimilar metal plates in this ionized solution starts the electro-chemical action. The SO_4 negative ions attack the surface of the zinc electrode, pulling positive ions from it; this charges the zinc negatively. At the same time, the positive hydrogen ions are attracted to the copper electrode, removing electrons from the copper to leave it positively charged. (The hydrogen ions, having regained their electrons, become whole again and rise to the surface as hydrogen gas, causing polarization.)

Although an external circuit enables the zinc's surplus electrons to reach the copper, they can never make up for the copper's deficit so long as chemical action continues (Fig. 14B).

Though the principle was discovered in 1800, the first

practical storage battery didn't appear until 1859. It used lead plates in dilute sulphuric acid. Today's greatly improved battery retains the acid but has one electrode of sponge lead, one of lead peroxide. It was invented in 1880 by Faure in France and Brush in America.

3

We can use the output of Volta's battery to make crystal clear the difference between *current* and *voltage*. Fig. 14A shows a battery with its external circuit *open* (not completed). The magnitude of its voltage is determined by the number of surplus electrons on the negative pole, which is always equal to the number missing from the positive pole. There is an electrical force or pressure between the two poles, even though it is not being put to any use. It is often called a *potential,* because it is there, waiting to go into action, like a boxer waiting for the bell. The commonly used word for potential is *voltage.*

Next, let's *close* (complete) the circuit of Fig. 14A, as shown in Fig. 14B. This permits electrons to move from the negative to the positive pole. Such a directed electron *move-*

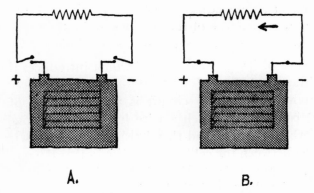

A.　　　　**B.**

FIG. 14.   Current and voltage. (A) Storage battery has voltage, even with circuit open. (B) Closing circuit permits current flow, distributing voltage throughout the circuit. Most of voltage will be across the resistor.

ment is called a current. The voltage, of course, is still there; though now that it accompanies the current it is said to be *distributed* throughout the circuit.

The size of the current flow is determined by the number of electrons that gets through the circuit in any given period of time. The time element is the clue to an understanding of current. A trillion electrons through a circuit each second means more than a trillion electrons each minute; just as a $100 salary does a man more good if he gets it every week than if he gets it every month. Current is measured in *amperes*.

You may be curious at this point as to just how many electrons pass a given point in a circuit each second when one ampere of current is present. It's a number which, if we were again dealing in dollars instead of electrons, would make the national debt look like small change. It is 6,250,000,000,000,-000,000 electrons; and as you can well imagine, it's not a number that is ever used in practical calculations. Almost as many electrons pass through a 100-watt lamp each second, for a lamp of this size uses almost an ampere of current.

Everything on this planet is constantly changing and nothing lasts forever; the battery is no exception. In the dry cell, the electro-chemical action consumes the zinc. Now, what is it that determines the *intensity* of cell action and thus governs its length of life? We find the answer to this in the nature of its external circuit, which introduces the idea of resistance.

Suppose the external circuit is a short length of heavy (thick) copper wire. Such a wire has so many loosely held outer-orbit electrons, and they have such a short, wide road to travel between the cell's two terminals, that the wire offers very little opposition to the voltage. The effect of this is to speed up its electro-chemical action to such a degree that it is quickly exhausted. The cell acts like an engine that has lost its governor. We say that it is *shorted,* and nearly every one knows that shorting a dry cell, or any kind of battery, is the handiest way to ruin it.

On the other hand, a large coil of very fine (thin) copper wire would limit the current flow to a mere trickle in comparison, and the electro-chemical action of the cell would be correspondingly less intense. The fewer vagrant electrons in the long, thin wire not only must fight their way through a narrower passageway, they also have much farther to go. An *iron* wire of the same size and length would offer still greater opposition to the cell's voltage, because iron has fewer loosely held outer-orbit electrons than copper.

The opposition offered by a circuit to an applied voltage is called its *resistance*. The unit of resistance is the *ohm*.

Each of the above examples illustrates one of the properties that determine the resistance of a circuit. 1. Its chemical composition. Silver, with the most loosely held electrons, has the least resistance; though copper is almost as good and is so much cheaper that it is the universal conductor. Gold is third, aluminum fourth. 2. The size of the conductor. The thicker it is, the lower its resistance. 3. The length of the conductor. The longer it is, the greater its resistance, because of the longer distance the electrons must travel. Ordinary house wiring has about four ohms of resistance per thousand feet of wire. The power lost in this resistance shows up on the light bill each month.

The relationship between the units of pressure, current flow, and resistance, is a happy one; one volt will force one ampere of current through one ohm of resistance. The beginnings of these basic units were not so happy. They had their origin in the mind of a struggling German scientist and teacher by the name of Georg S. Ohm, who, I think, deserves a chapter to himself.

6

GEORG OHM WRITES A LAW

GEORG S. OHM was born in the university town of Erlangen, Bavaria, on March 16, 1789, the year in which George Washington became our first president.

Ohm came from a family of locksmiths; his paternal grandfather, his father, his uncle, were all locksmiths, and his sister married one. His mother died when he was ten. The father had a taste for philosophy and mathematics, inherited by Georg and his younger brother Martin. He decided to give the boys a university education, providing they also applied themselves to becoming skilled locksmiths. He knew that philosophy and mathematics were meat and potatoes to a man's soul, but he was also convinced that when it came to providing these items for the table, locksmithing was more dependable. The boys disappointed him in this respect, for though both learned the trade neither followed it. Martin became a professor of mathematics at the Military College in Berlin, and Georg discovered a key that opened a vastly more important door than ever swung on a pair of hinges.

Georg Ohm studied philosophy, mathematics, and physics in the University of Erlangen. After three years, lack of means forced him to leave and take a job as tutor in a private school in Switzerland. A small and weakly youth, he made a bad impression at first, though he soon proved himself a good teacher. Later he was able to return to Erlangen for his degree as Doctor of Philosophy.

For the next six years Ohm's road was a rocky one. He was vitally interested in mechanics, light, and color, but he had little free time, from teaching, for experiment. He took a job at Bamberg, where he was miserable. He managed, however, to publish a book in 1817. He tried using the book as a lever to get him a teaching job that would leave him more time for research. The King of his own Bavaria wasn't impressed, but Prussia's King William III was, and he gave Ohm the post of instructor of mathematics and physics at the Jesuits' College at Cologne. At Cologne he found friends, appreciation, a library, apparatus, and freedom to pursue his research. His nine years there, until 1826, were the happiest of his life. Meanwhile his idea was slowly taking shape in his mind. He thought he could complete the work if given a year's leave of absence, which the college graciously granted him, and he went to live with his mathematician brother in Berlin. The following year, 1827, he published the pamphlet, *Mathematical Theory of the Galvanic Circuit,* which contains the basis of Ohm's Law.

At the time of its publication, experimenters knew that a short, thick wire was a better conductor than a long, thin one; but they lacked any proper system of electrical measurement. This was a serious drag on the progress of quantitative electrical investigation. Their only meter was a crude device, totally inadequate because they had no proper units of electricity (Fig. 20). One experimenter, the great English recluse-scientist, Henry Cavendish, used his body for a meter, gauging the amount of electricity by the quality of the shock it gave him. He was said to have become quite expert in the technique. Cavendish Laboratory is his memorial.

Ohm's basic idea was that each current has within it a definite *intensity* or *pressure*. The circuit naturally opposes this pressure, the size of the opposition varying with the conductor's thickness, length, composition, even temperature. In any given circuit, the volume or quantity of current flow is always directly proportional to the pressure.

This seems simple enough today. But in Ohm's time the theory was so revolutionary that only a few of his fellow scientists endorsed it; the rest of them opposed it with such vigor that Ohm was unable to return to his happy home at Cologne. These men must have taken it pretty hard, for they even went so far as to insist that its author must be crazy.

Recognition for his achievement finally came from Great Britain, in 1841, when the Royal Society of London awarded him the Copley Medal. The council, in making the award, stated that Ohm had established for the first time the laws of the electric circuit. Many were still not convinced, however, and two years later Sir Charles Wheatstone said in a lecture: "Ohm's Law is not yet generally understood and admitted, even by many persons engaged in original research." So, if you're having trouble with it, there's plenty of illustrious precedent.

The 1881 Electrical Congress in Paris agreed that pressure would be measured in volts, after Volta the Italian; volume in amperes, after Ampère the Frenchman, and resistance in ohms, after Ohm the German.

The Paris Congress took a leaf from Faraday's book of experiments when it chose the measuring method: the amount of current passing through a solution of nitrate of silver that deposits .0011800 gram of silver on the positive electrode each second. An ohm, said the Congress, is the resistance offered by a column of mercury of certain definite dimensions and a certain temperature. A volt is the pressure needed to push one ampere of current through one ohm of resistance. (These so-called international units differ slightly from the ones in use today.)

The relationship between volt, ampere, and ohm is beautifully simple; though mathematics will have to crash the party before we can put it to work. Mathematics, to a great many people, is a foreign language, one that uses symbols and numbers in place of words. But it's a language that always speaks right to the point, in a way that makes a simple declarative sentence look anemic. Its main concern is with the sizes rather than the sorts of things. Despite this, the things it talks about in electricity are only concepts, ideas, such as Ohm's electrical pressure, rather than the common-sense things we can see, smell, or touch directly. For example, it says: $I = E/R$. (I is for current flow, E for voltage, and R for resistance.)

Suppose we test $I = E/R$, bearing in mind that one volt will force one ampere through one ohm of resistance. Substituting these figures for E and R we get $I = 1/1$. Or, $I = 1$ ampere, which is correct. Next, combine the single volt with two ohms of resistance; with the resistance doubled, we would expect the current flow to be halved. Substituting again, $I = 1/2$ ampere, which bears this out. Finally, doubling the voltage should give us twice the current flow, and substituting once more we get $I = 2/1$. Or, $I = 2$ amperes.

If $I = E/R$, then it is also true that $R = E/I$, and $E = IR$. The logic of this is apparent if we substitute some simple numbers for I, E, and R in the first formula. Thus, if $3 = 6/2$, then $2 = 6/3$, and $6 = 2 \times 3$. If one knows any two of the three factors, the third can always be found by means of one of these formulas or equations.

$E = IR$ is easy to remember because EIR are the first three letters of Eire, the Irish Republic.

2

The electron theory tells us that when a voltage is applied to a conductor it receives electrons at the negative end, and almost at the same instant starts losing electrons at the positive end (page 30); Ohm's law enables us to figure the size of the electron current on the basis of voltage and resistance ($I = E/R$). Now let's put the theoretical and the practical together for a little further study of the simple electrical circuit.

The radio or television tube, versatile as it is, has one thing in common with an ordinary light bulb: a filament. The circuit of Fig. 15 has in it the filaments of a string of

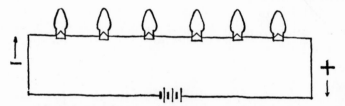

FIG. 15. Christmas-tree lights are often connected in series.

Christmas-tree lights, connected to a battery for power. It is a *series* connection, like the Abbé Nollet's monks. This method of hooking up lights has one disadvantage: if one lamp burns out, it opens up the circuit and darkens the whole string.

Practically all the resistance in this simple circuit is concentrated in the tungsten filaments. Some of the concentration can be accounted for because tungsten has about three times the resistance of copper; but most of it we must attribute to the *size* of each filament: each one is hundreds of times *smaller in diameter* than the copper wire (page 59).

A wire placed between a positive and a negative charge (voltage) gains electrons at one end *at the same rate* that it loses them at the opposite end (Fig. 6). In other words, the electrons leave the wire at the same rate that they enter it. This means there can be no damming up of the electrons at any point in the circuit. Therefore, in the circuit of Fig. 15, there must be just as many electrons passing through the high-resistance tungsten filaments as through the low-resistance copper wire each second. The law the kids in school wrestle with is this: *The current flow is always the same in all parts of a series circuit.* Even though each filament has hundreds of times the resistance of the copper wire, it must carry the same volume of current. How should the electrons act under these conditions?

The copper wire is not only much larger than the tungsten, it has many more detachable electrons available for current flow. It follows that if the same number of electrons are to get through the tungsten as get through the copper each second, they must travel at a much faster clip. Now, the heat and light are caused by collisions between the electrons and the atoms or molecules, just as in a Crookes tube. In the tungsten, therefore, the fewer available electrons must not only be faster moving to keep the volume of current the same, they must also battle their way through a narrower passageway. This means more violent and more frequent collisions with the atoms. As a result, the filament gets so hot it gives off light, while the copper stays as cool as Carlsbad Caverns.

What the tungsten filament really amounts to is a "bottleneck." A bottleneck in the highway would create a similar situation if the motorists, instead of slowing down for it, were forced to maintain their speed. The result would be a tangle of burning wrecks. An electron bottleneck in a wire always causes heat, even light if it is serious enough, as is the case in the light bulb.

This theory of resistance is supported by the fact that a metal's resistance increases with heat. The physicist can reduce the temperature of metals to within a small fraction of absolute zero, —273 C. At this stage of "coldness" electrical resistance in 22 elements, alloys, and compounds seems to disappear. On March 16, 1954, Professor S. C. Collins of MIT used an electric field to induce a current of several hundred amperes in a "supercold" lead ring. Two and one half years later the same volume of current was still flowing. Why the apparently *zero* resistance? It appears that the extreme cold so quiets down the normally restive atoms that the electrons pass through with small danger of collision.

Next, let's examine the relationship of our electron bottle-neck to Ohm's unit of pressure, the volt. The bottleneck, being the high point of resistance in the circuit, needs most of the battery voltage to get the electrons through it; and so most of the total applied voltage is "lost" there. The electrician says that this voltage is *dropped*. The voltage between each pair of filament terminals is called a *voltage drop*.

The voltage needed to push the electrons through the wire is also a voltage drop, but it is so small that it usually can, as the electrician says, be neglected. An ordinary voltmeter placed across one of the connecting sections of wire wouldn't even register.

This brings us to the second law of the series circuit: *The applied voltage divides among the various parts of the series circuit in direct proportion to the resistance of each part.* The filaments of Fig. 15, having practically all the resistance in the circuit, get almost all the voltage ($E = IR$).

Pockets of resistance, called *resistors,* are almost as plentiful in the wiring of a radio set as commercials on a station break. A radio may have a dozen resistors, a television receiver many more. A radio's volume control, for example, is a *variable* resistor, as are most controls and adjustments on video sets. The volume control may be placed in series with the detector tube; and as the total voltage will divide between the tube and the resistor, in direct proportion to the resistance of each, the larger the resistor the higher the voltage across it. A high voltage across the resistor is desirable, because its voltage is transferred to the next tube, an amplifying tube. Thus the set plays the loudest when all of the resistor (perhaps 500,000 ohms) is in the circuit. (See VC for volume control in Fig. 57. With arrow at top of resistor (jagged line) the amplifier gets full voltage, because all the resistance is then *across* that tube.)

Now a word about *power,* which is expressed in *watts.* Each lamp in Fig. 15 gives the same amount of light. We know that in this series circuit each filament has the same amount of current flow, and the same voltage across it. (Voltages are the same because resistances are equal: $E = IR$.) And it can be proved by experiment that the current flow and the voltage contribute equally to the power consumed. In the magic of mathematics, if we multiply the volts by the amperes we get the power consumption in watts: $P = EI$.

The tubes in the popular little a.c.-d.c. radio also have their filaments connected in series. Unlike the Christmas-tree lights, some of them need more power than the others, and these filaments have a higher resistance to give them more voltage. Remember the current is the same through all of them, and $P = EI$.

If the Abbé Nollet had connected his monks in *parallel,* he would have lined them up as shown in Fig. 16. The first difference you notice about this connection is that one or more monks can be added to or taken out of the circuit without breaking it; for each individual monk has a direct connection to the Leyden jars, receiving the full voltage. This explains the difference between series and parallel circuits. The former has only a single path for the electrons; the latter has as many paths as there are devices connected to it.

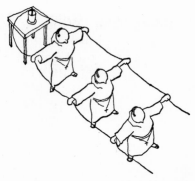

FIG. 16. The Abbé Nollet's monks connected in parallel.

The parallel circuit is the ideal one for use in home and factory. As Fig. 17 shows, you can plug in as many lamps or appliances as you wish: and with each electron bottleneck connected directly across the applied voltage, it draws current to an amount determined by the size of its resistance; the less the resistance the larger the current $(I = E/R)$. And at the same time any single bottleneck doesn't disturb the relationship of the others to the 110 volts. Of course, the number of bottlenecks is always limited, for if the sum of all the individual currents is too large, a fuse "blows" to protect the wiring—and the house.

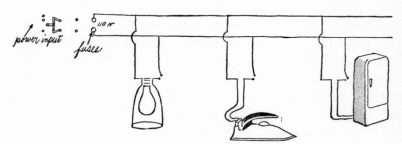

FIG. 17. Parallel circuit is best for the home.

In the parallel circuit, the lower the resistance of each device the more current it draws, and the more power it consumes $(P = EI)$. This might appear to contradict our statement that in a series circuit the device with the *most* resistance consumes the most power. However, it only consumes more power than the other devices in the circuit with it; the less the total resistance of the circuit the larger the current flow and the more power the circuit consumes. With the Christmas-tree lights, if we replace one of them with another of double the resistance, it will burn brighter than the first lamp; but at the same time the entire string will draw less current and the other lamps will be dimmer. How much brighter will the new lamp burn? Not twice as bright. This is the kind of problem that often makes young students of electricity wish they had taken up archery instead.

7

DO WE INHABIT A MAGNET?

MAGNETISM first found a practical use in the compass, which began to appear in the west over 800 years ago. Who invented the compass no one knows. His identity is buried under the same historical haystack that conceals the genius who first added tin to copper. There is evidence that the Chinese were familiar with it in ancient times, though it is doubtful if they ever put it to any good use. But we are certain of its presence on Arab, Italian, Portuguese, and Norwegian ships of the 12th century; and Baltic Sea vessels of the Finns and Lapps may have had it as early as the year 1000.

The gadget that bulges the pocket of a Boy Scout differs somewhat from this early sea-going compass, whose iron needle was fastened to a thin strip of cork or wood, or thrust into a reed, so it would float in a bowl of water. The needle was magnetized by contact with a natural magnet taken from the earth. When clouds hid the stars at night or shut off the sun in the daytime, the sailors must have found it as comforting to have on board as a rag doll to a child in bed.

As any encyclopedia will tell you, the natural magnet mentioned above is called a lodestone, which means *leading* stone, or a stone that leads. It was quite common in the ancient world. Lucretius, the Roman poet, wrote in 60 B.C. that the word magnet derives from the province of Magnesia, a district in what is now Asia Minor, where lodestones were plentiful. You can find them today at Magnet Cove, Arkansas. They are called magnetite, an iron ore (Fe_3C_4).

One of the best known of the ancient fables that sprang up around the mysterious stone told of "mountains in the north of such powers of attraction that ships had to be built with wooden pegs, because if iron nails were used they would be drawn from the timber."

Another Latin poet, Claudian (d. 408?), describes a miracle in the temple of Mars and Venus. A miniature scene shows a marriage chamber: purple coverlet, couch heaped with roses. The priest performs a marriage service for the two gods, followed by singing by the choir, with lights, color, and incense. Then the miracle! Venus, by her potent charms, suddenly draws Mars into her arms. As Claudian writes, she "clasps him to the bosom with amorous breath." The secret? Mars is made of polished iron, Venus is fashioned out of lodestone.

The materialism of the Ionians, which had its first apogee in the atomic theory of Democritus, failed to dent the main stream of Greek philosophy. Although Aristotle was the first classifier, the Greeks for the most part turned their backs on the material world. They felt that the practical arts were inferior. Nevertheless there were some instances of experiment and invention. Pythagoras reduced music to number when he showed that the tone from a plucked string was determined by its *length*—thickness and tension being equal. Strato, who succeeded Aristotle at the Lyceum at Athens, experimented with air pressures. He wrote: "The propagation of sound is due to air being an elastic medium which contracts and expands in accordance with the impulse imparted to it." Hero of Alexandria built a steam engine that operated on the jet principle, and there were a few other examples, such as Archimedes' screw. But as for the lodestone, there is no convincing evidence the Greeks knew that, if floated in water or suspended by a thread, it would come to rest in a north-south position.

As we have seen, the compass didn't appear on the scene in the west until something like 1,000 years later. Research on magnetism began during the years 1266–1269, when Charles of Anjou was besieging the city of Lucera in South Italy. In his camp was an engineer by the name of Magister Petrus de Maharne-Curie, who was better known by his Latin name of Peter Peregrinus. Peregrinus' job was to devise machines for hurling stones and fiery material at enemy fortifications. During the long siege, time hung heavy on his hands and he undertook to make some experiments with the lodestone. He described the results of these experiments in a long letter to a neighbor back home in Picardy. This letter, written in Latin, is the world's first treatise on magnetism.

Peregrinus was the first, so far as we know, to call the two ends of a lodestone the north and south poles. He writes of placing the lodestone on a large enough piece of wood to float it in water, and then noting which end pointed north. "If this pole were then turned away a thousand times, a thousand times would it return to its place by the will of God."

He describes how to make a mariner's compass with a scale and a lubber's line. And he states the fundamental law of magnetism: *Unlike poles attract each other, like poles repel each other.*

Peregrinus also notes that when he broke a magnet in two,

he didn't have isolated north and south poles; but instead, two complete magnets, each with a pair of poles.

Peregrinus, being an engineer, was a practical man, and he devised a method for putting the magnetic force to good use. In his letter he describes a machine with a magnetic wheel that "turns perpetually." He writes: "If it does not work, that fact is to be ascribed to the lack of mechanical skill on the part of the maker, rather than to inherent difficulties of the mechanism." It was plain that if his perpetual-motion machine slowed down to a stop there was nothing wrong with it that a little further tinkering wouldn't cure.

The kind of picture shown in Fig. 18 is familiar to every person who has ever cracked a book on elementary electricity. Peregrinus is credited with being the first to use bits of iron in this manner to reveal the magnetic force. Since Faraday we have thought of the force as consisting of *lines of magnetic force*.

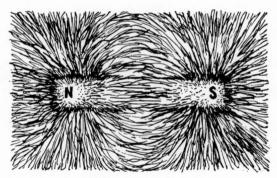

FIG. 18. Tiny bits of iron reveal "direction" of magnetic force.

It is apparent that the greater the distance from the magnet the weaker the field, not because the lines get weaker but because they are farther apart—just as the spokes of a wheel are farther apart at the rim than at the hub. The magnetic force diminishes with the square of the distance from its source—which is true also of electrostatic and gravitational forces (page 35).

Magnetic lines of force are certainly not "air-minded"! They much prefer travel through iron or the other magnetic materials, nickel and cobalt, where opposition to their passage is several thousand times less than it is in air. The U-shaped magnet brings the north and south poles close together, concentrating the lines of force in the shortest possible air path. Many electronic devices, including the loudspeaker, employ U-shaped or horseshoe magnets.

Peregrinus improved upon the mariner's crude floating compass, of doubtful value in rough weather, with a dry compass. He exposed the magnetized iron needle to the magnetic urge by balancing it on a pivot. But the device was still far from perfect; the first really good magnetic compass was Lord Kelvin's, introduced in 1876, the year of the American patent on the telephone. However, Peregrinus put his pivoted needle to good use in experiments with the "terrella," or "little earth," which he made. The terrella was nothing more than a chunk of lodestone, ground into the shape of the earth. When Peregrinus held a compass near his terrella, the needle aligned itself in relation to it just as it did in relation to the earth. But Peregrinus failed to see anything significant in this; to his dying day he clung to the poetic faith that the needle turned toward the "pole in the sky, deriving its power, in some way, from the whole of the universe." It remained for William Gilbert, over 300 years later, to discover from the same experiment that the compass needle points north and south because the earth itself is a magnet. However, Gilbert's theory that the earth is a giant magnet because it is made of a magnetic material, like the terrella, is no longer tenable. The magnetic field is supposed to pass through the earth's center; but if the earth's center is as hot as science believes it is, it can't possibly be magnetic.

Heat destroys magnetism. And the earth's crust contains very little magnetic material.

The latest theory has the earth a *dynamo*, like Faraday's original (page 92). There are electric *currents* in the earth's molten metal core (iron and nickel?) which may have *originated* in chemical action. They persist in the immense core as a result of its movement, caused by the earth's rotation. The individual currents add up to one with the proper direction for the earth's magnetic field (page 89).

The belief that it was a simple matter to *nullify* the lodestone's power persisted for a thousand years or so. All one had to do was to smear it with onion or garlic juice, or touch it with a diamond. Sailors who tended the compass were forbidden to eat onions or garlic, "lest they make the index of the poles drunk." It occurred to the 16th-century Italian, John Baptist Porta, to test this theory. He writes: "When I tried all these things, I found them to be false; for not only breathing and belching upon the lodestone after eating of garlic could not stop its virtues; but when it was anointed all over with the juice of the garlic it did perform its office as well as if it had never been touched with it, and I could observe almost not the least difference."

The happy thought that a telegraph system was available, in case of emergency, merely for the price of a pair of compasses also flourished in the 16th century. Each compass had to have the alphabet inscribed on its outer edge, so the needle could be made to point to the desired letter. Porta expressed his faith in the system in 1596 when he wrote: "I do not fear that with a long-absent friend, even though he is confined to prison walls, we can communicate with what we wish by means of two compass needles circumscribed with an alphabet." An Englishman, Sir Thomas Browne, is reported to have finally laid the theory to rest; no matter how many times he pointed the needle toward a certain letter, it had no more effect upon the other compass than the inner tension of today's impatient motorist has upon a red light.

2

William Gilbert's book, published in 1600, has the snappy title: *On the magnet, magnetic bodies also, and on the great magnet the earth; a new philosophy, demonstrated by many arguments and experiments.* There is only a short chapter on electricity, in which Gilbert points out that other substances besides amber can be "electrics," that is, can be electrified by friction.

Until this book appeared, there were many different theories on the compass, in addition to the "pole in the sky" theory of Peregrinus. Roger Bacon believed that the compass was influenced by the "four parts of the heavens as well"; and many, including Columbus, thought that the north star caused the needle to point north. There was also a popular belief in magnetic islands or rocks somewhere north of Greenland that attracted the lodestone. Some 16th-century charts show "magnetic mountains" rising out of the sea in the north. Gilbert put an end to all this with his theory that the earth itself is a "great magnet."

Gilbert tried to account for magnetic attraction both by means of a material effluvium and by an immaterial mind or soul. After Gilbert, however, philosophers began to lose interest in what was happening in the space between the magnet and the object of its affection, and concentrated on what took place inside the magnet itself. This type of speculation led to the fluid theories of magnetism of the 18th century, paralleling the fluid theories of electricity.

Franklin espoused a one-fluid theory, and Coulomb a two-fluid theory. According to Franklin, one pole of the magnet contained a different *amount* of fluid than the other; according to Coulomb, one pole contained a different *kind* of fluid than the other.

Today we lean upon the electron theory of magnetism, which states that the movement of the electrons around their central cores or nuclei makes each individual molecule a magnet. Each of those submicroscopic magnets has a north and a south pole, as indicated at the top of Fig. 19.

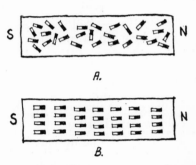

FIG. 19. Electronic theory of magnetism. (A) Partial magnetization. (B) Complete magnetization (saturation).

When a magnetic material such as iron or steel is completely magnetized, this vast army of tiny, individual magnets is lined up so that all north poles face in one direction, and all south poles in the opposite direction (Fig. 19B). Thus the billions of billions of individual molecular magnets, because they all face in the same direction, aid one another in creating a strong magnetic force. Such a magnet, at maximum strength, is said to be *saturated*.

With only partial magnetization, the number of mutually aiding molecular magnets is not complete; they're like a bunch of rookies that the sergeant has failed to line up properly. The result is a weaker field (Fig. 19A).

In an unmagnetized material, the individual molecular magnets are all "at ease"; the number facing in any one direction is always balanced by an approximately equal number facing in the opposite direction, completely canceling magnetic effect.

Many simple experiments support this theory of magnetism. 1. Either heating or jarring a magnet weakens it. Such treatment conceivably disorganizes the soldierly arrangement of the molecules. Jarring can also be used for the opposite effect; Gilbert made artificial magnets by hammering rods of iron on an anvil while they lay in the earth's magnetic field, pointing north and south. 2. Rapid magnetization or demagnetization creates heat in a magnet, which could be caused by the "frictional" effect of the rapidly reversing electron magnets. 3. An iron bar can be lightly magnetized by rotating it at terrific speed. Apparently the centrifugal force of rotation aligns some of the magnets parallel with the bar. This is known as cold magnetization.

But the electron theory of magnetism is still inadequate. Why aren't the molecules of *copper* magnetic? And why is it possible to obtain a magnetic material from an alloy of three wholly nonmagnetic materials, copper, aluminum, and magnesium? Another alloy, containing 85 percent iron, isn't magnetic at all. Your radio or television loudspeaker uses a small, powerful, permanent magnet made chiefly of aluminum, nickel, and cobalt, only the last two being magnetic. It is called *alnico*.

Quantum mechanics has theories which at least partially account for it, but they're beyond the scope of this book.

8

OERSTED'S COMPASS POINTS THE WAY

Good old gravity is the force that keeps us all pinned to the earth till our time comes; electromagnetism is the force that operates radio, television, movies, phonographs, and other devices to divert us while we're here. On the surface, these two forces seem as far apart as a squirrel cage and an atomic pile. Nevertheless, science has long been seeking a relationship, and after 30 years of labor Einstein may now have it in his new unified-field theory.

If Einstein's theory is verified, it will mean a truly great triumph for science. Science enjoyed just such a triumph in 1820, when Hans Christian Oersted (*Ur*-sted) discovered the relationship between electricity and magnetism. Prior to this, scientists generally had believed that electricity and magnetism were total strangers to each other: each was accounted for by a different kind of weightless (imponderable) fluid.

Compared with Einstein's new field theory, with its involved mathematics, Oersted's discovery of *electromagnetism* seems a simple affair. Despite this, however, it was a great discovery, for without electromagnetism our electrical age would not have been possible.

The first product of Oersted's discovery was the electromagnet, which is simply a coil of wire. Wound on an iron core, it becomes several thousand times more powerful. The power can be controlled by regulating the size of the current flow through the coil.

Until the advent of the electromagnet, the use of the direct current from Volta's battery, superior as it was to the high-voltage, spasmodic current from Leyden jars, was confined to the laboratory. Humphry Davy, Faraday's mentor, used his 4,000-volt battery in the experiments that led to the discovery of the elements sodium and potassium in 1807.

The first practical application of the electromagnet was to the telegraph. Wedded to Volta's battery, it produced the clicking telegraph sounder. Another issue from this marriage was the telephone, whose receiver later evolved into radio's loudspeaker.

But something much bigger was to come from the electromagnet: Faraday's generator. Only the generator can provide us with the vast quantity of cheap electric power necessary to light our cities, run our factories and street cars, and perform countless other tasks, from powering a mine hoist to heating a blanket.

Hans Christian Oersted was born in Denmark in 1777, twelve years before Georg Ohm. Both boys were fortunate in drawing fathers with a love for learning and a determination to give their offspring the very best kind of education. Oersted's father was a poor druggist on the island of Langeland, whose schools were also poor. Disregarding them, papa Oersted hired a German barber and wig maker to school Hans Christian and his brother Anders in German. The barber's wife taught them to read and write. Arithmetic was not the Teutons' strong point, and the job of initiating them into the mysteries of division and multiplication fell to a friendly schoolboy. The baker taught them some drawing, the burgomaster some French, the local surveyor what he knew of mathematics. To complete this educational cocktail, when Hans was twelve a dash of chemistry from his father's pharmacy was added. The cocktail proved potent enough to enable the boys to pass the entrance examination at the University of Copenhagen. The state paid part of their expenses, and they turned to teaching to earn the rest.

Hans and his brother, who was studying law, shared a common interest in their school subjects; they shared expenses and a common lodging; they even shared a single friend, Denmark's great poet, Oehlenschlager. But the poet had a sister, and she proved their cooperative Waterloo. She married Anders. Years later, Hans found conjugal happiness with Inger Bellum, a parson's daughter. They had three sons and four daughters. A good friend of Oersted's bequeathed to the youngest daughter the manuscripts of some fairy tales he had written. His name was Hans Christian Andersen.

Young Oersted's range of academic interests was wide. He won a gold medal for an essay "On the Limits of Poetry and Prose," and a prize for his efforts in metaphysics. His favorite philosopher was Kant, whose metaphysics oriented him toward a faith in a common identity for all the various manifestations of energy: heat, light, electricity, magnetism.

Hans earned his degree of Doctor of Philosophy in the same year that Volta introduced his crown-of-cups battery, 1800. He jumped at the opportunity for research provided by the new steady current flow. After vainly searching for an identity between electrical and chemical forces in the battery, he became intrigued with the possibility of a close relationship between electricity and magnetism. If a current flow can produce heat, for example, why shouldn't it also produce magnetism? He knew that lightning, at a distance, could reverse the poles of a magnet; and that the electric discharge from a Leyden jar could do the same thing. Franklin had seen in this evidence proof that lightning was electricity. Oersted was 42 years old when he demonstrated that electricity does produce magnetism.

Like Musschenbroek's discovery of the condenser and Galvani's discovery of his "animal electricity" that led to Volta's battery, it was something of an accident. But because he had been seeking such a relationship for so long, he immediately recognized its significance. Perhaps other experimenters before him had noted the same effect, but thought they must have been mistaken because it didn't fit in with preconceived notions. "Such accidents meet only persons who deserve them," Lagrange said, writing of Newton. And Pasteur said, "Chance favors only the prepared mind."

Oersted, along with others, had spent patient hours exploring the region around a charged Leyden jar with a compass; and he had many times placed a compass near a current carrying wire. In neither case had he gotten any results. In the case of the electrostatic charge, it has no magnetism; in the case of the current flow his mistake had been to place the needle at right angles to its direction of flow, expecting it to swing around parallel to the wire. In view of the prevailing theory for natural forces in the universe, any electromagnetic force should be exerted in the same direction as the current flow. But one day he said to his students, gathered around him, "Let us try once, now that the battery is handy, placing the magnetic needle *parallel* to the wire." (The story is told in a letter to Faraday, years later, by a Professor Hansteen.) As the professor carefully manipulated the gear, his heart suddenly started to race. The students looked at him inquiringly. The needle had moved! Or had it? Perhaps it was only his imagination.

After class he used a larger battery and there was no doubt about it: the needle swung around until it was at right angles to the wire, which meant that the magnetic force was exerted at *right angles* to the direction of current flow. (In Fig. 20, enough current in the coil will force the needle to a position at right angles to it.) In view of the physics of Galileo and Newton, all forces should act along a straight line joining the two attracting or repelling bodies. This was true of gravitational, electrostatic, and magnetic forces.

The name of the young poet-scientist of Copenhagen was soon famous all over Europe. The Royal Society of London, recognizing the importance of his discovery, awarded him the Copley Medal. Today's unit for magnetic intensity is the *oersted*.

The important discoveries that followed were all made by others: Ampère and Arago in France, Schweigger in Germany, Davy and Faraday in England, and Henry in America. The final, culminating discovery, that not only is a flow of current accompanied by magnetism, but that magnetism can produce a flow of current, was made by Faraday and is covered in the next chapter. But it was Ampère who first picked up the ball and carried it after Oersted's epochal breakthrough with the compass. The news of a kinship between magnetism and electricity galvanized him into action. He reasoned that if a wire carrying a current moved a permanent magnet (compass needle), such a wire must itself be a magnet. Therefore, two current-carrying wires should exert mechanical forces upon each other, just as two permanent magnets do.

Ampère needed only a few days to lay the foundation for electrodynamics (electrical forces) for all generations to come. Two current-carrying wires, if parallel, attract each other when the current flows are in the same direction in both wires; repel each other if the current flows are in opposite directions. He also provided the necessary mathematics.

It wasn't until some years after the development of Faraday's generator that an effective method for utilizing the electromagnetic force was discovered, in the electric motor.

Ampère and others soon learned how to concentrate the magnetic force that surrounds a current-carrying wire: by coiling the wire. The force is strongest close to either end of this *electromagnet*, which is also true of the bar magnet. An electromagnet, pivoted on its side, like a compass needle, will also come to rest in a north-south position.

Other revealing experiments quickly followed. Dominique François Arago, at Paris, saw that if an ordinary steel needle is placed inside a coil, lengthwise, the current flow in the coil will magnetize it. Sir Humphry Davy, assisted by Faraday, made the same discovery at about the same time. These men also found that a steel needle could be magnetized in this way when the current in the coil came from a Leyden

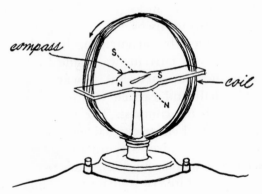

FIG. 20. First current-measuring meter. The earth's magnetism aligns the magnetized needle in a north-south position and holds it there—as long as there is no current in the coil. But current in the coil creates another magnetic field or force that opposes the earth's; the result is a "tug of war" between the two fields for the position of the needle. Most of today's meters are essentially the same, except that the earth magnet has been replaced by a U-shaped permanent magnet, the compass needle by a movable coil that turns on its axis. The current flows through the movable coil, whose magnetic field opposes the field of the permanent magnet. Attached to the coil is a needle that moves over a scale to register the size of the current flow.

jar which had been charged by a friction machine. This proved that chemical electricity from a battery is no different from frictional electricity—a point that had not been resolved up to that time.

A German chemist, Johann S. C. Schweigger, invented the first device for measuring electricity, now called the galvanometer (gal-va-*nom*-e-ter) after Galvani. Schweigger simply placed the compass needle inside a coil of wire (Fig. 20).

9

THE ANSWER: FARADAY'S COILS

CONDENSER, battery, electron current, magnet, electromagnet; our pace may seem slow enough to make Shakespeare's schoolboy crawling toward his books look as if he was shot out of a crossbow; though this step-by-step approach to electronics should pay handsome dividends later when we step off the deep end into its "magical" aspects. In this chapter we learn how Michael Faraday took Volta's current flow and Oersted's compass experiment and parlayed them into the foundation of our electrical and electronic age.

Would we have had our electric lighting, our motors and generators, radios and television sets, if this blacksmith's son had never lived? Undoubtedly, though the harnessing of electrical energy would perhaps have been somewhat delayed.

The scientist whose researches would have provided the foundation was Joseph Henry of Albany, New York. As a matter of fact, two of the three discoveries involved were made independently by both men, in slightly different ways. Henry was first with two of these. But Faraday was first to publish his findings, and to him has gone the credit. It must be admitted, though, that Faraday also contributed a theory, since proved invaluable. We can put this theory into three little words: *lines of force.*

We are already familiar with both kinds of these lines of force: those that surround a static charge, such as the charge on our pith ball or on the plates of a condenser (electrostatic), and those that surround a current flow (electromagnetic).

The man whose devotion to science was destined to have such an impact on our lives was born in Newington Butts, London, September 22, 1791, one of a family of ten children. Michael left home when he was thirteen to work in a London bookseller and stationer's shop. A year later he was apprenticed to his employer as a bookbinder. But this young man was far from happy, sitting all day long putting covers on books. He had within him an itch for self-improvement, both of mind and morals. He carried in his pocket Dr. Watt's *Improvement of the Mind,* and he dipped recklessly into the books he was binding. His master wrote of him: "His mode of living is temperate, seldom drinking other than pure clean water, and when done his day's work would set himself down in the workshop [to read], regardless of his fellow prentices. If I had any curious book from my customers to bind, with plates, he would copy such as he thought singular or clever. Ireland's *Hogarth* and other graphic works he much admired."

Michael was busy with his hands, too, during the few leisure hours the apprentice system allowed. He made a Volta battery and a small friction machine for generating electricity. He also acquired some chemicals and performed a few simple experiments.

Faraday's master "gave him leave" to attend occasional lectures on science, where he took notes. Later he would write out the lectures in full, enlivening the text with his own diagrams and illustrations. It was this habit that eventually enabled him, as he phrased it, "to escape from the vicious and selfish bookbinder's trade into the service of science." He had put together in his usual fashion some of the lectures of Humphry Davy and mailed them to the famous chemist. Davy was impressed, and later, when a laboratory assistant's post was open, he offered it to Faraday.

Davy was a reigning favorite of his time as a lecturer on science. He was among the first "popularizers" of science, and his lectures drew packed houses from among the élite. His long list of achievements includes the arc light, laughing gas, the miner's safety lamp, and discovery of the elements sodium, potassium, barium, boron, calcium, and strontium; though his greatest discovery, by far, was Michael Faraday.

Faraday went to work for the experts in 1813 when he was 22 years old at a smaller salary, 25 shillings weekly, than he had been earning; he had rooms over the laboratory at the Royal Institution, where he labored during the day. Sir Humphry (knighted the year before) reigned supreme. Faraday's salary was later increased to 100 pounds a year, with "lodging, coals, and candles." He remained at the Royal Institution for over half a century. In 1821 he married a fellow member of the strict Sandemanian sect, Sarah Bernard, to whom he was a devoted husband until his death in 1867. They had no children.

During the exciting years that followed Oersted's discovery of electromagnetism, while Ampère, Arago, Davy, Sturgeon, and others were experimenting with it, Faraday was wrestling with problems in chemistry. But he wasn't exactly holding himself aloof from the new magnetic force. He found time to repeat the experiments of the others and even make a few of his own. In one of them he used electromagnetism to move a short piece of wire around and around in a glass tube. The device has been called the first electric motor. He was really doing some thinking on the subject. And if electricity produced magnetism, why couldn't the process be reversed and magnetism be made to produce electricity?

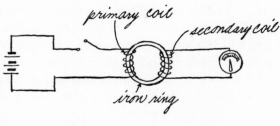

A.

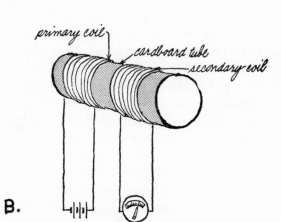

B.

Fig. 21.   (A) Circuit with which Faraday first obtained electricity from magnetism. (B) Faraday demonstrates that an *air*-core transformer also works.

While shadow boxing with the problem, Faraday often carried in his pocket a small coil of wire wound on a piece of iron. Later he wound two separate coils of well-insulated wire on an iron ring about one inch thick and six inches in diameter. The coils were wound on opposite sides of the ring so that the turns would all be parallel with one another. It was with this device that Faraday first obtained a current flow from magnetism. He connected the ends of one coil to a battery; the terminals of the other coil he connected together, so the circuit would be closed (complete). In this closed circuit, completely separate from the other, he placed a small compass meter (Fig. 21A). And when current flowed through the battery coil, or *primary* coil, a current was *induced* in the *secondary* coil: for the needle moved! But only for an instant—as Faraday made the connection to the battery. Then the needle came to rest, indicating that current flow in the secondary coil had stopped. But when he broke the connection to the battery, stopping the primary current flow, the needle moved again—this time in the opposite direction. In other words, a *rising* current induced a secondary current in one direction, a *falling* current induced one in the opposite direction. He noted too that reversing the direction of the primary current also reversed the direction of the secondary current. The date was August 29, 1831.

Strange to say, Faraday was not highly elated at these results. He had obtained a current flow from electromagnetism: but only for an instant, by either stopping or starting a primary current. And he was seeking a *steady* current flow.

Faraday proved that the induced current was no different from the battery current; in other words, was not altered in any way by the transformation. He was also curious as to what part the iron core had played in the process. He wound two coils on a cardboard cylinder, parallel as before, and got the same results (Fig. 21B); though when he substituted an iron for an air core, by slipping a soft-iron rod inside the cardboard cylinder, the needle always jumped farther.

To make doubly sure that the secondary current was induced by magnetism, in his next experiment he substituted an ordinary bar magnet for the primary coil. Holding the bar magnet in his hand, he thrust it down through the center of a coil that was connected to the same crude galvanometer. The needle moved. He pulled the bar magnet out of the coil and the needle moved again—this time in the opposite direction (Fig. 22).

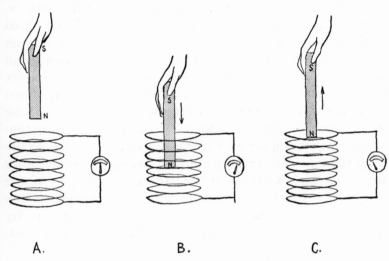

A.   B.   C.

Fig. 22.   Faraday generates electricity with an ordinary bar magnet.

The first practical device, the first *gadget,* to be spawned by these revolutionary experiments was the *induction coil.* Your car, without its induction coil, wouldn't run any farther than it would without its motor. The induction coil is Faraday's two parallel-wound coils on an iron core, but with something added: a device to *interrupt* continuously the direct current flow from the battery. This is the interrupter or vibrator, which operates like an electric bell. A battery current that is constantly being interrupted is either building up for an instant after the contact is made, or dying out for an instant after the contact is broken. Result: a continuously *changing* current through the primary coil. Changing is the key word in understanding electromagnetic induction; it means that a conductor is being subjected to a changing magnetic field. It doesn't matter whether the magnetic lines of force are rising and falling, or whether it's the conductor that's on the move; in both cases a change is taking place. However, the lines must always cut *across* the conductor.

The rapid development of the induction coil is a good example of how invention marches on over the paving stones of theory, laid down by the scientist. Callan and McGauley in Ireland, Bachhofer in Germany, and Page in America all had induction coils operating in their laboratories by 1838. Others, notably Ruhmkorff in Germany, added vital improvements. Toward the end of the century, Hertz was to use a Ruhmkorff coil, as the induction coil was known in Germany, to generate the first wireless waves. But in the beginning the new coil served mainly as a convenient device for providing high voltages in the laboratory; it is a voltage raiser when it has more turns of wire in the secondary than in the primary. The secondary coil's larger number of turns, when subjected to the primary's changing lines of force, acts like a gear box to multiply the input voltage. If the secondary has twice the primary's number of turns, it delivers twice the voltage. It works the other way around too: a secondary with half the number of turns of the primary delivers half its voltage.

Thus the job of an induction coil is to *transform* a voltage. Faraday's twin-coil iron-ring device can be used without the interrupter to transform a voltage—providing one of the coils is fed with an *alternating current,* which is always changing: either rising or falling. Faraday's laboratory gadget was, therefore, the world's second *transformer.* (Henry's was first.) But there was no need for a transformer until an alternating current was available, some years after the appearance of the magnetic generator, which evolved from Faraday's second basic experiment, October 28, 1831.

Faraday's model of the magnetic generator may seem a simple machine to have waited several thousand years for.

He mounted a 12-inch copper disc so it could be turned by a crank; as it turned, its outer edge passed between the poles of the largest horseshoe magnet he could lay his hands on, a compound steel magnet owned by the Royal Society. Fig. 23 is drawn from Faraday's own sketch of the device.

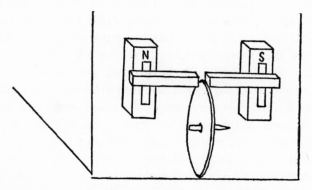

FIG. 23. The first magnetic generator of electricity, drawn from Faraday's own sketch.

Examine it closely and you will see that it has something in common with his previous experiments: a conductor of electricity is subjected to a changing magnetic field: the outer edge of a copper disc is moved through the field of a stationary magnet, cutting across its lines of force.

Faraday drew current from his revolving copper disc by means of two sliding contacts or *brushes*. One brush pressed against the disc's outer rim, the other one pressed against the shaft on which it was mounted.

Though the world's first generator was far from practical, the principle was there: it converted mechanical power to a current flow. Inventors in various countries were soon building much more efficient machines: *dynamos,* they were first called. The basic improvements were two: 1. the substitution of electromagnets for Faraday's permanent magnet, thus providing a much stronger magnetic field; 2. the use of a coil in place of Faraday's copper disc. By 1870, the coils were being wound longwise in slots on a soft-iron core, called a *drum*. Such a coil-carrying device is now known as an *armature*.

From the brushes of Faraday's copper-disc generator came a flow of direct current, which was what he wanted. On the other hand, the wire-wound armature machines that replaced it generated an alternating current; though when it came to the *power* produced, the latter machine was as superior to Faraday's as a horse is to a horsefly.

An alternating current is one that rises to a peak and falls to zero again, then reverses its direction and does a repeat performance. When each of these movements starts, the number of electrons moving through the circuit is close to zero; but, like a crowd gathering at a fire, the number quickly reaches its maximum, then melts away to zero again, just as the current flow reverses its direction. A direct current can be described on paper by means of a straight line (Fig. 24A).

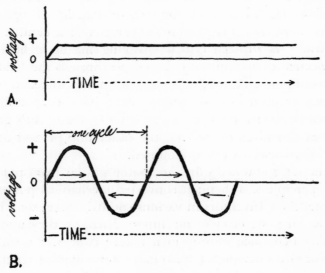

FIG. 24. (A) Direct current. (B) Alternating current.

As time passes, the voltage stays at a constant level above the zero-voltage line. An alternating current can be pictured by a wavy line, as in Fig. 24B. Above the zero-voltage line is indicated one direction of flow; below it, a flow in the opposite direction. One direction is said to be positive, the other negative. Note that, after starting at zero, the voltage rises to a peak and then drops back to zero, then repeats in the opposite direction. One complete back-and-forth movement is called a *cycle*. Our home power-circuit frequency is 60 cycles per second. The more conservative British prefer 50 cycles.

Now, the discharge current from a condenser also oscillates in this way (at an extremely high frequency), though each succeeding surge of the electrons is weaker than the one before, and the current quickly dies out. And the experimenter, having long before replaced condenser current with the smooth, unidirectional current from Volta's battery, was disappointed that his wonderful new magnetic generator had turned out no better in this respect. But he was equal to the occasion. He brought out the ends of the coils on the armature to segments at the end of the shaft. These segments were all insulated from one another; and the ends of the coils were connected to them in such a way that the brushes, rubbing against them, picked up a direct current by reversing the direction of flow of every other half cycle. This automatic switching device is called a *commutator*. Your car's genera·tor has a commutator because it must furnish a direct current to charge the battery. All the early generators of electric power were commutator-equipped direct-current machines. But direct current for power proved later to have more limitations than virtues. The famous Serbian inventor, Nikola Tesla, who worked for Edison for a time after coming to this country, argued with Edison on this point. Tesla liked alternating current, Edison said only direct current was practical. Tesla's espousal of a.c. proved to be well justified.

He sold his a.c. system to Westinghouse for a million dollars. Our hydroelectric systems wouldn't be feasible with direct current; a high voltage is necessary for economical transmission of power to the cities; and only an alternating current can be *transformed* to a higher voltage. Current from the giant alternators at Boulder Dam, Arizona, is raised to 287,000 volts for transmission, reduced to 110 and 220 volts for use in home and factory.

The evolution of Faraday's iron-ring transformer into today's power transformer is a large and fascinating subject in itself. The inventor who first took a model of a transformer to the United States Patent Office was turned away. The examiners patiently explained that such a device was useless, because "no more current could be taken from it than was put into it." And if they were trying to say that no *power* is gained, they were correct. In fact, some power is always lost in a transformer, used up in heat. But the examiners completely missed the point and thus assured themselves of a secure place on electricity's All-Time Bonehead Team, together with the Italian Government that turned down Marconi's wireless (sending him to England), and the picture companies that rejected De Forest's Phonofilm.

Faraday's two coils on a cardboard tube (Fig. 21B) was an air-core transformer. Most radio and television transformers are of this type; though a few use an iron core, on the model of his iron-ring transformer. The symbol for a transformer is a pair of loops or spirals (Fig. 55). These transformers are like the men in a bucket brigade: they receive and pass on the radio wave's energy. In more technical language, they act as *coupling* devices. One transformer couples the antenna circuit to the first tube, another couples the first tube to the second, etc. The alternating current of the radio wave, because any alternating current is continuously changing, readily passes through the transformers.

Note that the final transformer, the one between the final

tube and the loudspeaker, has some straight lines between
its primary and secondary coils; this means it has an iron
core.

2

In a transformer, a changing primary current induces a
current in the secondary coil; it is, then, a mutual affair
between two separate coils and is quite properly called
mutual induction. But there is also what is called *self-induction,* which was Faraday's third and final basic discovery
in electromagnetism, though Henry in fact was first with it,
unknown to Faraday. It was the self-induction of a coil that
made possible the tuning of wireless waves 70 years later.
Note that most of the coils of Fig. 57A have condensers connected across them to form *tuners.*

Faraday had a sympathetic ear for anyone with a problem,
and he listened patiently when a young man named William
Jenkins came to him, puzzled by something very strange
about a simple electric circuit (Fig. 25). That a spark should

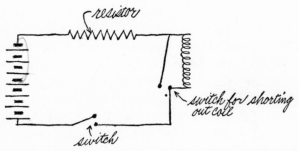

FIG. 25. This circuit led Faraday to the discovery of self-induction. Spark at
switch is greater when coil is in the circuit.

appear at the switch when he broke the circuit seemed natural
enough; but why, if he inserted a coil in the circuit, should
the spark be larger than before? Faraday soon had the answer.

In a transformer, the primary's rising and falling current is accompanied by rising and falling lines of magnetic force that cut across the secondary coil, inducing a current in it also. (It is more proper to say that the changing field induces a *voltage;* for a current flow is present only with the circuit closed. See pages 57-58.) Now, it occurred to Faraday that the lines of force must also cut across the primary coil itself; after all, the primary coil is much closer to its own magnetic field than any secondary coil could possibly be. This, naturally, would create *self-induction.*

Consider a coil in a circuit with an applied alternating-current voltage. The coil's changing magnetic field induces a voltage in it. So we have two voltages, the impressed voltage and the self-induced voltage. Or do we? If we pour port and sherry into a glass, do we still have two kinds of wine? It's the same with the two voltages: we end up with a single voltage, a net voltage. The secret of what the net voltage is like derives from Lenz's Law: *The self-induced voltage always opposes any change in the impressed voltage.*

If the impressed voltage is rising, the self-induced voltage opposes its rise; if the impressed voltage is falling, the self-induced voltage opposes its fall—tries to hold it up. This opposition to both the rise and the fall of the impressed voltage tends to lower its peaks—to smooth it out, in other words. Smoothing out a frequency is the function of the coil in filter circuits of radio and television sets.

Because it is "agin" both the rise and fall of the impressed voltage, the self-induced voltage is called a *counter voltage,* or a *counter electromotive force.*

The counter voltage is larger the faster the impressed voltage changes as it rises or falls. (In the case of an alternating current or an interrupted direct current, this means the counter voltage is larger the higher the frequency.) Here we have the explanation for Jenkins's big spark when he opened the switch with the coil in the circuit. With the voltage suddenly removed, the current's lines of force collapsed on the coil. Collapsing lines of force move at an extremely rapid rate, which induced a very high counter voltage; a counter voltage that caused quite a spark between the switch points. The old Ford ignition coil was a single-coil spark producer like Jenkins's. The fluorescent-light starter uses a single coil to obtain a momentary voltage higher than the 110, necessary to complete ionization in the tube.

The size of the counter voltage induced depends also upon the circuit's *self-inductance*. Every circuit has *some* of this inductance, even a straight piece of wire. Inductance is enormously increased, however, by coiling the wire, which concentrates the magnetic field to increase the inductive effect. The more turns in the coil, and the closer together the turns, the greater the inductance. The unit of inductance is the *henry*, after Joseph Henry. The symbol for inductance is L. In electronics it is more convenient to use the smaller units of the *millihenry (mh.)*, one thousandth of a henry, or the *microhenry (µh.)*, one millionth of a henry.

An early Marconi antenna was tuned simply by clipping to the required number of turns of a coil in the circuit. But how, when a tuner has a condenser *and* coil (Fig. 9)? Any circuit also has some capacitance, together with its inductance; even a straight piece of wire has a little. And the Marconi antenna shown has considerable capacitance, the overhead wires and the earth acting like the two plates of a condenser (Fig. 45).

The tuned circuit is not the simplest little gismo to evolve from man's curiosity about the physical world, and we shall discuss it more fully in Chapter 11. Next, are some of the many devices still in use that evolved from the electromagnets of Joseph Henry, American, who anticipated Faraday in the discovery of both mutual induction and self-induction.

10

THE MARVELOUS MAGNETS OF HENRY

In the year 1837 the House of
Representatives in Washington was asked to appropriate
some money to build a telegraph line from New York City
to New Orleans. A Captain Hunter of Baltimore suggested
that the British system would be best. About fifty-six stations, eight or more miles apart, would be needed, he said.
Arms at the top of a mast, moved by ropes, would spell out
the words. He estimated that in the daytime, if there was
no fog, mist, or rain, such a visual system could flash a news
dispatch from Broadway, New York, to Canal Street, New
Orleans, in one hour; which meant that the message would
have to travel at the incredible speed of something like one
hundred miles for each five minutes.

The proposal evoked a protest from a professor of art in
New York, who urged caution. It would be unwise to spend
money on a semaphore telegraph, the professor wrote, be-

cause he, the writer, was at that very moment working on an *electric* telegraph. His new system promised to be both faster and more reliable. The letter was signed Samuel F. B. Morse.

Although England had the first sight telegraph, France built the first extensive system during the wars that followed the French Revolution (Fig. 26). She found that faster com-

FIG. 26. Semaphore telegraph station.

munications helped to win battles. By 1830 Claude Chappe, the engineer who conceived and built the system, had 533 stations in operation, covering about 3,000 miles of line. But before he concentrated on the sight telegraph, Chappe had tried an electric system. As Volta had not yet given the battery to science, he was forced to rely upon the high-voltage, spasmodic current from Leyden jars. He used clocks with second hands only. The face of each clock was divided into spaces numbered from one to ten. With the two clocks synchronized, the hand on the sending clock always pointed to the same number as the hand on the receiving clock; thus an operator, by watching his clock, could telegraph any number from one to 10 merely by sending a surge of current from his Leyden jars through the circuit. The 10 numbers, singly or in combination, stood for letters, words, or even phrases. The system failed because it was impossible to insulate the high voltage for distances of greater than one mile.

Claude Chappe's unhappy experience with the clocks and jars is just one example of a number of abortive attempts to telegraph with friction-generated electricity. Even after battery current was available, the telegraph still had to wait on a device that grew out of Oersted's discovery of the relationship between electricity and magnetism: Joseph Henry's electromagnets.

2

One summer's day, shortly after the dawn of the 19th century, a little boy who was visiting his uncle in a small town near Albany, New York, chased a rabbit. The rabbit led him under a church, and he couldn't help noticing that some of the floor boards were missing. This presented more of a temptation than we can decently ask a venturesome small boy to resist, and inside the church he discovered a shelf of books, some of them on science.

The boy who chased the hare to the science books was Joseph Henry, the son of a day laborer of Scottish ancestry. He was born in Albany, December 17, 1797.

In his early teens, showing little interest in study, Joseph was apprenticed to an Albany watchmaker. But, as with Faraday and his bookbinding, clocks and watches failed to monopolize his interest. After the day's work was done, he invested his evenings in amateur theatricals; and he dreamed of abandoning watchmaking some day for the theater, proudly touring the young nation's cities as an actor in the plays of Will Shakespeare. But in his 16th year Joseph happened to read a book for young people called *Lectures on*

Experimental Philosophy, Astronomy, and Chemistry, by an English clergyman, Reverend George Gregory. It sent him back to school.

After a spell at night school he enrolled at the Albany Academy as a regular student, paying his way by teaching in country schools. For a time he specialized in a premedical course; he didn't turn to experimental science, with emphasis upon electricity, until he became professor of mathematics and natural philosophy at the Academy some years later at the age of 29.

Like Faraday, Henry was a poor-boy genius. The accomplishments of the two in electromagnetic research ran parallel for some distance; when Henry turned off on a side road it was to concentrate on the electromagnet. Henry created the "spool"- or "bobbin"-wound electromagnet, which he first used for lifting. By the year 1830 he was lifting over a ton with one of them. Unscrew the cap from your telephone receiver and you will see a magnet that is essentially the same as that devised by Henry 124 years ago.

Henry called one type of his U-shaped magnets an *intensity* magnet. On each of its two poles he wound a coil composed of many layers of fine, silk-covered wire, with the two coils connected in series. His wife contributed the silk from one of her petticoats. The fine wire, with its thin silk insulation, enabled Henry to concentrate a great many turns close to the iron core of the poles. And because field strength decreases with the *square* of the current's distance away, the closely clinging coils were extremely effective.

So many turns of such fine wire added up to a high resistance; this called for a battery with many cells connected in series so as to provide the necessary high voltage for pushing enough current through the coils (page 55).

Now let's look in on the Albany Academy, on an afternoon in the year 1831, the same year that Faraday completed his great experiments. In one of the classrooms, Joseph Henry is performing an experiment of his own that, taken with his other work, ranks in importance with Faraday's.

On the table is a U-shaped electromagnet and a battery. Connected to them, and suspended around the room, is a mile of wire. A small bar magnet is pivoted so that it swings horizontally, like a compass needle. One of its poles rests between the two poles of the U-shaped electromagnet, the other pole close to an office bell. Henry completes the circuit; current flows through the mile of connecting wire and the coils of the electromagnet; the suddenly magnetized poles of the magnet cause the pivoted bar to swing around and strike the bell.

Henry had put together for the first time the basic components of a practical telegraph system: an electromagnet and battery capable of magnetizing iron *at a great distance*. And Henry pointed out, in an article in *Silliman's Journal* in 1831, that the way was now clear for the invention of the electromagnetic telegraph.

While professor of natural philosophy at Princeton (1832-1846), Henry installed an experimental telegraph on the University grounds. He tried a single wire, using the earth as the return conductor. He also used a *relay* for the first time. This consisted of an electromagnet built to operate with an absolute minimum of current; its armature, instead of being used directly, merely opened and closed a local battery circuit that sent a larger current through a second electromagnet. The second one did the work.

One year after Henry's classroom preview of the telegraph, Samuel F. B. Morse, recently returned from a trip to Europe, started out bravely to give to the world a battery-powered telegraph system. Morse, an artist by trade, was unacquainted with previous efforts in that direction; this was fortunate for his initial optimism, because he was also innocent of any knowledge of electricity. His great good fortune, as it turned out, lay in the fact that Henry had not patented the application of his intensity magnet to the telegraph. Years later, during a trial involving the validity of Morse's telegraph patent, Henry was attacked in court by a lawyer representing Morse. In reply, Henry stated: "I considered it incompatible with the dignity of science to confine the benefits which might be derived from it to the exclusive use of any individual. In this perhaps I was too fastidious."

Morse began his experiments with a copy of Sturgeon's magnet, a crude affair wound with a few turns of bare copper wire and completely unsuited to the task required of it. After several fruitless years of experiment, Dr. Leonard D. Gale of New York University, where Morse had his laboratory, introduced him to Henry's intensity magnet and showed him how to use it with a high-voltage battery.

From that time on, Morse was assisted by Gale as well as by a young mechanic named Alfred Vail. On several occasions he even had some advice and a pat on the back from Henry himself. Several years later the combined efforts of Morse and his two assistants resulted in a good, workable system, better than the English "needle-pointing" system —which, however, was two years ahead of Morse. Its superiority lay in its relative simplicity. Most European countries soon adopted it. Even France, in 1855, after considerable debate in Parliament, installed it in place of the waving wooden arms of Monsieur Chappe.

In the Morse telegraph instrument, Henry's intensity electromagnet had evolved into an ingenious and highly practical device. Henry admitted as much when he saw it.

His instrument finally perfected, Morse went to Congress, hat in hand, for a $30,000 grant to install a trial unit. Many discouraging years passed before he finally got the money. Chosen for the test were the 44 miles between Washington and Baltimore, and it was over those wires that, in 1844, the now-famous "What hath God wrought?" message was sent.

After it became apparent that there was a ready and growing market for the almost instantaneous transmission of intelligence, "smart money" was attracted to the electromagnetic telegraph like electrons to a positive voltage. The numerous rival companies that sprang up used Morse instruments, or variations of them, and his company always brought suit for infringement of patents. During the many court battles the defense often tried to prove that Henry, not Morse, was the true inventor of the electromagnetic telegraph, and that this invalidated the Morse patent. Although the people lined up pro and con around the cracker barrels, the judges on the bench were unanimous in favoring Morse.

Morse, the promoter, deserves much credit for his leadership, his faith and perseverance, though he was not the inventive genius pictured in the popular mind; in fact, he was hardly an inventor at all. And Henry, the scientist, whose intensity magnet was indispensable to Morse and his associates, hardly deserves oblivion. When Henry died in 1878, at the age of 80, the former watchmaker's apprentice and amateur actor had become a beloved national figure. Memorial services in the House of Representatives at Washington were attended by all the high government officials, including the President. Much of his fame rested upon his work as the first Secretary of the Smithsonian Institution, which he developed into a popular and useful establishment. His extensive meteorological work there led directly to the creation of the United States Weather Bureau.

3

Henry's electromagnets found their first use in the dynamo as a replacement for Faraday's permanent horseshoe magnets. Then, after their application to the telegraph, the telephone inventors picked them up. Here their task was a more subtle one: to convert the air waves of sound to electrical waves, and vice versa.

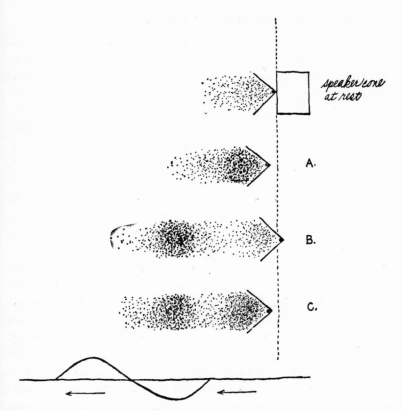

FIG. 27. The loudspeaker's cone, as it vibrates, bunches and rarefies the air to create the sound waves.

Any vibrating object, if it vibrates above 20 cycles, creates air waves we can hear, though above 17,000 cycles or so they fade out. Fig. 27 pictures the vibrating diaphragm of a loudspeaker creating these waves. Moving rapidly in and out, it forms the molecules of air into *layers;* in every other layer the molecules are closer together, raising the air pressure above normal; in the intervening layers the molecules are farther apart, dropping the air pressure below normal. The layers travel out from the diaphragm at a speed of about 1,100 feet per second.

The graph in Fig. 27 describes an air wave on paper. As a

matter of fact, almost everything in nature can be *pictured* as rising and falling in wave form. Even our spirits. We could make a chart showing the progress of our "ups and downs" from day to day (Fig. 28).

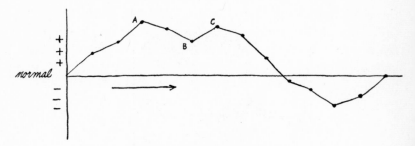

FIG. 28. "Happiness" wave.

The straight line across the page represents the *average* state of our well-being. The dots above the line stand for the days we feel better than average; the higher our spirits the higher the dot; those below the line stand for our below-average days. Some psychologists call this wavy line the life cycle, or the happiness cycle. There is a definite regularity about its rise and fall: it has a definite *frequency*.

We shall call it the *fundamental frequency,* because it isn't the only one. Little things like a disastrous evening at penny ante, or a long spell with no letter from the girl friend, can make a slight dip in the fundamental, such as at B. A small rise, such as at A or C, might be caused by finding a forgotten sawbuck tucked away in a dresser drawer, or by the news that the jalopy's clutch isn't burned out after all. These small dips and rises tacked on to the fundamental frequency are the result of other, added frequencies, called *harmonics*. At least that's how the mathematician analyzes an irregular wave such as the happiness wave. To the technician, also, it's a fundamental *sine wave* (Fig. 29A) with a number of sine-wave harmonics added. He can prove he's right by imitating any musical instrument simply by mixing a fundamental with the correct harmonics. Harmonics are whole multiples of the fundamental, the 2nd harmonic being twice the fundamental, 3rd three times, etc. The *pitch* of a sound is determined by its fundamental. Even though the fire siren and the contralto's high note may share the same pitch, the latter's characteristic quality and timbre are explained by the number and variety of added harmonics. Fig. 29 shows the wave forms of a fundamental 256-cycle frequency, both with and without some harmonics. The harmonics or *overtones* were discovered by Baron von Helm-

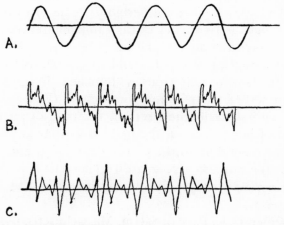

FIG. 29. (A) Fundamental 256-cycle frequency with no harmonics. (B) Piano note of same fundamental. (C) Cello pipe organ of same fundamental.

holtz (1821-1894), distinguished German scientist, half a century before we had an oscilloscope to picture them (Fig. 99).

Fig. 30 shows how the harmonics are produced by a piano string. The string not only vibrates as a whole, between its two ends, but also in several of its parts at the same time—at frequencies determined by its length, tension, etc. For example, you could take hold of it at its center when it is

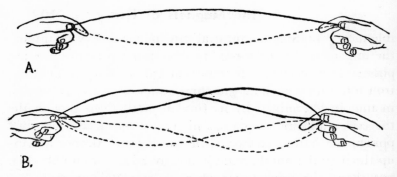

Fig. 30. Vibrating string producing (A) fundamental frequency, (B) second harmonic.

vibrating and hear (faintly) a note twice the frequency of the fundamental: the *second harmonic*. The third harmonic is three times the frequency of the fundamental, etc.

We can describe an alternating current on paper in the same way as an air wave of sound (Fig. 31). We can even think of the current's electrons as "bunched" in the wire, just as the air wave's particles are compressed (Fig. 27). At the end of each half cycle, the electrons reverse (alternate) their direction of flow. Between the half cycles they are normally at rest, corresponding to the point of normal pressure of the air wave. We can also give to a *direct*-current flow the properties of a wave—simply by causing it to rise and fall at a rapid rate.

In 1837 Dr. C. C. Page of Salem, Massachusetts, used a flex-

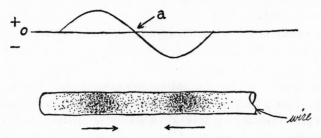

Fig. 31. Graph of alternating current. At zero point, *a*, there is no electron movement in the wire.

ible metal diaphragm, vibrating against a metal point under the impact of the air waves, for the transmitter of his telephone. His receiver was electromagnetic, with a floating iron rod for a core. The core was mounted so it could move in and out of the coil in step with the current waves through the coil, reproducing the sound. But the transmitter's diaphragm, vibrating against its metal point, tended to chop up the battery current, instead of converting it to waves, and nothing intelligible was transmitted.

In 1854, in an article in *L'Illustration,* a Frenchman named Charles Bourseul tossed off a suggestion how to build a telephone. His transmitter was essentially the same as that which Page used, but his receiver was worse: it was the same as the transmitter. (Bourseul later suggested an electromagnetic receiver.) Impractical as it was, however, it proved to be worth more than the paper it was diagramed on, for it sparked the interest of a young German, Philipp Reis, in the problem.

In 1860 Reis built a transmitter based on the same principle as the one of Page and Bourseul, though it functioned better. He used an ear drum made from a pig's bladder, mounting it inside a replica of the human ear carved out of wood. He pasted a thin strip of platinum foil on the membrane to provide a path across it for the electricity. Touching the foil at the membrane's center was a small spike, attached to a springy metal strip.

For his receiver, Reis used an electromagnet, with an iron knitting needle for a core. One end of the needle touched a violin; and as the electric waves passed through the coil they caused the needle to vibrate against the violin, reproducing the sound (explained by the fact that the iron needle gained slightly in length when magnetized by the rising and falling current). Reis improved upon these instruments later. But we can see, in his wooden-ear transmitter and his violin sounding board, the same faint-hearted approach that impelled our first auto builders to place the engine in a buggy —some, it is said, even retaining the receptacle for the whip, just in case a horse might be needed. In one model of his telephone, Reis built in a telegraph key, just in the event an emergency might require the dots and dashes.

Reis's telephones were distributed in many countries and written up in at least fifty scientific journals. Some complained that the voice was not distinct, though it was usually admitted that the device transmitted music very well. That the instrument was not developed to the point of commercial use, can be attributed to the tremendous lack of interest in a telephone; people just weren't excited at the prospect of extending the range of speech, and gave Reis no support. He died, a disappointed man, before he was forty. Nevertheless, he was the first to build a workable telephone. In 1897 the Germans belatedly placed a memorial tablet on his home at Friedrichsdorf.

America's next telephone wasn't a telephone at all: it was Elisha Gray's "harmonic telegraph," first demonstrated for Western Union in 1874. Gray was trying to replace the clicks of the telegraph sounder (which had replaced Morse's tape machine) with musical tones—though not with the idea of entertaining the operators at work. The scheme was to send several messages over a single line at the same time. Gray got the tones by vibrating metal reeds. Western Union called it a telephone on the grounds that "it was the first step toward doing away with manipulating instruments altogether, when operators will talk with one another instead of telegraphing." It wasn't a success.

Another inventor who was struggling to perfect a harmonic telegraph was a Boston teacher of the deaf, who had come to this country from his native Scotland via Canada, Alexander Graham Bell.

In 1876 Bell applied for a patent on a telephone. He was granted the patent just 21 days after application, which was unprecedented, for it usually takes years. This was before he had actually transmitted the human voice over wires. It is said that when he finally accomplished this feat he used an acid-cup transmitter of Gray's.

The hastily granted patent was a cruel disappointment to the numerous other telephone inventors, many of whom, notably Gray, were at least as far along as Bell. They didn't take it lying down. A tidal wave of litigation engulfed the courts for more than 20 years, costing the Bell company almost two and one half million dollars. In one case the Supreme Court justices split four to three in Bell's favor, two not voting.

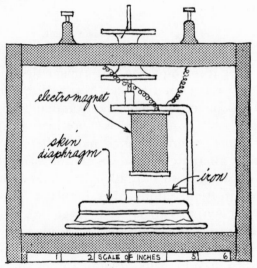

Fig. 32. Bell's telephone patent. The same device was used for transmitter and receiver.

In Fig. 32 a diagram of the Bell patent is shown. Fig. 33 shows this type of instrument in a simple telephone circuit. You can talk against either diaphragm and, theoretically at least, the other diaphragm will reproduce your voice. The receiver isn't difficult to understand: the rising and falling current, by varying the coil's magnetism, pulls and pushes the iron diaphragm; it's like a dog wagging its tail. Though how the transmitter's vibrating diaphragm *produces* the current waves may be puzzling. How does the tail manage to wag the dog?

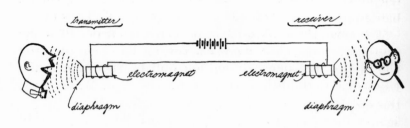

FIG. 33. Simple telephone circuit.

It does it by disturbing the coil's magnetic field, making it alternately stronger and weaker. You realize that the magnetic field is stronger the closer the iron diaphragm is to the magnet's core—where the field is more intense. As the diaphragm vibrates, moving closer to and farther away from the core, the field alternately improves and deteriorates, causing the lines of force to rise and fall: rising, they induce a voltage in one direction; falling, they induce a voltage in the opposite direction, as Faraday saw (page 90). The induced voltages add to or subtract from the steady, unidirectional battery voltage to create the current waves. (Adding to and subtracting from your bank account causes the balance to oscillate in the same way.) The engineer would explain all this simply by saying that the diaphragm, as it vibrates, varies the *reluctance,* his term for resistance to the magnetic force.

The telephone of Fig. 33 will also operate without batteries. In this case, the transmitter's iron core must be permanently magnetized, so the vibrating iron diaphragm can *generate* voltage waves in the circuit. All power is supplied by the sound waves. You could snip off a couple of telephone receivers, connect them through a pair of wires, and have yourself a private telephone circuit, though the telephone company doesn't recommend it. Even in this electronic age, the United States Navy looks with favor upon sound-powered telephones: no electric-power failure can silence them. A battleship has one at each of its 2,000 or so battle stations.

The current variations from the early magnetic telephone transmitter were too feeble, however, for any good use. Bell had one in the system he exhibited at the 1876 Centennial Exposition at Philadelphia, and only by shouting into the transmitter, while the wonder-drunk listener pressed his ear against the receiver's diaphragm, could an occasional word be guessed at. Dom Pedro II de Alcantara, Emperor of Brazil, was among the many visitors who were nevertheless greatly impressed. (What will they think up next!) The telephone's practical usefulness had to wait on the carbon transmitter, or *microphone*. The first one was devised by scientist David E. Hughes, a professor who had emigrated to America from England at the age of 7. It is shown in Fig. 34.

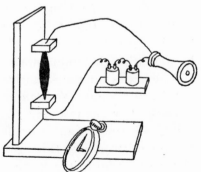

Fig. 34. First carbon microphone, by Hughes. The carbon pencil touches the carbon blocks lightly, top and bottom. Sound waves from the watch cause the pencil to vibrate slightly, varying the resistance between it and the carbon blocks; this periodic resistance variation in the electrical circuit causes the receiver to reproduce the sound.

Seeking a practical transmitting instrument, the inventors first experimented with a solid piece of carbon against which a metal point vibrated. But the final solution was the carbon microphone of Hennings and Edison (Fig. 35). Its little

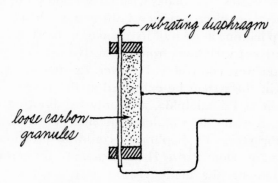

FIG. 35.   First practical microphone.

brass cup (the *button*) is filled with pulverized anthracite from the coal bin. The cup is held solidly in position. Pressing against its grains of carbon is the flexible metal diaphragm. The loosely packed carbon grains offer considerable resistance to a current flow through them: packing them more tightly together lowers this resistance. Thus the diaphragm, vibrating against them, alternately lowers and raises the resistance in step with the sound waves. Actually, the carbon transmitter operates on the same basic principle as those of Page, Reis, and Gray: *resistance variation*. But it works very much better because the conversion of air waves to current waves is smooth and complete.

The double-button microphone (Fig. 36) early replaced the single-button type for radio; it is more efficient because the vibrating diaphragm produces a wider range of current-flow variation. It is still a good instrument, rugged and efficient. A drawback is the fact that the carbon granules do not offer an absolutely stable resistance to the battery voltage, and the slight variation of current flow causes an annoying hiss or "frying sound." It is no longer used for broadcasting, though it finds a wide range of usefulness in communications work.

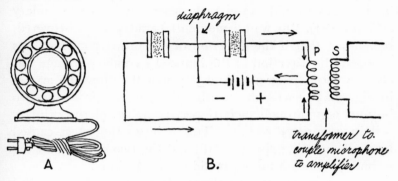

FIG. 36.   Radio's double-button carbon mike.

The double-button mike, a classic in ingenuity, was patented by inventor E. H. Colpitts, a name long familiar to radio men. It applies principles discovered by Faraday. Tracing its action for the first time will make you sympathize with the psychologist's rat, threading its way through a maze to earn its dinner; though your reward, if you negotiate it successfully, will be intellectual rather than intestinal.

The diaphragm of this microphone is *between* the two buttons. While it is packing the carbon granules of one button more solidly (decreasing the resistance) it is loosening the carbon granules of the other button (increasing the resistance), and vice versa.

The primary coil of the transformer is *split,* that is, it is tapped in the middle. As the current flow of one button passes through half of the coil, at the same time the current flow of the other button passes through the other half. And as one button's resistance is decreasing while the other's is increasing, one current flow will always be rising while the other one is falling, and vice versa. Now, as Faraday discovered, a rising primary current induces a secondary voltage in one direction; a falling primary current induces a secondary voltage in the opposite direction. So it would seem that because the two induced voltages are opposed and equal in size, they should cancel each other out in the secondary coil (Fig. 41). But wait a moment! Faraday also discovered, remember, that if the *direction* of the primary current was reversed, the direction of the induced secondary voltage was also reversed (page 90). And if you will follow the arrows in Fig. 36, you will observe that the currents from the two buttons pass through their respective halves of the primary coil in *opposite directions*. This reverses the effect caused by their opposing rise and fall, and the two currents in the secondary coil are mutually aiding at all times.

It is known as a *push-pull* circuit. Colpitts also patented its application to vacuum-tube amplifiers, and if you have a quality amplifier you are using it now. No amplifier that makes any pretensions to fidelity of reproduction would be caught dead without a final stage of push-pull amplification. But I am getting ahead of my story.

Radio has tried many different kinds of mikes in addition to the carbon: condenser, crystal, velocity, dynamic. The latter two are pretty much standard today in radio and television, and I shall describe them. Both are the same in principle: miniature, sound-powered dynamos. As the sound waves cause their diaphragms to vibrate, they generate wave currents in unison.

This was also true of the inadequate early telephone transmitter just described. But there is a difference. In the transmitter of Fig. 33, the iron diaphragm generates current waves in the magnet's coil. But the velocity mike's magnet is the permanent type, with no coil; its diaphragm a metallic ribbon suspended between the two magnetic poles; as the ribbon vibrates in the magnetic field it generates the current waves *in itself*.

The dynamic mike operates on the same principle. A small, light coil of wire is attached to its diaphragm; the coil is suspended so that it is said to "float" in the magnetic field between the magnet's two poles. The current waves generated in the coil, though stronger than those in the velocity mike's ribbon, still require considerable amplification before they can be used.

These current waves, or voice currents, shown graphically in Fig. 29, are known as the *audio frequency*. They are not broadcast directly. After amplification, they are used to *modulate* another frequency, a much higher one called the *radio frequency*. The radio frequency carries them to the receiver, and for this reason is called the *carrier*.

4

Radio's first loudspeaker was merely an overgrown telephone receiver with horn attached. The horn provided some amplification. (The horn-shaped air column acts as a *coupler* between diaphragm and room, enabling a given movement of the diaphragm to move more outside air than otherwise.) This speaker spoke softly because the vibrating diaphragm had to be so close to the magnet (for sensitivity) that strong signals caused it to touch the magnet, creating a rattle. It contributed its share to the popular theory of the day that radio broadcasting was just a passing fancy, useful as a hobby for those who lacked intelligence to collect stamps or manipulate a ouija board.

Because its diaphragm was iron, it was called the moving-iron type of speaker. Many ingenious improvements were made on it, but I shan't describe them because today's speaker works on a little different principle: it has a moving coil, like the dynamic microphone. In fact, it's a *dynamic speaker*. In the dynamic microphone, the vibrating coil generates current waves in itself; in the dynamic speaker, the current waves in it cause it to vibrate. One is a generator, the other a motor.

The dynamic speaker of Fig. 37 is the PM type. PM stands for permanent magnet and not, as Peregrinus would have had it, for perpetual motion. All loudspeakers used electromagnets at first, until General Electric engineers, while searching for alloys with better magnetic properties, developed alnico (aluminum, nickel, and cobalt). Alnico PM's were first used solely in the smaller speakers, later graduating to the 10- and 12-inchers and larger.

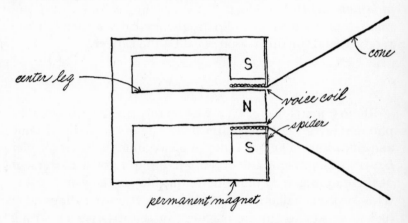

FIG. 37. PM (for permanent magnet) loudspeaker.

The coil in the slot between the poles of the PM is called the *voice coil*. Attached to a flexible material, the *spider,* the voice coil can be moved in and out of the slot. Its copper wire, being nonmagnetic, is no more a magnet than is a spool of thread, and the intense field of the permanent magnet has no effect upon it. But tune in a station, and the audio-frequency waves passing through its turns make it an *electromagnet*. Now, with two magnets, we have mutual reaction. The audio frequency flows through the voice coil, first in one direction, then in the opposite direction, changing its polarity on each alternation; on half the cycle the mutual reaction pushes the coil out, on the other half it pulls it in. A 1,000-cycle frequency, for instance, moves it in and out 1,000 times per second.

A vibrating coil alone, like a wheelbarrow without a bottom, wouldn't be very efficient; so a large paper cone is attached to it. (Actually, the cone may also contain wood, kapok, or other materials.) The cone carries with it enough air as it moves in and out to create a good volume of sound. Like the string of Fig. 30, the paper vibrates in all its parts, enabling it to reproduce a *range* of frequencies. However, this range may be too limited for good reproduction. A large cone, with its relatively large mechanical resistance, reproduces the frequencies down in the bass range much better than it does the higher frequencies. On the other hand, a small cone, 8 inches in diameter or under, favors the highs at the expense of the lows. For this reason it is common practice to divide the audio range among from two to four speakers. Distortion is also minimized by this arrangement. The low-frequency speaker may, for example, only be asked to reproduce frequencies up to 600 cycles, the mid-range speaker those from 600 to 4,000, and a third all those above 4,000. When a single speaker is made to do, the cone is doctored in various ways to increase frequency range. For example, the apex area (near voice coil) is stiffened by impregnating the fibers with some chemical. The fast-moving high frequencies take hold of this stiffened area and force it to vibrate by itself. The slower moving lower frequencies move the entire cone. We say that the cone automatically decouples itself for the highs, explained by inertia. A speaker has a natural (resonant) frequency of its own that it may reproduce with much greater volume than the others, unless it is mounted in the proper *enclosure*. Enclosures are discussed on page 209.

The newest type of speaker is the *electrostatic,* which operates in reverse to the condenser mike of Fig. 61.

11

NEXT STOP, TUNERVILLE

Cʜᴀᴘᴛᴇʀ 12 tells the story of the world's first transmitter and receiver of the waves we use for radio, television, radar, and many other types of electronic apparatus. To prepare us for an easier understanding of this pioneer laboratory rig, I think we should pause here first for a close-up view of the waves, with accent both on theory and tuning.

The authors of elementary radio books, in seeking some sort of concept of radio waves that the reader can roll under his mind's tongue, have almost invariably solved the problem in the same way: by comparing radio waves from a transmitting antenna with the water waves from a stone falling into a quiet pond. The number of stones tossed into quiet ponds by these writers down through the years, if fitted neatly together, could easily pass for a respectable stretch of old Roman road. However, I can think of no alternative to this hoary method, so here goes ours. Kerplunk!

Watch the waves travel outward from the splash in ever-widening circles (Fig. 38). If you take a pencil and draw a cross-sectional picture of the wave, the result will look like the graph used merely to *represent* an alternating current, or a sound wave, or the state of our spirits from day to day.

FIG. 38.   Water waves have long been used to dramatize our concept of radio waves.

Now we throw a bottle into our imaginary pond. Is the bottle washed ashore by the waves? No. It merely bobs serenely up and down. (Objects are blown ashore by the wind, washed ashore by breakers or tides.) This proves that the water itself doesn't travel outward from the splash, just the waves. This very significant fact can be even more eloquently demonstrated with a piece of rope. Fasten one end to a building (Fig. 44) and vigorously move its free end up and down. From the look of the waves, the rope is actually moving toward the building, an absurdity if I ever saw one. The wave is merely traveling *through* the rope from one end to the other.

Despite the fact that the individual particles of water themselves have little or no movement toward the shore, there is a definite movement of force or energy. The shore feels this force or energy where a wave contacts it; the building feels it at the point where the rope is attached. We say that the water is the *medium* through which the water wave travels, and the rope is the medium for the rope wave. Air, you will recall, is the medium for sound waves.

The standard broadcast station has a steel tower which serves as an antenna, and the current from the transmitter moves up and down (oscillates) in it (Fig. 63). Now, this oscillating antenna current is surrounded by the electric and magnetic fields of Faraday and Maxwell; and as we shall see in the next chapter, such is the peculiarity of this kind of circuit that its oscillating current, instead of being converted to heat in the conductor, is converted to another kind of energy: electromagnetic waves, better known as radio waves.

As the oscillating current in the antenna changes direction, upwards of half a million times each second, the waves are "pumped" out in all directions. The energy in the waves produces an electrical pressure (voltage) in any conductor in their path; and such a conductor could very well be the antenna of your radio. But what is the *medium* for the radio waves?

Electromagnetic waves will pass through a vacuum, which rules out air as the answer. Modern science, though it had no proof, thought that the medium must be there just the same. They called it the *ether*.

Sometimes this kind of strategy works out very well. The scientist is convinced that something *should* exist to explain certain experimental evidence, and by and by he is able to demonstrate that it *does*. But the ether failed him. Proof finally came that there is no such animal, and he abandoned it.* Though, like Santa Claus, we could ill afford to dispense

* From the Michelson-Morley experiment, made in Cleveland, Ohio, in 1887. These American scientists rigged up an ingenious contrivance for measuring the speed of light. They measured the speed of light traveling both with and against the motion of the earth through space, and at right angles to this motion. They hoped to find that light traveling against the earth's

with it entirely. The fact that neither one exists is beside the point. We *need* a common-sense, mechanical view of nature for practical purposes. Dirac has even suggested recently that the mathematical physicist would find it helpful to revive the concept of the ether.

The Quantum Theory of Planck and Einstein goes right into the whirling electrons themselves for an explanation of how electromagnetic energy is released. The smallest unit of released energy, according to this theory, is a particle called the *photon*. Whether it is what we call heat, light, violet rays, X-rays, gamma rays, or the radiation from a television antenna, the energy is released in bursts of photons. There is proof for this, just as there is proof for the wave theory.

For proof of the wave theory, imagine a radio wave in space. Each half cycle rises and falls, but between the two half cycles is a point where the wave has no effect upon a receiver. This couldn't possibly be, if the energy consisted of bursts of photons; for *particles* must be felt at any and all points in their path, as every hen-house raider who must dodge the farmer's shotgun appreciates.

One way to get around this would be to assume that it *is* possible for each burst of particles to travel from point to point without passing through parts of the intervening space; like an automobile that journeys from New York to San Francisco and appears only in the cities and towns, never on the roads between them. St. Thomas Aquinas, in his 13th-century *Summa Theologica,* considers this possibility. He asks himself the question: "Can angels move from one point to another without passing through the intervening space?" His answer

---

motion would be moving faster than light traveling with the earth's motion; just as on the highway a car going in an opposite direction to your car is moving faster (relative to you) than its speedometer indicates. But Michelson and Morley were disappointed. Light has a single speed, regardless of whether the observer is moving toward its source or away from it. Thus, if there is an ether, the earth is standing still in it. This is the experiment that started Einstein on the road to his theories of relativity.

is, yes they can. However, the scientist still has some way to go before he beds down photons with the angels.

Assuming that waves consist of particles, then it should logically follow that *particles are waves;* and the scientists actually have proof of this. Each particle is a wave, whether it's a flying electron or a speeding bullet.

From a practical standpoint we must choose the theory that serves us best; and when it comes to tuned electrical circuits the choice is waves.

We have already discussed briefly radio's "gate keeper," the coil-and-condenser tuner that lets in one frequency and shuts out all the rest. I'll return to this technical view of resonance in the next section, but right now I'd like to compare electrical resonance with mechanical resonance. As an example of the latter we shall use a child in a swing: a pendulum.

A little cooperation from a grown-up always spices the child's play; and as Galileo discovered with the swinging lamp in the church, you may observe that the child swings back and forth a definite number of times each minute. This is the swing's natural movement, its *resonant frequency*. To change the resonant frequency, we must alter the length of the ropes.

It is apparent that for best results you must push the child at the precise moment the swing reaches the top of its arc. In other words, the frequency of your pushing must continue to be the same as the natural frequency of the swing; for, if you change it and push too soon, the swing's backward motion cancels out some of your effort, and a push that is too late also wastes effort. Maximum efficiency demands that your motion stay in resonance with the motion of the swing, in step or rhythm with it.

Now, compare the swing with the oscillating electrons from a tuned-in wave in your radio or television set. See the secondary circuit of the tuner of Fig. 39. The signal is an alternating or oscillating current; its electrons oscillate between

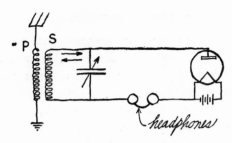

FIG. 39. Tuned secondary circuit of simple radio receiver.

the plates of the variable condenser, passing through the coil connected to it.

The tuner's resonant frequency is determined by the amount of inductance and capacitance, just as the swing's resonant frequency is determined by the length of the ropes. Adding either inductance or capacitance slows down the electrons, thus lowering the frequency. When you turn the knob on your receiver to maximum capacitance, you open the door for the lowest frequency on the band. (In this position the condenser plates are completely meshed. On the standard broadcast band this is 550,000 cycles.)

A single batch of electrons, once started by a tuned-in wave, would swing back and forth between the condenser plates forever, if it weren't for one thing: the ordinary ohmic resistance in the circuit. Electrical resistance is comparable to the friction encountered by the swing; we could no more have an electrical circuit without some resistance than we could have a swing without some friction. Hence the size of the current in each half cycle is smaller than the one before it, and the oscillations quickly die out. In a tuner, however, each half cycle of the tuned-in wave starts a new movement of electrons, and at just the proper instant so there is no interference with the movement started by the previous half cycle: like giving the child in the swing a push at the proper moment each time. Thus the resonant circuit recruits enough fresh electrons each half cycle to make up for the losses caused by resistance.

The voltages generated by the waves not tuned in are out of step with the natural back-and-forth swing of the electrons, and so produce relatively weaker currents in the tuner. The farther a wave is from resonance, the weaker the current. Some tuners are more *selective* than others; that is, they favor the resonant frequency more. We say that the more selective a tuner the *sharper* it tunes. Take a look at the graph of Fig. 40 and you will see where we get the word sharpness. The less the ohmic resistance the sharper the peak.

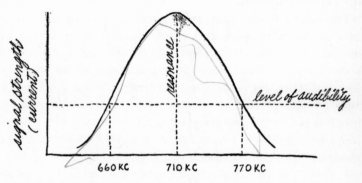

FIG. 40. Graph showing quality of a tuned radio circuit. The circuit is tuned to 710 kilocycles. The *peak* of the graph reveals that this frequency is causing a maximum current flow (signal strength) in the circuit. Note that the response to frequencies on either side of 710 kilocycles drops off quite rapidly until frequencies below 660 and above 770 kilocycles are too weak to be heard in the speaker. The peak could be *flattened* by inserting ordinary ohmic resistance in the circuit, because current flow used up in resistance is not tunable. This is often done in television receiver circuits which must amplify a wide *band* of frequencies.

It is quite common not to tune the primary circuit of a radio receiver's antenna tuner to individual stations. The inductance and capacitance in coil and antenna give it a resonant frequency near the middle of the broadcast band; and it tunes *broadly* enough to let in all the stations on the band quite well. Finer selection takes place in the other tuned circuits that follow.

2

Now we'll stop our Tunerville bus for a more technical view of the resonant circuit. This section may hurt a little, so skip it if you just want theory. Though it is essential to the technician, there is nothing in it that will ever fit in a crossword puzzle or win you the Panama Canal on a quiz show.

In Chapter 9 we learned how Faraday (and Henry) explained the effect of putting a coil in a circuit in which the current flow is continuously changing. Its surrounding magnetic field creates a counter voltage that opposes any change in the impressed voltage. There is a technical term for this effect of a coil in a circuit: *reactance*. The reactance reduces the current (by lowering its peaks), but it reduces it more for high frequencies than it does for low frequencies. Like ordinary resistance, reactance is expressed in ohms. Its symbol is X.

In Chapter 5 we learned that the condenser also offers some opposition to a changing current; but unlike the coil it suppresses a low frequency more than a high one. This means that the condenser also generates a counter voltage and has reactance. It is possible to visualize this.

As the condenser charges, on each half cycle of the alternating current, it is something like a toy balloon being blown up. At the moment you start to blow, there is no opposition; but as the air accumulates in the balloon, it constitutes a back pressure that opposes you. And when a condenser first starts to take a charge, the impressed voltage meets no opposition, permitting the electrons to flow into it rapidly. But as the electrons accumulate on the negative plate (and are removed from the positive plate), a back pressure develops that slows down the rate of electron accumulation. Which is to say that a condenser generates a counter voltage.

To distinguish between the two reactances, inductive reactance is written X_L, a capacitive reactance X_C.

We just noted that a coil suppresses a high frequency more effectively than a low one, while a condenser has an opposite effect. In technical man's talk: The reactance of a coil increases as the frequency increases, or $X_L = fL$, the f for frequency; the reactance of a condenser decreases as the frequency increases, or $X_C = 1/fC$.* This works out in a *time* difference involved between X_L and X_C: the two counter voltages rise and fall at different times. When one is rising the other is falling, and vice versa. As a result, the two counter voltages tend to cancel (neutralize) each other (Fig. 41).

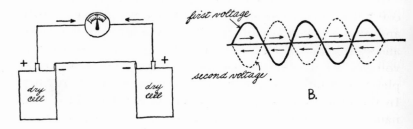

A

FIG. 41. How voltages neutralize each other. (A) The positive voltages of the two dry cells are connected together, as are the negative voltages. Positive opposes positive, negative negative, and if the two cell voltages are equal no current will pass through the meter. (B) Two alternating-current voltages which also neutralize each other. We say that the two voltages are 180 degrees out of *phase;* in other words, they are always directly opposing as they rise and fall, and if they are always equal, no current can flow, as in the case of the dry cells. The two voltages are like a pair of Japanese wrestlers who, having equal strength and being equally alert, cannot budge each other. Change the phase relationship by moving one voltage a little ahead of or a little behind the other, however, and there will be current in the circuit. Current will also flow if one voltage is made greater than the other. Sound waves can also neutralize each other. The army has developed an earphone that reduces a loud roar to a whisper through phasing. The device contains a tiny microphone whose output is fed into the earcup opposite in phase to the sound that arrives direct. Designed for artillerymen, ground-maintenance and jet-bomber crews, it also has a future among riveters and husbands whose wives have a high decibel rating.

* To make these formulas work, add 2 π, which is 6 2/7. Thus, $X_L = 2 \pi fL$, and $X_C = 1/2 \pi fC$.

In a circuit such as the secondary of Fig. 39, the reactances of coil (X_L) and condenser (X_C) directly oppose each other; the value of each reactance is determined by the frequency applied. Suppose we apply a low frequency, 100,000 cycles, to the circuit. From the formula above, we know that the coil's reactance to this frequency will be small; though the other formula tells us that the condenser's reactance will be large. The *net* reactance will be equal to their difference; and because the capacitive reactance is so much greater, we say that the net reactance is capacitive.

But as we slowly increase the frequency over 100,000, the coil's reactance rises, while the condenser's reactance falls; and soon we must reach a frequency at which the two reactances are equal. This is the one at which the two counter voltages are also equal and, being directly opposing, completely neutralize each other. This is the resonant frequency. In the neat symbols of math, when $X_L = X_C$ we have resonance; and the only remaining opposition to the oscillating current is the ohmic resistance.

Simple? Sorry. Anyway, it's just like the child in the swing.

12

MAXWELL'S MATH TO HERTZIAN WAVES

ONE of the most revolutionary discoveries in the whole history of science was this: a certain kind of electrical circuit can be made to produce waves, waves that are essentially the same as light waves. It was realized through the efforts of three men: Faraday, Maxwell, and Hertz.

The discovery was another of those ground gainers on the field of science, similar to the one from Edison to Fleming to De Forest that gave us the radio tube; though these men were inventors, while Faraday, Maxwell, and Hertz devoted their lives almost entirely to pure science.

Faraday used his electric and magnetic lines of force to account for the way electricity acts on bodies at a distance. He speculated upon the nature of these lines of force, and their relationship to other forces in nature. How did they act in their journey from one point to another? Did they vibrate like light? Did they travel at the same rate of speed as light? Were they the *same* as light, essentially? He thought they might well be, and by means of a powerful magnet he managed to effect an extremely minute change in light rays, indicating some connection between magnetism and light at least. Faraday was the Prince of Experimenters, and he worked longer hours than a Chinese laundryman, but this was something that called for a theoretical physicist, a scientist who could use the mathematics developed by Newton and Leibnitz as an instrument for probing the electric and magnetic fields. Fortunately a man came along at the time who was well qualified for such a job. His name was Maxwell.

James Clerk Maxwell was born in Edinburgh in 1831, the year, you may remember, in which Faraday made his great discoveries in magnetic induction. His father was a well-to-do farmer, a Scottish laird. His mother died when he was eight years old. Like most children, James Clerk was full of questions, his favorite being "What's the go of it?" But the answers he got seldom satisfied him. Instead of signing off with a meek "Oh!" he usually had a second question: "I know, but what's the *particular* go of it?"

The father who raised him was very much interested in science and technology. He was also a great individualist. Even in the matter of clothes he rejected conformity, taking it upon himself to design his son's outfits. Naturally these originals got the lad into trouble at school. His mates nicknamed him "Dafty," no doubt good 19th-century English for "Goofy."

Young Maxwell's singularity, however, was not confined to the sartorial; he had a habit of tossing off puzzling remarks, and often he would laugh for no apparent reason. Teasing "Dafty" became a popular playground sport. Sometimes he would turn and fight his tormentors. If those Edinburgh schoolboys had had their way and managed to cut their nonconformist playmate down to size, we might not have our radio and television today. But fortunately the youth had what it took to preserve his inner integrity.

James Clerk Maxwell entered Edinburgh University when he was 16. During his three years there he distinguished himself through some research on light. In 1850 his father sent him down to Cambridge. The great Faraday was still tirelessly searching for truth in his laboratory at the Royal Institution.

At Cambridge, Maxwell began to speculate on Faraday's lines of force, preparing the material for his first paper on electromagnetic theory. He worked on it for eight years, at the same time that he was doing significant work on the theory of gases.

Consider the negative charge on one plate of a condenser, the same negative charge as the one on our pith ball or glass rod of Chapter 2. It is surrounded by *electrostatic* lines of force. Now discharge the condenser. The electron current is surrounded by *magnetic* lines of force. Have the moving electrons lost their *electrostatic* lines? No, a current flow has both fields. A current flow is merely a charge in motion. You can take a charged piece of amber, whirl it rapidly on the end of a string, and it will be surrounded by the magnetic force. And here is our point: *the faster you whirl it, the stronger the surrounding magnetic force.* Maxwell reasoned that the faster a charge moves *through a conductor,* as a current flow, the greater its surrounding magnetic force. So the size of the magnetic force from a charge of a given size would reveal its speed of movement. Using a new method he had devised, Maxwell made some exact measurements of the electrostatic force between charged plates, and of the magnetic force from the charges moving in a conductor; and the intensity of the latter, compared with the former, was great enough to indicate that the electricity was moving with the velocity of light. This would also be true of the two fields of his hypothetical waves. He wrapped up the proof in a page of mathematical equations. Maxwell had found the *particular* go of Faraday's lines of force.

As the wave spreads out in space with the velocity of light, its two forces, electrostatic and magnetic, are at right angles to each other, and at right angles to the direction of travel. One pair of fields produces another, which produces a third, and so on indefinitely, just as though there was always a circuit there to pick them up and pass them on.

Maxwell's equations soon led to wireless telegraphy, then to radio broadcasting and television. But to the purely scientific mind, these things are just by-products, gadgets. Of vastly greater importance is the fact that the equations were a necessary prelude to Einstein's calculations that crystalized in the theories of relativity.

Maxwell's fellow scientists on the continent were skeptical of his revolutionary new theory. Maxwell had failed to provide a circuit capable of *producing* the waves, like light waves, to go with the page of equations; he was so sure of his figures that he hadn't bothered to seek physical proof. He was not primarily an experimenter anyway. Physical proof didn't come until 1888, nine years after Maxwell's early death at the age of 48. A young German scientist, Heinrich Rudolph Hertz, put together the necessary gear in his laboratory at the Technical High School in Karlsruhe, where he was professor of physics.

Hertz's father was a Jewish lawyer in Hamburg; his mother came from a long line of Lutheran ministers. He was given the best kind of education available, a well-rounded one that included science, the classics, and modern languages. Grandfather Hertz was an amateur experimenter, and his apparatus gave young Heinrich his initial interest in science. He thought at first that he would like to be an engineer, but he soon realized that his love for theory better suited him for pure science. He was given a good start in this direction in Berlin, where he studied under two great scientists, Helmholtz and Kirchhoff. It was Helmholtz who suggested that he seek confirmation of the new electromagnetic theory.

By this time it was well known that the discharge current from a condenser swings back and forth between the plates; is, in a technical word, oscillatory. Now these were the oscillations that Maxwell had said could be made to radiate electromagnetic waves. For years, scientists and experimenters all over the world had been producing them, on occasion, without being aware of it. One experimenter who was aware of it was an eighteen-year-old science teacher at the Philadelphia High School, Elihu Thomson. Three years before Hertz began his experiments, Thomson confirmed Maxwell's theory when he drew sparks from metal pipes on the side of the room across from an oscillatory circuit. Later, in England, Fitzgerald experimented with the waves. So perhaps Hertz doesn't stand quite alone in his confirmation of the Faraday-Maxwell theory, as it was known on the continent, even though his confirmation was complete and conclusive. Hertz designed both a transmitter and a receiver for the waves, carrying out a series of brilliantly planned experiments that proved the electromagnetic-wave theory up to the hilt.

It will be helpful if, before we consider the Hertz transmitter, we first examine the circuit of Fig. 42A.

The interrupter, *a*, breaks up the direct current from the battery to provide the *changing current* that Faraday found was necessary for induction. The secondary winding, having many more turns than the primary, delivers several thousand volts. The secondary voltage is *alternating*. (This is because the secondary voltage opposes any *change* in the primary current, and moves first in one direction and then in the opposite direction, trying to prevent its rise and fall. See page 98.) Frequency is determined by how fast the interrupter works.

Each half cycle of alternating current charges up the condenser. The spark gap acts like a valve. The distance between

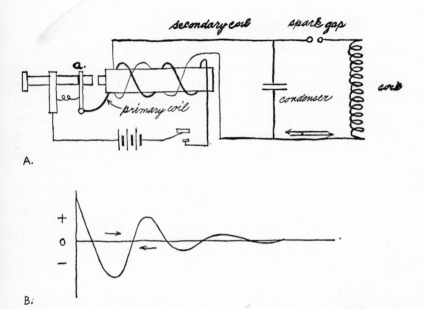

A.

B.

FIG. 42. (A) Diagram of a spark transmitter, which produces (B) a *damped* wave.

the gap's electrodes is adjusted so that the air has just the right amount of resistance to break down when the voltage on the condenser has built up to maximum, at the peak of each half cycle. The breakdown of the air permits the condenser to discharge across the gap.

The condenser discharge current is *oscillatory;* it swings back and forth between the condenser plates at the resonant frequency of the circuit. But because each half cycle must jump the high-resistance spark gap, the current quickly dies out after only a few alternations (like a pendulum that encounters considerable resistance). Such a *damped* series of oscillations is pictured in Fig. 42B. Another series of oscillations occurs on the second half of the frequency cycle. Thus there are two series, called *trains,* of highly damped oscillations for each complete cycle of alternating current from the induction coil. Bear in mind the two frequencies: 1, the total number of trains per second, determined by the mechanical vibrator; 2, the frequency of the oscillations in each individual train, governed by the amount of inductance and capacitance in the circuit.

Now let's remove the coil and spark gap from the circuit and start opening up the condenser. As we separate the plates, the capacitance decreases (Fig. 7); but even wide open, as in Fig. 43A, it still has some capacitance (page 99). And even with the coil gone, the two short pieces of wire still have some inductance. So we still have a resonant circuit, even

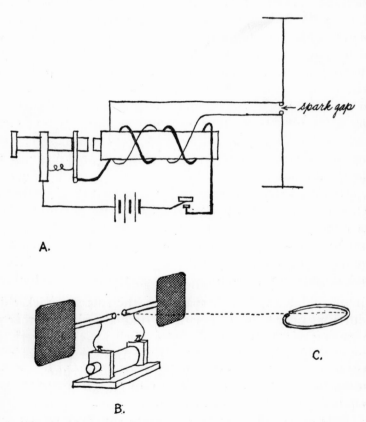

spark gap

A.

B.

C.

FIG. 43. The original transmitter of electromagnetic waves, by Hertz. (A) Schematic. (B) How it looked. (C) Receiver.

though its resonant frequency, with so much less inductance and capacitance, is very much higher than before. And with the spark gap put back in, as shown, the circuit will produce two trains of damped oscillations for each alternating-current cycle from the induction coil, just as before. Fig. 43A is a diagram of the *oscillator* used by Hertz. It is pictured in 43B.

There is an important difference between the two circuits. In the Hertz oscillator, the capacitance of the circuit is not confined, concentrated, or, as the technician says, *lumped* as it is in the circuit of Fig. 42A. Separating the condenser plates is like opening a door; the voltage between the two plates and the two wires is released. In other words, the electrostatic field spreads out into surrounding space; and with the coil gone so does the magnetic field. *Now* the energy in the fields doesn't all collapse back on the circuit; succeeding fields *push each other out*. And as Maxwell predicted, each oscillation creates an *electromagnetic wave,* one following the other like those that spread out from the pebble in the quiet pond.

Hertz used metal plates or balls on the ends of his oscillator. This increased the capacitance slightly. Without them, we have today's *dipole antenna,* used for television, short wave, and some radar, both in sending and receiving. However, we have long since discarded the Hertz spark gap; a tube is a vastly superior generator of the high-frequency oscillations.

The Hertz receiver was a small loop of wire with a spark gap in it to reveal the presence of received energy (Fig. 43C). The loop picked up so little voltage, even when very close to the oscillator, that the distance between the gap's electrodes had to be extremely short for the spark to jump it. He adjusted the distance between by means of a micrometer, and watched for the spark in the dark.

Hertz called his receiver a *resonator,* because its size and shape gave it just the correct amount of inductance and ca-

pacitance to resonate to (be in tune with) the oscillator
frequency.

The laboratory radio system built by Hertz was the world's
first; though the countless changes and refinements that have
since been grafted upon it have changed its appearance completely. It's like an old pair of shoes that have been patched
and repaired so many times that any trace of the original
leather has all but disappeared.

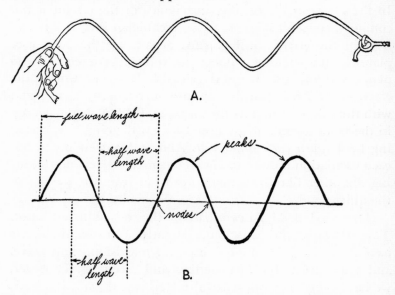

Fig. 44.   (B) Graph of a Hertzian (radio) wave resembles (A) the wave in a
rope.

If you were to feel along the rope of Fig. 44A in the dark
you would note that there are places, between the waves or
loops, where the rope is scarcely moving at all. These quiet
points, where no energy is present, are called *nodes.*

Hertz used his resonator to "feel" along the beam of energy
sent out by his laboratory transmitter. He discovered there
were points where he got a maximum spark, and precisely
between two of these points he got no spark at all.

This seemed ample proof that the electromagnetic energy travels outward from its source in wave form, with the same loops and nodes as a mechanical wave traveling along a rope.

The distance between two nodes, or between two peak voltages, gave him half a wave length (Fig. 44B). Knowing the wave length and the speed of travel of the waves, he was able to calculate the number of waves released each second: the *frequency*.

For example, suppose the measured length of a *complete* cycle (including two loops and two nodes) is one meter. A one-meter wave, traveling at a rate of 300,000,000 meters per second, will travel for 1/300,000,000th of a second before a second wave starts; therefore 300,000,000 of these waves will go out each second, which is its frequency. A two-meter wave will travel for 1/150,000,000th of a second before a second wave starts; 150,000,000 will go out each second, and this will be its frequency. (To obtain frequency from wave length, divide 300,000,000 by wave length. To obtain wave length from frequency, divide 300,000,000 by the frequency.) Hertz experimented with frequencies as high as 300,000,000 cycles.

Hertz made many experiments with his oscillator and resonator (transmitter and receiver), and all of them buttressed the wave theory. He *focused* the waves by means of a parabolic reflector, made of metal. (It has the same shape as the reflector behind an automobile headlight.) He *beamed* the waves at a sheet of metal, and the waves were *reflected,* just as light waves are reflected from a mirror or a polished surface. (This is the basis of radar.)

He did find, however, that unlike light waves his generated waves passed right through solid materials that were non-metallic, what we call insulating materials; which explains why an indoor radio antenna may work very well. In fact, the waves *prefer* other insulating materials to air; a glass rod can be used as a *wave guide.*

It seems perfectly evident from Hertz's experiments that

his electrically generated waves, like light waves, take time to move from point to point, and therefore are not instanta-neous, like thought or the force of gravity. If Faraday and Maxwell torpedoed the action-at-a-distance theory, which said that the effect was instantaneous, Hertz gave it the *coup de grâce* that sank it out of sight. He demonstrated by ex-periment that the forces of electricity and magnetism can leave one body and travel to another body in the form of an electromagnetic wave. The wave, it was assumed, existed by reason of changes in the state of a medium—the ether.

The stage was all set for the entrance of the Boy from Bologna, Guglielmo Marconi.

13

MARCONI HATCHES WIRELESS

IN 1894 the clatter of 'horses' hooves was heard, galloping out onto the quiet stage of calm scientific inquiry. The determined young man in the saddle was Guglielmo Marconi. Guglielmo was born in 1874, the son of an Italian businessman of Bologna and a Scotch-Irish mother from Ireland. Anne Jameson, of the Dublin family of whiskey distillers, had gone to Bologna to study music and learned about love instead.

While the family summered in the Alps, or wintered in the south of Italy, young Marconi and his two brothers received most of their education from private tutors. Guglielmo attended technical schools in Florence and Leghorn for short periods, and it was at one of these schools that his imagination was set on fire by a demonstration of the new Hertzian waves. In 1892 Sir William Crookes, of Crookes tube fame, had written an article in the *London Fortnightly Review,* suggesting that the Hertzian waves had a future in the field of communications. He said: "Here is unfolded to us a new and astonishing world, one which it is hard to conceive should contain no possibilities of transmitting and receiving intelligence." Young Marconi read this and everything else he could find on the new waves. And if the waves could be harnessed to a wire-less telegraph system: why shouldn't he be the one to do the hitching? Timorously at first, the 20-year-old youth began to experiment, setting up his gear on the family's country estate.

Meanwhile, the scientists had been repeating the Hertz experiments in their laboratories, and a French professor of physics, Edouard Branly, greatly improved the receiver. For the Hertz spark gap, he substituted a *coherer*. This device consisted of a small glass tube filled with powdered metal filings. Powdered metal offers a high resistance to the passage of a current flow, except when it is excited by Hertzian waves, which greatly reduce the resistance. Thus the coherer acted as a relay; the received waves, passing through it, caused it to turn on a local current to operate a signaling device, such as a telegraph sounder. And if the waves were broken up into dots and dashes, so would be the local current (Fig. 45).

The coherer liked to stay in its "frozen" state, and to remedy this a gadget called a *decoherer* was added: a little tapping hammer, operating like an electric bell, that restored the tube's high resistance between dots and dashes.

Young Marconi elevated one end of the Hertz dipole antenna and began lengthening it until it was soon 40 feet long. Later he *grounded* the other end by attaching it to a metal plate buried in the earth. Thus was born what has ever since been known as the Marconi antenna (Fig. 45). The increased physical size of this antenna over the little Hertz dipole meant greater inductance and capacitance, and so a much lower frequency. There is an especially large capaci-

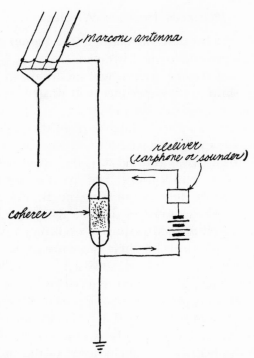

FIG. 45. Marconi's first receiver, using coherer. Only one end of the Marconi elevated antenna is shown.

tance effect between the overhead wires and the ground, the two acting like the plates of a condenser.

Marconi managed to send his signals a little farther with his big grounded antenna. He naturally concluded that the lower frequency was best. It wasn't until the early 1920s that the engineers began to realize the superiority of the higher frequencies for most purposes.

For his receiver, Marconi tried different kinds of powdered metals in Branly's coherer. He thought that placing the tube's metal terminals (electrodes) closer together, almost touching, gave better results. At any rate, within a year he was blasting the Hertzian waves out across his father's chestnut trees for distances up to a mile and a quarter. When he got up to a mile and three quarters, he felt he was doing well

enough to offer his new "wireless" to the Italian government.
The officials politely turned it down.

Guglielmo's mother, with whom he always spoke English,
encouraged him in his experiments. It was her influence that
sent him to Great Britain in 1897.

One of the first things young Marconi did upon arrival in
London was to apply for a patent on his system. British patent
number 12,039, it was granted on July 2, 1897, four months
to the day after application. The specification shows the
Hertz oscillator in the transmitter; the Branly coherer, decoherer, and Morse sounder in the receiving instrument.
There was a well-defined raising of eyebrows among the scientists when they learned their laboratory gear had found
its way into the patent office. Only a few, notably Crookes,
Sir Oliver Lodge, and Ernest Rutherford, had given any
thought at all to its practical use. The waves that Hertz generated in his laboratory traveled in a straight line. This would
make them useless for telegraphy over distances of more than
30 or 40 miles because of the curvature of the earth. But the
waves of lower frequencies that Marconi stumbled onto, with
his big antenna, hug the earth. They have a *ground wave*.
And it was later discovered that all waves up to around 30
million cycles are "reflected" back to earth by the *ionosphere*.
Television frequencies are above 30 million.

Marconi was a shy and sensitive though personable young
man, who besides being eminently practical was also ambi-
tious. His practical side was not confined to his experiments
—it extended into his business dealings. With the basic wireless patents in his pocket, he excited the interest of the British post-office department, for whom he was soon carrying
out numerous experiments. The newspapers were filled with
stories about the strange goings-on of the young Italian and
his crew, who were stringing up wires all over the English
countryside, frightening the livestock with the ominous
crackling of their electric sparks. It wasn't long before the

copper plate Marconi had buried for a ground at the foot of his first antenna turned to gold. Less than a year after his arrival in London, a group of wealthy men joined with him to form the Wireless Telegraph and Signal Co. (In 1900 it became the Marconi Wireless Telegraph Co., Ltd.) For his patents, which involved his ingenuity and foresight, young Marconi was made one of the new company's six directors, placed in charge of its technical program, presented with $75,000 in cash, and given $300,000 worth of stock out of a total capitalization of $500,000. Some stock was offered to the public, though on slightly different terms.

The world's first wireless company had the full backing of the British government's post-office, war, and navy departments. Among the government men were Sir Oliver Lodge and Professor James A. Fleming, inventor of the Fleming valve (some time later) that Lee De Forest transformed into the audion. Fleming became the company's scientific adviser.

The post-office department's engineer, Sir William Henry Preece, worked with Marconi in the field. At one stage of their experiments, Sir William issued a comment that has turned out to be a classic example of British understatement. He said, "The distance to which signals have been sent is remarkable. On Salisbury Plain, Mr. Marconi covered a distance of four miles. In Bristol Channel this has been extended to over eight miles. *And we have by no means reached the limit.*" (Italics mine.)

Marconi was first of all concerned with getting more and more distance with his gear, and he didn't bother much about tuning. In his first patent there was no reference to it. In 1898 Sir Oliver Lodge patented the use of a coil in the antenna circuit.

A coil in series with the antenna circuit of the Marconi transmitter didn't reduce radiation very much, and its turns could be varied to change the frequency: the more turns the lower the frequency. The receiver was tuned in the same way.

The patent went to Marconi's new company. In 1904 the company patented a vastly improved tuner, the two-circuit job, with which we are already familiar (Fig. 55A).

In 1913 I had one of these tuners, connected to a spark-coil transmitter, spluttering away in one corner of the woodshed. But the little interrupter wouldn't handle much current and I replaced it with a transformer, hooked to the 60-cycle house current. The standard ship's generator provides a direct current; and in making this change on board ship, one had to install a direct-current motor for turning a 500-cycle alternating-current generator—a *motor-generator* set. The transmitter converted each half cycle of the 500-cycle a.c. frequency to a wave train of high-frequency waves for a total of 1,000 per second (pages 136-137).

Ionization between the open gap's electrodes was also a problem. It was first replaced by a rotary gap, and then by the highly efficient quenched gap, invented by the German physicist Max Wien. With the 500-cycle generator, it produced a beautiful 1,000-cycle note that was relatively easy for the operator to fish out of the grinding, crashing, hissing static so prevalent on the old ship-to-shore frequency of 500,000 cycles (600 meters). This frequency is still widely used for establishing contact between ship and shore and for SOS calls.

Tube transmitters didn't begin to replace the old shipboard spark sets in any great number until the middle 1920s. The first SOS, sent out by Jack Binns of the S.S. *Republic* when she collided with the *Florida* in 1909, went out over a spark transmitter, as did the SOS from the *Titanic* when she rammed an iceberg in 1912. At the time they were jettisoned, the quenched-gap transmitters were highly efficient pieces of apparatus compared with the early Marconi sets.

You can readily see why the spark transmitter's 1,000 wave trains per second could not be used for radio telephony or broadcasting. The high, radio frequency was already broken up by its own wave trains—into a single 1,000-cycle note. The sending operator, with his key, separated this single note into dots and dashes. Radio telephony or broadcasting needs an unbroken radio frequency, a *continuous* wave (Fig. 44B); then the frequencies of voice and music can be impressed upon it to "break it up" into their own lower frequencies. This is the process known as *modulation*.

The weakest link in Marconi's first shipboard receiver was the coherer and decoherer. It was soon replaced by the detector. The detector *demodulates* the signal, which, in plain language, means that it separates the audio frequency from the radio frequency. Magnetic and electrolytic detectors appeared first, then the crystal detector, which proved the best. Many an early broadcast fan remembers when a good headphone signal was the climax to a successful search for a sensitive spot on galena or silicon with the cat's whisker. A detector is still necessary in a radio or television set. And today a superior type of crystal is coming into favor—*germanium*.

In the popular mind, Marconi has always been to radio what Columbus is to America. For many years Marconi's name was nailed over the doors of most of the radio "shacks" on the world's passenger ships. When I was going to sea, during and shortly after World War I, a member of my profession was often referred to in foreign ports as "the Marconi"; and once, in a Latin-American port, a young man respectfully addressed me as "Señor Marconi." But we have seen that the famous Scotch-Irish-Italian inventor didn't reach up and pluck the "wireless" from a low-flying cloud. His contribution was in making the beginnings of a practical system out of an experimental one. Let's say that Hertz laid the egg and Marconi hatched from it a very queer bird.

The first Marconi wireless sets were installed on British

light ships, anchored a few miles off shore. As early as 1900, the company was putting them on ships that *sailed* the seas. For the signal with which the Atlantic Ocean was first spanned, on December 12, 1901, Marconi used 20 kilowatts of power. This is a great deal of power, even for one of today's big broadcasting stations. The transmitting antenna at Poldhu, Cornwall, England, was of peculiar construction—an inverted cone 200 feet high. The frequency was 300,000 cycles (1,000 meters).

Marconi himself was in Newfoundland on the receiving end for this occasion. His receiver used a gadget similar to a coherer, consisting of a glass tube with a metal electrode at each end. Inside the tube, between the two sealed electrodes, was a single globule of mercury. Connected with it was a battery and, in place of the Morse sounder, a telephone receiver. The receiving antenna was a single wire attached to a kite.

Marconi managed to hear, buried among the maddening crashes of static, the three little dots signifying the letter *s,* the prearranged signal. Not everybody believed he had really heard them, and he may have been a little uncertain himself. After all, it could have been his imagination. Among those who took his word for it was Edison, and Marconi was very grateful for this evidence of faith on the part of a fellow inventor.

Sending the three little dots across the broad Atlantic cost the Marconi Company something like $200,000 for all the necessary equipment and preparations. It was Marconi's greatest triumph, after his early successful experiments. But trans-Atlantic wireless was never to be a success with Marconi spark transmitters, despite all the millions sunk in the project.

In 1919 Marconi acquired a luxurious yacht, the *Elettra,* and thereafter, until his death in 1937, he spent a good part of his time at sea, but was still at work on radio, measuring ranges on signals of different frequency. Largely as a result of those experiments, the high frequencies (short waves) were made available for communication, as we shall see in Chapter 20. Following his early success with the spark system, however, he left it to others to make new discoveries in the field he had pioneered. One of them was Fessenden, hero of the chapter that follows.

14

A 1906 BROADCAST

On Christmas Eve, 1906, astonished wireless operators at sea on the Atlantic heard some strange sounds in their receivers. In place of the customary dots and dashes, there was a recording of Handel's "Largo," a violin solo: "O Holy Night," and a Bible reading. They could hardly believe their earphones, and nervously passed them to fellow crew members; not so much through generosity, I imagine, as to reassure themselves of their sanity. They had no cause to be alarmed. It was merely a radio broadcast coming from Professor Fessenden's experimental radiophone station at Brant Rock, near Boston, on the Massachusetts coast. This was probably the first radio broadcast in history. The program was picked up as far south as off the Virginia coast. Soon Fessenden was sending speech 3,000 miles across the Atlantic to a receiving station at Machrihanish, Scotland. A little later than this, another American, Lee

De Forest, was also getting results with radiophone equipment.

These two men were America's most noted pioneers in the wireless field: Reginald Aubrey Fessenden, a professor at what is now the University of Pittsburg, and Dr. Lee De Forest, who had a Ph.D. from Yale. Both were of old New England ancestry, although Fessenden was born in Canada, De Forest in the Middle West.

Marconi had patented all the basic apparatus used by the scientists to send and receive the Hertzian waves in their laboratories. But this didn't daunt inventors of the caliber of De Forest and Fessenden. De Forest, still alive and active, was a few months older than Marconi, Fessenden seven years older.

In Chapter 13 we learned how the 500-cycle generator of the improved spark transmitter charged up a big condenser 1,000 times each second. Each of the 1,000 spark discharges of the condenser fed a wave train of damped high-frequency oscillations into the antenna (Fig. 42B). Tuning in the high frequency of the wave trains, the receiving operator heard the audio frequency's 1,000 note in his headphones. Now, as you know, the high-frequency oscillations in a resonant circuit are merely alternating current; they're the same as the 60-cycle current in your home, except for their higher frequency. And why not, Fessenden reasoned, dispense with all the apparatus between generator and antenna, and obtain the high frequency *direct from the generator?* Such a wireless transmitter would consist of little more than a generator hooked to the antenna.

Other inventors, notably Marconi's Fleming, in England, were skeptical. They didn't think that alternating current direct from a dynamo would produce the Hertzian waves. They believed there had to be a spark. Fleming said, "It's doubtful if any appreciable radiation would result."

But there was a small monkey wrench banging around in

the machinery of Fessenden's simple scheme: *frequency*. The frequency of his alternating current was determined by the number of times the generator's armature turned over each minute. To build a generator with an armature that could be turned fast enough for a wireless frequency without flying apart was one of those engineering jobs that just couldn't be done. It therefore took a little time. G.E.'s Dr. Ernest F. W. Alexanderson, who worked with Fessenden, finally perfected the device, called an Alexanderson alternator. It is a beautiful piece of machinery, producing a frequency of 100,000 cycles per second with high power, and until recently it still found a limited use in trans-Atlantic telegraphy.

The advantage of the alternator over the old spark transmitter was profound: it produced *continuous oscillations* (Fig. 44B). A continuous wave carries better and it tunes more sharply. These factors made the alternator superior for wireless telegraphy. But continuous oscillations also made possible radio telephony, because they can also be *modulated* by the audio frequencies of the voice. Fessenden was primarily interested in radio telephony. As early as 1900 he had succeeded in sending speech by radio over a distance of about one mile. (He did it by voice-modulating the wave trains of a special spark transmitter, whose frequency was 20,000 cycles, too high to be heard by the human ear. But this kind of "secondary" modulation didn't work well and he abandoned the idea.) By 1905 he had extended this distance to 25 miles and, as I have said, in 1907 he spanned the Atlantic with the spoken word.

At about this time De Forest was using the continuous waves from an electric arc. (Valdemar Poulsen, of Denmark, had developed a version of the ordinary electric-arc street light that converted a direct current to high-frequency oscillations suitable for radio.) Fessenden was trying out the first, not very satisfactory, models of his alternator. The main stumbling block for both experimenters was modulation.

Both were using a carbon microphone to impress the audio frequencies of voice and music on the continuous waves. They placed the microphone directly in the antenna circuit, or coupled it to the antenna circuit in some way. We explained in the section on the telephone how, when the sound frequencies strike the carbon mike's diaphragm, its vibrations create a varying resistance in step with the air waves; and the varying resistance creates electrical waves of the same frequency. This works very well in a telephone circuit, where very little current is necessary. But the early transmitters had to have quite a few amperes in the antenna circuit in order to radiate much power; and the resistance variations of a carbon mike's granules just won't vary a heavy current flow to any appreciable degree. The *percentage of modulation,* says the technician, is very low. Good modulation had to wait on the electronic tube.

Fessenden had over 500 inventions to his credit when he died in 1932. Roy Weagent, one of his early assistants, who later became a famous radio engineer, once said of him, "He was the greatest creative genius of all time in the realm of wireless." And Elihu Thomson called him "the greatest wireless inventor of the age—greater than Marconi." One of his most fruitful ideas was the *heterodyne* principle, used later by Armstrong to give us the *superheterodyne* receiver.

2

Although transoceanic telegraphy with the spark transmitter failed, the powerful new continuous-wave transmitters were a success: despite static and fading of signals, the Alexanderson alternator was pushing considerable commercial traffic across the Atlantic, and the Navy was having good success with the Poulsen arc, especially over the long reaches of the Pacific. After World War I, General Electric's Alexanderson alternator seemed to hold the key to domination of transoceanic wireless, and the Marconi Company placed an order with G.E. for a number of them. The United States government wasn't too happy at the prospect of a British monopoly in world communications and, prompted by President Wilson, some Naval officials suggested to G.E.'s vice president, Owen D. Young, that his company acquire the American Marconi Company's properties, contracts, and patents and establish an American company for operation of the alternators. As a result of this suggestion, the Radio Corporation of America was formed. The event marked the end of almost 20 years of world-wide wireless domination by the British.

The telephone company, with Western Electric, soon acquired stock in RCA and signed cross-patenting agreements with the new company. The only large electrical manufacturing firm still outside the fold was Westinghouse, whose subsidiary, International Radio and Telegraph Company, also owned some valuable patents. In 1920 these patents were pooled with the others when Westinghouse joined the group.

Until 1920 interest was confined to international telegraph and telephone communication and ship-to-shore traffic. Then the fuse that was to set off the bomb called radio broadcasting began to sputter. When the bomb burst, months later, the five companies mentioned above had the patent situation pretty well in hand. They later acquired from Edwin H. Armstrong his superheterodyne circuit, which had so much to do with the rapid growth of broadcasting.

In 1930 the government started suit against RCA under the antitrust laws. Two years later the corporation was broken up under a consent decree, and RCA became an independent corporation.

15

RADIO'S FIRST TUBE

Rᴀᴅɪᴏ, in the popular mind, distinguishes the ether's broadcast programs from its dots and dashes, the latter coming under the head of wireless. This assumption was arrived at without any help from history, for the Germans proposed radio as a replacement for wireless long before the dawn of broadcasting; they had the word substituted for wireless in the articles of the International Wireless Telegraph Convention of 1903. The new word didn't begin to catch on until much later, however, and even today in Great Britain it's still "the wireless."

Any device that uses tubes similar to the ones in a radio set is an electronic device, ranging from battery charger to image orthicon. Electronic tubes are familiarly known as vacuum tubes, or radio tubes. The simplest one is the *diode*. (Don't confuse it with the dipole antenna, first used by Hertz.) Every radio receiver has one diode, most of them have two, and a television set may have more. The experimental Crookes tube was a diode, and so is the X-ray tube. It isn't the most versatile member of the tube family, by any means, but it was the first, and it still gets plenty of work. (Transistors, discussed in the final chapter, are beginning to replace many types of tube.)

The most common diode has in it a short length of wire (filament) that is heated by a current flow; an "electron bottleneck," we called it in an earlier chapter. One doesn't need to have a sheepskin from Cal Tech to realize that it isn't light, as from a light globe, nor heat, as from an infrared lamp, that we want from the filament in a radio tube. What, then? Electrons! Electrons pushed out of the filament.

Heat isn't the only method for freeing electrons from a solid. They can also be freed by means of light. In fact, it is this connection between light and electrons that has made possible the television-camera tube, in which both methods are used. Here we are concerned with the heat method only, which is common to all the tubes in a radio or television receiver.

The effect of heat upon all matter, whether solid, liquid, or gas, is to speed up the movement of the molecules. Gas "pressure" is merely the bombardment of the walls of its container by the restless molecules. In a solid the closely packed molecules are almost quiet, though there is still some movement at ordinary temperatures. To quiet the molecules completely, it would be necessary to reduce the temperature of the solid to absolute zero (page 66). When a metal is heated to the boiling point, some molecules escape, like steam from boiling water. The blackening on the inside surface of an old light bulb is a deposit of tungsten that has slowly "evaporated" from the filament. Naturally, such a molecular disturbance seriously disturbs the electrons, especially those "vagrant" electrons that make up a current flow. The circuit of Fig. 46 illustrates this.

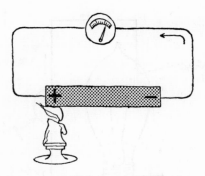

FIG. 46. Heat creates a current flow. Electrons are forced out of the hot end of the metal bar into the cold end. This leaves the heated end positively charged, while the extra electrons at the cold end charge it negatively. The unbalanced condition causes a current flow through the meter in the direction shown.

If the temperature of a metal is raised above a certain point, some of the electrons are forced out of it completely, which is what happens with the hot cathode of a radio tube.

It was our own Thomas A. Edison who first noted the effect of *electron emission* from a hot filament. The year was 1883, 16 years before Thomson's discovery of the electron. Edison was puzzled as to why his experimental lamps got black inside. Searching for a way to prevent it, he placed a piece of metal close to the filament. He connected this second electrode to one side of the filament through the base. In the external circuit, he placed a galvanometer (Fig. 47).

To Edison's amazement, the galvanometer registered a tiny current flow, despite the fact that inside the lamp the circuit was *broken*—there was an open space between second electrode and filament. The only clue to what was happening was this: the connection to the filament had to be made to its positive side for current to flow; when made to its negative side there was no movement of the galvanometer needle. Edison didn't understand the strange results of his experiment, neither did he see anything immediately practical in it. But he took out a patent anyway, just in case the principle might be used as the basis for a measuring device.

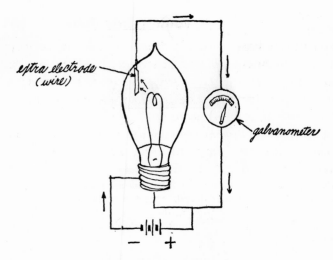

FIG. 47. Diagram showing the Edison effect.

Twenty-one years later, in 1904, Ambrose Fleming entered the picture. Fleming, who died in 1945 at the age of 95, was Marconi's chief technician when the Marconi Company was first organized. He later worked for the Edison and Swan Lighting Company in London, and he had some of Edison's lamps with the extra electrode inside, which he used in experiments. It occurred to him that this "Edison effect," as it has been called since, might be useful as a detector of wireless waves. For his second electrode he used a flat piece of metal that almost completely surrounded the filament (Fig. 48). This was the Fleming valve.

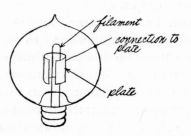

FIG. 48. Fleming valve.

We call this type of tube a diode, because it has only two electrodes, one negative, the other positive. The negative or cathode provides the electrons, and may be simply a filament; the positive electrode is called the *anode,* more commonly referred to as the *plate*.

Fig. 49 shows a diode connected to two batteries. One, the A battery, heats the filament. The other, the B battery, is between the plate and the filament.

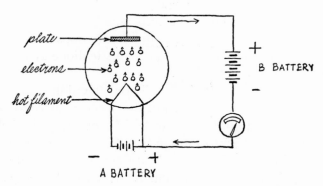

Fig. 49. The diode that evolved from Edison's tube and the Fleming valve. With the filament heated, a positive plate voltage keeps the negative electrons moving through the circuit.

Heat forces electrons out of the filament, leaving it with a deficiency of electrons, or positively charged. Now a positively charged filament right away pulls the electrons back again. One of these electrons is like the runaway boy; after a brush or two with the cold world his home suddenly becomes uncommonly attractive to him, and he rushes back to mother as fast as his little legs will carry him. But with a B battery connected as in Fig. 49, the plate has a positive charge on it too, a positive charge that competes with the filament's positive charge for the emitted electrons. A high-enough plate voltage will snatch up all of them, or almost all of them. The loss of so many electrons to the plate should build up a large positive charge on the filament; but note that the filament is connected to the negative side of the B battery, and it gets its electrons back from that direction. As a result of these pressures, a steady electron current flows through the circuit, called the *plate circuit*. The plate current flows as long as the filament is kept hot and the positive charge stays on the plate.

But suppose we turn the battery around, putting a negative charge on the plate, a positive charge on the filament. What happens then? The negative plate looks to the negative electrons like a red light to a conscientious motorist, and all traffic through the tube and plate circuit stops. Not a single electron passes. Now let's look at the little diode as a detector of the electromagnetic waves.

The signal current in your radio or television tuner moves first in one direction and then in the opposite direction—call it an alternating current or an oscillating current. Suppose we connect the tuner to a diode as in Fig. 39. Note there is no B battery, just an A battery to heat the filament. As the signal current moves in one direction it gives the diode's plate a positive charge (by pulling the electrons away from it); as it moves in the opposite direction it charges the plate negatively (by piling up electrons on it). Thus the diode's plate is alternately positive and negative once each cycle. Positive, it attracts electrons from the filament and current flows through the tube; negative, it blocks all electron flow. As a result, all current flow in the plate current must be in one direction only; we get a *direct current* from an *alternating current* simply by blocking the negative halves of each cycle. The process is known as *rectification,* or *detection.* How rectification separates the audio from the radio frequency in a radio, or the video from the radio frequency in a television set, is described in the next chapter.

When Fleming incorporated the Edison effect in a detector tube, he didn't realize that a pure stream of electrons was possible. He believed that some gas had to be present in the tube if it was to operate, as in the case of the Crookes tube, which had no filament: merely two cold-metal terminals for the cathode and anode. Today we call this type of diode a *cold cathode* tube.

Radio and television receivers use hot cathode diodes not only to rectify (detect) the received signal, but to rectify the power supply as well. Rectification is the first step in getting a smooth direct current from the 60-cycle alternating current to use in place of the B battery with the amplifier tubes.

Valuable as Fleming's diode has proved to be, its range of usefulness is limited; rectification can even be accomplished by other devices. In the chapter that follows we shall see what happened when De Forest added something more to Edison's experiment: a third electrode.

When radio broadcasting started, in 1920, Edison showed no interest; he said they were trying to put over a "laboratory experiment." He hung a sign on his office door: I WILL NOT TALK RADIO TO ANYONE. Perhaps the great inventor was chagrined that De Forest had *merely* added a third electrode to *his* filament and plate. Merely? Others had experimented with a carbon-filament electric lamp before Edison: he had *merely* discovered a *carbon* filament that worked better.

16

DE FOREST'S MAGIC LAMP

ALTHOUGH Roentgen discovered X-rays in 1895, and Fleming patented the diode in 1904, our electronic age was not really born until 1906. The blessed event took place when a descendant of John Alden, Dr. Lee De Forest, inserted a third electrode in Fleming's diode. The new baby was christened the *audion*.

The infant was not immediately popular outside the family, consisting of De Forest and his assistants. A few years of growing up were necessary before its role as the greatest child prodigy of its time was even to begin to be evident. Its spectacular career had barely started, in March 1912, when De Forest and the officers of his radio company were arrested on charges of having used the United States mails to defraud. Two of the company's officers were found guilty, while De Forest and one of his associates were acquitted of criminal intent.

The fraud charges were based on the contention that the

company's only assets were the De Forest patents, "chiefly directed by a strange device like an incandescent lamp, which he called an audion, and which device had proved worthless."

The district attorney stated: "De Forest has said in many newspapers and over his signature that it would be possible to transmit the human voice across the Atlantic before many years. Based on these absurd and deliberately misleading statements of De Forest, the misguided public, Your Honor, has been persuaded to purchase stock in his company, paying as high as ten and twenty dollars a share for the stock. . . ."

Some of De Forest's classmates had raised $2500 for his defense. When he paid it back soon after, one of them, George McLanahan, said to him, "Now, De Forest, that you are out of that mess, the best thing for you is to forget you are an inventor, and find a 'garden variety' of job. . . ." This bit of advice he fortunately ignored.

When De Forest was presented with the Edison Medal on January 28, 1947, by the American Institute of Electrical Engineers, David Sarnoff, then President of RCA, hailed the "worthless" device as "one of the twenty greatest inventions of all time."

Sarnoff said that modern telegraphy, telephony, radio, motion pictures, phonographs, transportation, navigation, aviation, and hundreds of industrial operations now employ De Forest's basic invention. And he added that it still continues to enlarge its field of usefulness.

It was the American Telephone and Telegraph Company that first put the new audion to work on a grand scale. De Forest had submitted it to the company as a solution to the problem of long-distance telephony, and was given no encouragement. Later an A.T. & T. agent who, it is stated in De Forest's biography, disclaimed any connection with the company, approached him. De Forest was hard pressed for funds, usually a chronic condition among independent inventors, and he signed away all his rights in the audion for use in telephone circuits for the modest sum of $50,000.

With the new *three*-electrode tubes operating every fifty miles or so in the telephone lines, pumping new life into the dying voice currents (amplifying them), every subscriber in America could soon talk with every other subscriber, regardless of the distance that separated them.

Lee De Forest was born in Council Bluffs, Iowa. His father was a Congregational minister, his mother the daughter of a minister. But Lee early showed a preference for science over theology, and when he entered Yale, his father's school, he specialized in that branch of learning.

Graduated from Yale, after a difficult struggle, young De Forest enlisted in the war with Spain, returning to Yale for his Ph.D. after its end. He found employment with various electrical companies for several years, mostly around Chicago. At one time he was on the staff of an electrical magazine at a weekly salary of $10. But the writings of Nikola Tesla had directed his imagination toward wireless, and he usually had a makeshift laboratory set up, perhaps in his hotel room, seeking improvements upon the Marconi apparatus. Marconi, by the way, was also a Tesla fan.

The pressure was on for a better detector, and De Forest's dreams were wrapped up in what he called a *responder:* a glass tube containing oil, water, peroxide of lead, and a metallic powder. But there was no magic in the mixture and it was an early casualty. He worked out a complete wireless system, which he installed on the American boat during the 1901 international yacht race. Marconi had his system on the rival British schooner. Each had a contract to report the progress of the race for competing newspapers ashore. However, neither apparatus was properly tuned, and the dots and dashes were so jumbled up together the shore operators could decipher nothing.

De Forest thought there might be enough interaction between wireless waves and a Welsbach gas burner for a detector. Mistaken, he switched successively to a Bunsen burner, a carbon-arc lamp, and finally to an incandescent filament in an evacuated glass bulb. He connected the antenna to a positively charged platinum plate next to the filament. Seeking more positive control, he wrapped tin foil around the bulb for the antenna. Next he moved his control element *inside* the bulb, in the form of a second plate opposite the first. Finally, he placed the second plate *between* the filament and the first plate, punching holes in it so it wouldn't block the passage of the gas. Success! A piece of wire, bent back and forth in the shape of a *grid,* worked better and the audion was born. His grid patent, No. 879,532, was granted on Feb. 8, 1908.

De Forest wasn't thinking of an *electron stream* between filament and plate as we do now; he believed some gas had to remain in the tube to provide an ionization that was affected by the Hertzian waves. Nobody seemed to understand it at first, just as it was with Volta's crown of cups.

De Forest's assistant, C. D. Babcock, named the new grid-operated tube the *audion.* (Latin *audire,* to hear; Greek *einai,* to go. Audion: to hear the movement of electricity.) It was a better detector than the Fleming valve, because it *amplified* at the same time that it detected. Not until this virtue became apparent did the little audion's tremendous possibilities begin to be realized. It was soon found that the signal could be amplified not once but many times, merely by coupling together several tubes. This *cascade amplifier* could build up a feeble signal to large proportions.

There were formidable engineering problems to be solved in such an amplifier. De Forest and an assistant, Charles V. Logwood, developed an audion amplifier in 1912, in the Palo Alto California lab of the old Federal Telegraph Company. It was at this stage in the audion's evolution that De Forest sold it to the telephone company.

A lamp works manufactured the early audions for De Forest, who sold them to amateurs. Others, notably Langmuir, greatly improved the audion by giving it a much higher vacuum and replacing the old filament with one that yielded a more satisfactory supply of electrons. Patent difficulties interfered with its early commercial application. However, radio men at sea were soon building their own tube receivers to replace the crystal set. As late as 1919, as radio officer on a trans-Pacific liner, I supplied my own three-tube battery-operated receiver, strictly against the law. Fortunately for all concerned, the United States port inspectors had very poor eyesight in those days and didn't even notice the extra unlicensed equipment.

Before we raise the curtain on the secrets of this heart, brain, and sometimes pituitary gland of electronics, the three-electrode tube, or *triode,* suppose we review briefly the terms applied to its parts and simple circuits.

In most modern tubes the electrons don't come directly from the filament, but from a small metal tube (sleeve) that surrounds the filament and is heated by it (Fig. 50D). But whatever the construction of the *electron emitter,* it is called the *cathode.* The positive electrode may be called either *anode* or *plate.*

De Forest named the batteries used with early receivers and still required by portable sets, A, B, and C batteries. The A battery supplies a current for heating the filament, the B battery puts a steady d.c. positive voltage on the plate, and the C battery supplies a negative voltage for the grid. The reason for the C battery voltage will soon be evident.

In Chapter 15 we saw how the electrons from a hot cathode, being negative, flock to the positive plate like women to a wedding. It is no problem at all to make the voltage on the plate high enough to soak up practically all of the electrons, when the tube is said to have reached the *point of saturation.*

Remember that the grid has open spaces in it; the electrons pass through the grid like a swarm of gnats through
chicken wire. In Fig. 50A, a C battery is connected between
grid and cathode so as to give the grid a negative charge.
Now, what effect does this have on the electron stream? A

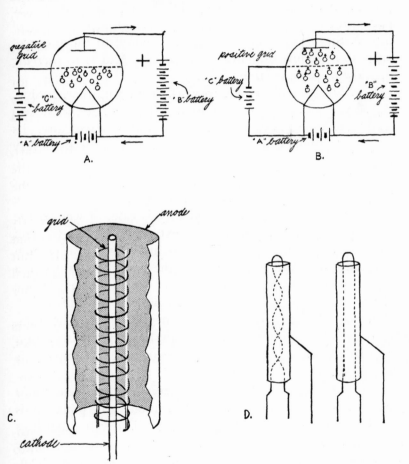

FIG. 50. De Forest's audion had cathode, grid, and plate or anode. (A) Negative grid blocks electrons. (B) Positive grid increases flow of electrons. (C) How
the three elements are arranged in the tube. (D) The electrons are usually
obtained indirectly, from a metal sleeve heated by the filament.

negative charge repels electrons: therefore, the grid *decreases* the flow of plate current. A large-enough negative grid voltage could even shut off the electron flow completely, as a closed Venetian blind shuts off the light.

Next we turn the 6-volt C battery around so its *positive* pole is on the grid (Fig. 50B). The positive grid helps the plate pull electrons away from the cathode (providing, of course, the plate voltage hasn't been raised to the point of saturation). Thus the effect of a positive grid is to *increase* the flow of plate current.

Now let's put the triode to work as an amplifier. In Fig. 55A, the C battery has been replaced by tuners (first two tubes). Even at best, the radio frequency wave, after its journey through space, is capable of producing only a very slight potential in the tuner, perhaps one of only a few *millionths* of a volt. Satisfactory operation of a loudspeaker without some amplification is out of the question. So we see the great need for amplification in this case, as well as the problem of amplifying such an extremely feeble voltage; a voltage that is also constantly changing, literally faster than lightning. Suppose, for example, the wave comes from a broadcast station whose frequency is 1,000,000 cycles. At one instant the grid gets a minute positive charge; half a millionth of a second later the grid is negative. Now the question is, will the tube's plate current rise and fall in unison with this kind of voltage change on its grid? The answer is a loud yes.

Here we put our finger on the seeming magic of the radio tube. Its electron stream between cathode and plate lends itself to a fantastically delicate *control*. The vast quantities of submicroscopic particles, the electrons, lack appreciable inertia; neither is there any amount of friction among them.

If it is possible, in some way, to obtain even an extremely feeble voltage from *any* kind of operation, electronic tubes can build it up to the point where it may be used for almost any job. Some familiar examples, in addition to the radio or television receiver, are: the tiny voltages generated by the microphone in the broadcast studio or by the camera tube in the television studio; the minute voltages that accompany brain activity (picked up by placing electrodes in contact with the scalp); the voltages obtained, by means of a photo-tube, from the faint light of distant stars.

By using a succession of tubes, placing the voltage from one plate current on the grid of the following tube, it is possible for five or six stages to build up an antenna potential of a few millionths of a volt to several volts.

An amplifying tube usually requires a steady negative voltage on its grid. Technicians call this voltage, whether from a C battery or some other source, a *bias*. The negative bias, being steady at all times, doesn't *vary* the plate current. The signal voltage goes right on top of it, the cycle's negative half making it more negative, its positive half less negative. Making it less negative really amounts to making it positive (page 31), and the plate sees the grid swinging negative and positive.

Radio-tube manuals give the proper grid bias voltage for each type of tube. Only with the recommended bias does the plate current's rise and fall closely mirror the grid's voltage changes. Of course, the grid can never cause the plate current to follow its voltage rise and fall with *complete faithfulness;* if it could, many thousands of radio engineers would have been done out of careers, for the resulting *distortion* has always been a major problem. This grid-plate disagreement is technically called *nonlinearity*. It causes both *amplitude* and *intermodulation* distortion (page 199).

2

De Forest was seeking a better detector when he added the grid to the diode. How much better he built than he knew at the time! For it soon became evident that his little triode not only would detect and amplify but would generate waves (oscillate) as well.

As an amplifier, a triode has its grid voltage from some outside source, such as a radio tuner, to control the plate current's rise and fall. But when a tube oscillates, the plate current must rise and fall without any outside help. How does it manage this? It supplies its own grid voltage, as indicated in Fig. 51. Note the extra coil, called the *tickler* or *feedback coil*. This is the little "gimmick" that enables a tube to be self-sufficient in the matter of grid voltage.

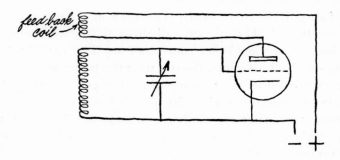

FIG. 51.   A feedback coil enables the tube to oscillate.

The feed-back coil is the primary coil of an air-core transformer. Its secondary coil is in the grid circuit; thus any changing current in the feed-back coil will induce a voltage in the secondary coil that will be felt by the grid. And as the feed-back coil is connected directly in the plate circuit, any change in the plate current will provide such a voltage.

No plate current can be *completely* stable, and suppose a very slight rise occurs in it. The rise induces a small voltage on the grid through the feed-back coil. If the current is passing through the coil in the right direction (a matter of connecting to the proper terminals) the induced voltage will be positive. Now a positive grid voltage will further increase the rising plate current, which will further increase the positive grid voltage, which will further increase the plate current, etc., etc., and "inflation" is in full swing.

Unlike Amos and Andy, this can't go on forever. A point is soon reached where no amount of positive grid voltage can make the current rise any higher, which is the point of saturation. At this instant, the plate current starts to fall. And if a rising current through the feed-back coil induces a positive voltage on the grid, a falling current will give it a negative voltage, as Faraday discovered; and the falling current will also be tied to a grid voltage. The plate current falls until the negative grid voltage stops its flow completely, then starts to rise again.

The tuned circuit of coil and variable condenser is a factor too: its inductance and capacitance exercise control over each half cycle by allowing it only so much time to rise or fall; in a word, the tuned circuit controls the *frequency* of the oscillations, the total number per second.

Just a small dose of feed-back can be used to good advantage in a receiver to increase the amplification in a tube. This is called *regeneration,* and was very popular in the early days of tube sets. The amount of feed-back voltage must be carefully regulated, for if it rises above a critical point the tube "breaks down" and oscillates. Then it becomes a transmitter as well as a receiver. When World War II broke out, many British merchant ships still carried three-tube regenerative receivers. These had to be replaced in a hurry, because a signal from one of them could reveal the ship's position to an alert German sub.

Who discovered the triode's additional virtues of regeneration and oscillation? This is still a question in some minds, though our courts have made a valiant attempt to answer it. (Lawyers seem to have profited more from invention than inventors.) On January 31, 1913, Edward H. Armstrong notarized a circuit with the audion in which there was regeneration. Later he filed applications for two patents at two different times; one for the regenerative circuit, another for the oscillating circuit. A patent for the regenerative circuit was issued to him in the fall of 1914. Meanwhile De Forest wasn't idle. He filed for a patent on what he called his *ultra-audion,* and he attacked the Armstrong claims on the grounds that they revealed nothing new. De Forest then filed another patent application which, in effect, claimed for his circuit the functions of both regeneration and oscillation.

Court decisions mostly favored Armstrong, except the final one, which the Supreme Court awarded to De Forest. The justices accepted as proof of priority a diagram in one of the old note books of Herbert Van Etten, an assistant at the Palo Alto Laboratory. This diagram shows feed-back at an audio frequency. The difficulties the courts have had in the technical land of invention indicate that the legalistic mind is no more at home there than a Tibetan monk in Tahiti. The feed-back circuit was the last of De Forest's basic patents. It expired in 1941.

The triode is vastly superior to the arc or alternator as a generator of continuous waves; it is cheaper, more convenient, and adaptable, and has a much wider frequency range. So here at last, 15 years after Fessenden first transmitted the human voice through space, was everything needed for a good radio telephone: an ideal source of continuous waves; an efficient system for modulating the waves by an audio frequency; a "magic" amplifier of an oscillating current, for use both in transmitter and receiver; and a sensitive detector of the waves. These ingredients were soon to be baked into a much tastier pie to be set before the public: radio broadcasting.

In 1915 the telephone company's Western Electric built the country's first big tube transmitter, for the Navy. In testing the new tube transmitters, a radio engineer often found it a novel relief to substitute a phonograph record for his voice. De Forest, who had broadcast Caruso in Grand Opera from New York's "Met" in 1910, using an arc transmitter, was back with his "Radio Concert" tube transmitter in the summer of 1916. Columbia supplied him with records, making him the first disc jockey. At 11 P.M., Tuesday, November 7, 1916, he confidently announced that Charles Evans Hughes had been elected President, and went to bed. Despite this pioneering, the broadcast idea didn't begin to take tentative hold on the imagination until late in 1919. Apparently quite a few were first, just as the Seven Wise Men of Greece were seventeen.

Also in 1916, Harold J. Power, of Medford Hills, Massachusetts, began serenading the avid amateurs with an occasional record. Dr. Frank Conrad, a Westinghouse engineer, who had played with a radiophone in his garage in 1916, came on the air early in 1920 with a station relicensed as 8XK, soon to become KDKA, Pittsburgh. A Detroit station, now WWJ, started broadcasting recorded music at about the same time as 8XK. Each of these pioneer stations now claims priority over the other. Lester Spangenberg, W2ZM, Lakeview, New Jersey, was sending out regular nightly broadcasts in February 1920. There were other early birds, both in the United States and Canada.

On November 2, 1920, KDKA broadcast the Harding-Cox election returns to a listening audience, mostly amateurs, estimated at 500 people; two years later, the United States had that many broadcast *stations* on the air. The new radio was stepped up a notch in class in 1921, when David Sarnoff, RCA General Manager, arranged a broadcast of the Dempsey-Carpentier bout.

Sponsors came knocking at the doors early, sparkling commercials in hand. N. W. Ayer of Philadelphia, one of the oldest and most conservative of the advertising agencies, broke the first one to harness: the Shur-On-Optical Company. Ayer also handled National Carbon's Eveready Hour, first regular series of sponsored broadcasts, in the same year, 1922. Both programs were placed with KDKA.

The telephone company paid De Forest $250,000 for his rights in the audion when used for radio telephony. De Forest didn't own the full rights. The Marconi Company, owner of the Fleming valve patent, the simple diode, had battled him through the courts, claiming infringement. The final verdict was a "split" decision, the judges dividing the tube right down the middle. The third electrode, the grid, belonged to De Forest all right; there was no doubt of that; but the filament and plate were still the property of the Marconi Company. Thus, neither De Forest nor Marconi could use the revolutionary new device without the consent of the other. This has always seemed a strange decision to radio men. By the same logic, the Wright brothers should share their glory with the inventor of the box kite.

3

I have said that any receiver, whether of radio, television, or radio-telegraph waves, must have a detector. Today we're back to a version of Fleming's diode. It isn't sensitive, but it detects with a minimum of "dat old debbil" distortion, and sensitivity is no longer a problem with tubes to amplify the signal.

Before we learn how detection separates the audio from the radio frequency in the radio receiver, we should first become acquainted with how the transmitter "packages" these two frequencies for shipment.

The American Indian, standing over his campfire with blanket in hand, modulated the even rise of the column of smoke in such a way that, to the eye of the viewer, the altered column carried intelligence (Fig. 52). In the broadcast station, the audio frequency from the microphone mod-

Fig. 52. The Indian telegraphed by modulating a column of smoke.

ulates the even flow of the radio frequency in such a way that, to the ear of the listener, the altered continuous waves carry intelligence.

The audio frequency from the microphone (after suitable amplification) goes to a modulator tube or tubes. This modulator circuit uses the audio frequency to vary the power on its way to the oscillator; as the audio frequency rises and falls, it causes the power to increase and decrease alternately. Thus the audio frequency controls the amount of *power* that goes into the antenna, just as the Indian with his blanket controls the amount of *smoke* that goes into his column.

What modulation does to the radio frequency is graphically revealed by Fig. 53. Fig. 53A represents the microphone's audio frequency. (In this case it's a pure, steady note, such as would come from a pitchpipe.) Fig. 53B represents the radio frequency from the oscillator. Fig. 53C shows how the one modulates the other, by controlling the power, which varies the *amplitude* of the radio-frequency current. The radio frequency is still there, for tuning purposes; but it now has the audio frequency fastened to it, top and bottom. It's a plain case of coat-tailing a ride. Now

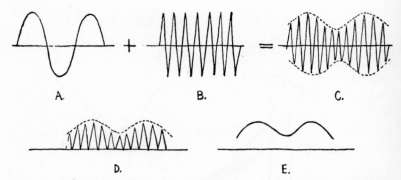

A.   B.   C.

D.   E.

FIG. 53. How we modulate a carrier wave. (A) Audio frequency from mike. (B) Radio frequency (carrier). (C) Radio frequency modulated by audio frequency. (D) Detection in receiver "wipes off" one audio frequency. (E) Remains of radio frequency filtered out.

we're ready for the detector, so let's jump to the receiver.

To begin with, the receiver's loudspeaker has no use for the radio frequency; no voice coil could vibrate at the rate of upwards of half a million cycles per second; and even if it could, you wouldn't hear anything, around 17,000 cycles being about the top limit for the human ear. The loudspeaker wants the *audio frequency*.

Now, with the audio frequency attached to both top and bottom of the carrier wave, the speaker is confronted with the problem of *two* audio frequencies. Examine them and you will see that they are always opposing each other: one is always rising when the other is falling, and vice versa. Furthermore, they are at all times of equal magnitude. If we put them both through the loudspeaker's voice coil they would cancel each other out (Fig. 41) and no more sound would emerge than from the Indian's column of smoke. But if we *rectify* our modulated radio frequency by means of a detector, we get rid of one of them. One audio frequency is completely scraped off, as shown in Fig. 53D. The single audio frequency, almost as pure as when it came from the studio microphone, is just what the voice coil ordered. (The radio frequency *peaks* must still be filtered out, as shown in Fig. 53E.)

Although the triode is still the basic electronic tube except for ultrahigh and superhigh frequencies, it has been improved upon, largely by the addition of more grids. I shall give some of the reasons for these extra grids in the chapter that follows, which is mainly devoted to putting together a complete radio receiver.

17

LET'S BUILD A RADIO

Now that we're familiar with the history and functioning of condenser, coil, resistor, and tube, it should be fun to fit them all together into a radio set (in our fancy, of course).

The same or very similar combinations of the identical condensers, coils, resistors, and tubes are also found in most other electronic devices, amplification and filtering being especially common; so if I seem to devote too much time to the radio receiver in this book on electronics, there is more to it than sentiment on the part of one who strung the wires for his first flat-top Marconi antenna after school back in 1913.

A radio receiver has two gates: one through the antenna that lets the signal through to the set, the other through the rectifier tube that passes the current flow necessary to power the tubes' filament and plate circuits. We shall tail the antenna current through to the loudspeaker first. The block diagram of Fig. 54 supplies a rough idea of what we'll find ahead.

We know that the radio or carrier frequency arrives at the receiver's antenna with the audio frequency "built in" for shipment, as indicated in Fig. 53C. The carrier, sweeping through the antenna, creates in it an electron current, a current that oscillates after the manner of a pendulum. (It's the electrostatic component of the wave that the antenna picks up.)

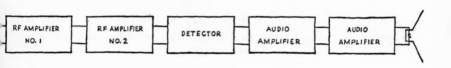

FIG. 54.   Block diagram of radio receiver.

The antenna gate is wide open to the waves within certain frequency limits, because of its inductance (L) and its capacitance (C). This inductance and capacitance is inherent in the circuit, just as color and form are inherent in a rainbow; though both can be increased, in lumps, by adding a coil, such as L_1, and a condenser, such as C_1 (Fig. 55A). C_1 is a small fixed condenser. We say that the antenna circuit is tuned broadly enough to let in all of the frequencies on the standard broadcast band almost equally well.

It is obvious that L_1 is the primary winding of a transformer; and just as in Faraday's air-core transformer, it will pass on any changing current to the secondary, L_2. L_2 is part of a second tuned circuit.

The secondary coil of this air-core transformer has more turns than the primary coil. This steps up the voltage some, but transformation of the voltage is not its primary function.

Its primary function is to serve as a means of *coupling* the two separate circuits together. C_2, as the arrowhead indicates, is a variable condenser for making the L_2C_2 circuit resonant to the desired frequency. C_2 enables us to pluck the program we want from L_1C_1.

Note that the tuned circuit L_2C_2 is connected directly across tube 1, between its grid and cathode. The voltage of the circuit's oscillating current will be felt by the grid. And as you well know, it is no simple voltage. Even unmodulated (with no sound reaching the studio mike), it is a voltage that changes from positive to negative and back to positive again many hundreds of thousands of times each second. Modulated, its peaks also carry a mixture of audio frequencies, which may swing through a frequency range of from 40 to 14,000 cycles per second. However, the sensitive tube is not "dismayed" by this feeble grid voltage that changes with lightninglike speed. The plate current follows its variations as relentlessly as the spectator's head at a tennis match follows the flight of the ball. The plate current is larger than the current on the grid side; it will yield a higher voltage for the grid of tube 2, which means *amplification*.

Now take a look at L_3 in the plate circuit of the first tube. It is the primary coil of a second air-core transformer. You will note that it has no condenser. However, any coil has some capacitance in it to go with its inductance, and L_3 is responsive enough to (closely resonant to) all the frequencies on the broadcast band. It would be better, of course, to tune L_3 more sharply to the selected frequency, but we must be careful to keep the number of expensive condensers that must be adjusted for each station to a minimum. So we tune only the secondary circuit of this transformer, by means of C_3. The rapidly rising and falling voltage developed in L_4C_3 goes to the grid of tube 2. Tube 2 is coupled to tube

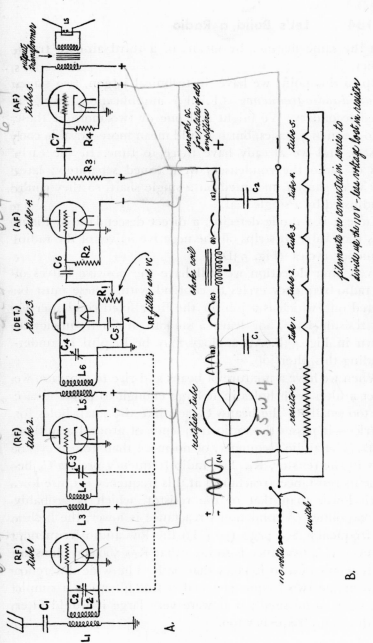

A.

B.

Fig. 55.   Circuit diagram of receiver of Fig. 54. (B) Power-supply circuit.

3 in the same manner by means of a third air-core transformer.

Up to this point we have, in technical jargon, two stages of *tuned-radio-frequency* (T.R.F.) amplification, using a tuned secondary. We might add one or two more of these radio-frequency stages, but it would mean more variable condensers, and we already have three to tune. In the early days of radio the condensers were tuned separately; later they were *ganged,* mounted on a single shaft, so they could be adjusted by a single dial.

Tube 3 is a diode detector, a direct descendant of Fleming's 1904 valve. It strips off the negative halves of the radio-frequency cycles (Fig. 53D).

Even after detection we still have the positive halves of the radio-frequency cycles to contend with. These must be filtered out, which is a job for the little fixed condenser C_5 and resistor R_1. They leave a smooth audio frequency as shown in Fig. 53E. An analogy may be helpful in understanding this filter job.

When we have a mixture of beans and rice to separate, we select a filter with holes in it large enough to pass the rice but too small for the beans. C_5 acts like the small holes for the rice—it passes the radio frequency of around a million cycles. The audio frequency, of no more than 10,000 cycles, stays in the resistor, R_1. The radio frequency prefers C_5 because its resistance (reactance) at this frequency is quite low, much lower than that of the resistor, which is probably 500,000 ohms. (A condenser's reactance is lower, the higher the frequency. See page 130.) To the low audio frequency, however, C_5's reactance is so high that R_1's 500,000 ohms actually seems low, so it takes that path. The wide difference between the two frequencies makes this filter job a simple one. C_5 is quite small; if it were very large it would filter out the audio frequency too.

Now that we have detected the signal and stripped it of its radio-frequency wings, it will operate a loudspeaker; and we could, if we wished, connect the speaker's voice coil in series with the diode so the same current would flow through both. But the current flow might not be large enough for a satisfactory volume of sound, so it is customary to add two more stages of amplification, called the *audio frequency stages*. Though we are finished with tuning, we still have a *range* of frequencies to amplify, say from 40 to 10,000 cycles, and this could give us some trouble. Suppose, for example, one of the circuits fails to amplify the whole range evenly; the result would be *frequency distortion,* different from the amplitude distortion between grid and plate mentioned before (page 171).

In a series circuit the voltage divides among the various parts in direct proportion to the resistance of each (page 66). The detector tube and R_1 are in series: which means that R_1 must have a high value, perhaps 500,000 ohms, so as to capture as much of the circuit's voltage as possible for passing on to the grid of tube 4 for further amplification.

Note the arrowhead on the connection to R_1. No curtsy to the Indian, it means the resistor is *variable*. It is the set's *volume control.* With all its 500,000 ohms in the circuit (arrow at top), it passes on its maximum voltage to tube 4 and maximum volume comes from the speaker. You can see that, with the arrow in that position, grid and cathode are across the whole resistor. (Both the lower end of R, and the cathode of tube 4 are shown as *grounded;* this grounding connects them.)

With no more need for tuning, an audio frequency amplifier can use simple resistors (and a small condenser) for coupling between stages. Tube 4's plate circuit has a large resistor, R_3, say of 250,000 ohms. The voltage across R_3 goes to the grid of tube 5 for final amplification. The connection from the top of R_3 doesn't go direct to the grid of tube 5, however, but is separated from it by a fixed condenser, C_7. Why C_7?

Examine the circuit closely. The plate of tube 4 requires a steady positive voltage in order to attract electrons from the cathode, upwards of 40 volts; and if it weren't for C_7 this positive direct-current voltage would also appear on the grid of tube 5. What tube 5's grid wants, of course, is a small, steady, *negative* voltage or bias; and you can well imagine the disastrous consequences of a 40-volt *positive* bias. The grid would draw off most of the cathode's electrons, making the tube totally inoperative. Although C_7 successfully blocks the plate's steady, direct-current voltage, like any condenser it is helpless before a *changing* voltage; so the signal voltage, which constantly rises and falls, passes through it to the grid. C_7 is a coupling condenser, sometimes called a blocking condenser.

When the grid of tube 5 goes positive on the positive half of each cycle, it attracts electrons; because of C_7 these electrons would be trapped on the grid, were it not for R_4. R_4 provides a path for them to leak off. It also provides a means for applying a negative bias to tube 5. R_4 should have a value several times that of R_3. Proper values for both resistors and coupling condenser for use with the various types of amplifiers are found in the radio-tube manual.

Now, if you're in the mood for trouble, you can find some in this resistance-capacitance (RC) coupling of this audio frequency stage. Trouble in the design of an amplifier usually means distortion. I have just pointed out, in connection with C_5, that a condenser's reactance (resistance) is greater for the low frequencies than it is for the high ones. Our little coupling condenser is certainly no exception to this rule: it passes the higher audio frequencies better than the lower ones, which creates a certain amount of the frequency distortion mentioned before.

Tube 5, the final audio frequency amplifier, must deliver as much current as possible to the speaker. The speaker's voice coil wants power (voltage times current), whereas each tube's grid only wants as much voltage as possible from the preceding tube.

Suppose we place the voice coil of the speaker directly in the plate circuit of the power-amplifier tube. Such an arrangement is not good. For one thing, the steady plate current is present in the voice coil at all times, magnetizing the coil and causing it either to push or to pull the diaphragm off center (depending upon the direction of the current flow). As a result, when the signal current (audio frequency) arrives, it finds the voice coil out of position, and the diaphragm doesn't vibrate as it should. Volume will also be feeble because of a poor *impedance* match. So we couple the tube's plate circuit to the voice coil through an iron-core transformer (Fig. 55A), which passes only the varying signal currents. Its many primary turns (for the high-impedance tube) and few secondary turns (for the low-impedance voice coil) permit maximum transfer of power.

2

Now for the second gate into the radio, the one that lets the 110 volts of alternating current from the plug in the wall through to the rectifier tube (Fig. 55B). This current also heats the filaments.

To change this alternating current to direct, the rectifier blocks every other half cycle of current. After rectification, of course, the pulsating d.c. must be smoothed out. This calls for a filter. The filter circuit of Fig. 55B is standard in small radios. It is essentially the same as the C_6R_1 filter used with the detector tube, though I think we can best visualize how it works by reference to the condenser's *time constant*. The time constant of a condenser is the time in seconds required either to charge or to discharge it; in other words, the time a current, or most of it, needs to get in or out (page 241).

It is plain to see that C_1 of Fig. 55B is connected directly *across* the rectifier tube (parallel to it) like a basket under a chute; from which we can infer that each individual half cycle from the rectifier drops into it. As the rectifier passes current only in one direction, this will be a direct current. C_1 is a large condenser, with a capacitance of from eight to 80 mfds., so that it always takes considerable *time* for the d.c. half cycle, or pulse of direct current, to flow into or out of it; and each charging half cycle is still in the process of discharging when the next one starts. This smooths out the ripple by holding up each pulse—holding it up near its peak voltage.

A water-tank analogy is good. Think of the water flowing into the tank in spurts; after the tank is partially filled, a *smooth* flow will leave through a valve below the water level.

C_1 discharges its filtered d.c. voltage directly into the coil, L, which is in series with one side of the line from the rectifier tube. L is a *choke coil*, designed to choke off a frequency. It consists of several hundred turns of wire wound on an iron core, giving it a high value of inductance. Inductance, we learned before, opposes both the rise and fall of a current; thus, L further irons out the ripple.

C_2, another filter condenser, usually with the same capacitance as C_1, also connected directly across the line, takes good enough care of what ripple remains, so that very little 60-cycle hum is heard in the speaker.

When a radio develops a bad hum, or a sound that suggests it is harboring an outboard motor, the trouble can most likely be traced to a defective filter condenser. Next to the tubes, the filter condensers are perhaps the most vulnerable parts in radio and television receivers. They are of a special type, called *electrolytic condensers,* and seldom last for more than five years, whether the set is in use or not.

Finally we come to the current needed to boil the electrons out of the filaments or cathodes. Can we use the a.c. direct from the wall plug, or must we rectify and filter it first? Well, in the old days, the filament current had to be rectified and filtered; otherwise, the rising and falling 60-cycle current would have interrupted the supply of electrons twice each cycle, to cause a dandy hum in the loudspeaker. But today we can put the 110-volt a.c. direct on the filaments without any ill effect. For today's tubes are *indirectly* heated. The actual emitter of the electrons is not the filament itself, but a metal sleeve that surrounds it (Fig. 50D). The metal sleeve holds the heat between alternations of current, which prevents any critical interruption of emission. This type of cathode is used in the tubes of all modern radio and television receivers, except some of the battery-operated portables. And here we have the reason why your set takes a little time to "warm up" after you switch it on; the filaments need half a minute or so to heat the metal sleeves.

Fig. 55B shows how the filaments of small radios are connected together, in series, so as to divide the 110 volts among them.

For simplicity's sake I have omitted the grid-bias circuits from our receiver of Fig. 55. If you are curious how a grid bias for an amplifier is obtained without use of a C battery, one method is shown in Fig. 103. The direct-current flow moves upward through the resistor into the tube; thus its lower end is negative, its upper end (and the cathode) is less negative, and therefore positive with respect to the lower end. Or, we can say that the lower end is negative with respect to the cathode; and connecting the grid to the lower end makes *it* negative with respect to the cathode also. The condenser connected across the resistor filters (smooths) out the audio frequency of the signal, leaving a *steady* negative grid bias. It is a much larger condenser than the C_5 (Fig. 55A), big enough to filter out the audio frequency itself.

3

One of the first audions sold to amateurs, which I purchased as early as 1918 for $5, was about the size of a three-inch length of broom-handle. Three filament leads protruded from one end (there was a spare filament), plate and grid leads came out the other end. To mount the tube, you fastened the wires to binding posts on the front of the panel. This pioneer audion would often "break down" into oscillations. It didn't require the special feed-back circuit of Fig. 51 to do this; for, instead of electromagnetic induction, it relied upon electrostatic induction, first explained in Chapter 2. When a changing current flows in a circuit having a condenser, it does so by virtue of electrostatic induction between the condenser's plates (page 40). Now, the plate and the grid of a triode act just like the two plates of a condenser; the rising and falling signal current in the plate circuit feeds back through this condenser to induce a voltage on the grid.

Any triode is prone to feed back enough voltage to oscillate, especially at the radio frequencies. This is something no amplifier should do. Neutralizing circuits may be used, but they have many disadvantages, so new tubes were developed to solve the problem. (Old-timers will remember the Neutradyne set of the early 1920s.) The best one is the *pentode*, with a total of three grids. All today's radio and television sets use pentodes for voltage amplification, and many use them for power amplification also (the final stage). Details on how the extra grids function to prevent feed-back may be found under Fig. 56.

The first triode transmitting tube, no bigger than a tea cup, developed 25 watts of power. The radiophone station built by Western Electric for the Navy at Arlington, Virginia, in 1915, used 500 of them and had a power rating of one kilowatt and a half. A couple of years later they were

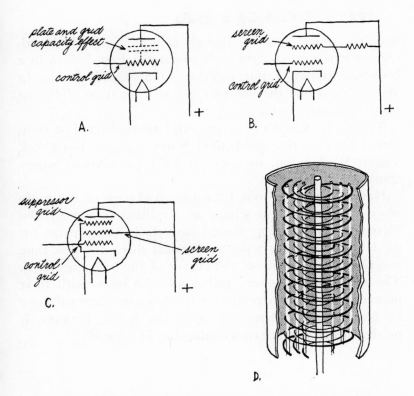

FIG. 56. The story of the pentode. (A) Triode. Dotted lines indicate capacity effect that creates feedback, causing tube to oscillate. (B) Screen grid added. By connecting this grid to the plate side of the tube, most of the electrostatic feedback is prevented. The screen grid's *positive charge* helps pull electrons from the cathode, most of them passing through its mesh to the plate. With the screen voltage ahead of it, the plate voltage has less effect upon plate current. This gives the control-grid voltage more effect than it had before, greatly increasing amplification. The control grid can also be more closely meshed, further increasing the *amplification factor*. The electrons tend to "cluster" around the cathode, forming a *space charge*, which restricts further emission. The added screen voltage tends to neutralize the space charge. However, the speeded-up electrons, striking the plate, now dislodge electrons from the metal itself, called *secondary electrons*. These electrons, attracted to the higher potential positive screen grid, create a second current through the tube, in the wrong direction. This is prevented by the suppressor grid (C). Connected to the cathode, the suppressor grid's negative voltage (with respect to the plate) shoos the electrons back to the plate again. (D) The pentode's three grids are mounted one inside the other.

making 250-watt triodes, though most of the early broadcast stations were content with 50-watters; I used them in a broadcast station I put together in Shanghai, China, in 1922. Next came the water-cooled 10-kilowatters, followed by 100-kilowatt giants.

Today, the world's most powerful transmitter, just completed by RCA for the United States Navy at Jim Creek Valley, Washington, uses special RCA 500-kilowatt supergiants.

Having completed our little tour backstage of the radio receiver and seen how science accomplishes its sorcery, the hieroglyphics of Fig. 55 should have shed their mystery for us. However, I must warn you against shock the first time you see the underside of the chassis of the radio set itself. The resistors, condensers, coils, and tube bases, with their maze of connecting wires, look as if they were dumped there by Martin and soldered into place by Lewis. Patience is needed at first to trace each connecting wire (lead).

18

SUPERHET BY ARMSTRONG

THE pioneer radio fan, as he sat most of the night hunched over his little tube set, must have seemed a strange creature to his family. His god was Distance. What he heard in the headphones clamped to his ears as he patiently adjusted knob and dial—a high note from an old Caruso recording, or a low joke from an amateur comic —was of no particular interest unless it came from some station way on the other side of the continent; then it would send him off in a transport of joy.

Along about the midtwenties he started babbling about a new kind of receiver with the strange name of *superheterodyne*. Today all home radios are superhets, just as all cars have self-starters, and nobody bothers to mention it. People have forgotten that the auto didn't begin to be popular until the self-starter was added, nor radio either until the superhet replaced the T.R.F. set.

The superhet is credited to the late Edwin H. Armstrong. While director of the Signal Corps Labs in Paris during World War I, the Hammond Labs, near Gloucester, Mass., sent him a receiving set incorporating the heterodyne principle for performance checks. Starting with this circuit, Armstrong later developed the superhet broadcast receiver. On Oct. 5, 1920, he sold it to Westinghouse, which later turned it over to RCA under a patent-pooling arrangement (page 156). The price, with the regenerative circuit thrown in, was $335,000, payable over a ten-year period.

Edwin Howard Armstrong was born in 1890 in New York City. His father was American representative for the Oxford University Press. When Edwin was 14, his father returned from a business trip to London with an armful of boy's books, including *The Boy's Book of Invention* and *Stories of Inventors*. The latter book included the story of Marconi. Two years later young Armstrong's wireless signals from his Yonkers attic earned him a measure of local fame. He went to Muhlenberg College and to Columbia University, and held degrees from both schools.

Armstrong's instructor at Columbia was Michael Pupin, another of the great pioneers of radio. Pupin invented the electrolytic detector and developed a method for analyzing complex currents in resonant circuits. In recognition, the American Institute of Electrical Engineers presented him with the Edison Medal in 1920. Twenty-two years later, in 1942, the Institute presented the Edison Medal to Armstrong, who, until his death on February 1, 1954, sat in Pupin's old chair of Electrical Engineering at Columbia. For Armstrong, this was the climax to a long list of such presentations, ranging from the *Légion d'Honneur* from the French government to the Modern Pioneer plaque from the National Association of Manufacturers.

In his acceptance speech at the Edison Medal ceremonies, Professor Armstrong told the story of the superheterodyne invention. The Army had sent him to France during World War I as a captain, though he was soon promoted to major. One night, while watching a bombing raid, he fell to wondering at the ineffectiveness of the anti-aircraft fire. It wasn't too important, because the aim of the bombers was even worse.

Planes were located by their sound waves. A big metal ear, with microphone inside, was swung around until the noise from the plane's propeller was loudest. It occurred to Major Armstrong that a better way would be to tune in the electromagnetic waves broadcast by the ignition system of the plane's motor. But these waves are of a very high frequency, too high for the tubes and circuits then available. A new type of receiver was needed. The Major used the heterodyne principle for *lowering* the frequency of the received wave before feeding it to the tubes for amplification. This was his first superhet.

Although the superhet was never used for the purpose for which it was devised, it proved better for receiving any kind of radio signal; in the next world war it was incorporated in the receivers of the radar sets that locate an enemy plane by sending out a wave and picking it up again on the rebound.

Fig. 57 shows the block diagram of a typical superhet. It does away with all but one of the radio frequency stages of the T.R.F. set, and some of the cheaper superhets even elim-

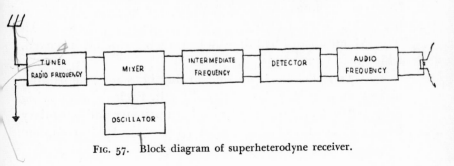

FIG. 57. Block diagram of superheterodyne receiver.

inate that. After tuning in the carrier frequency, the super-het reduces it to a lower frequency, called the *intermediate frequency,* usually referred to as the i.f.

The superhet reduces any frequency tuned in to this same i.f. Its key is streamlined simplicity, which, after all, is in tune with the modern trend. Like prunes, for example, which are routed straight through from orchard to dryer to wholesaler to chain store to kitchen stove in neat two-pound packages with an absolute minimum of labor and conversation. When you switch on your superhet, a circuit takes over that changes the tuned-in frequency to the intermediate frequency, which carries the signal through all the i.f. stages to the detector with comparable efficiency.

The standard broadcast band is from 550,000 to 1,600,-000 cycles. One thousand cycles is one kilocycle, so let's say from 550 kc. to 1,600 kc. Now, a tuning circuit has trouble with such a *wide range* of frequencies. The superhet's i.f. stages have only a *single* frequency to manage. They amplify the whole range more evenly, provide greater amplification per stage, give higher fidelity, and do a better job of keeping out unwanted stations—though this usually requires a stage of T.R.F. Much of the superhet's virtue rests on the fact that tuning *both* the primary and secondary circuits is no problem; for the i.f. stages are *fixed-tuned. They need no dial,* which also makes the superhet simple to operate. This helped more than anything to break down the resistance of the average housewife to a "talking piece of furniture" in her living room (to lift an immortal phrase from Fred Allen). About all you had to do was to turn it on and it played, which made sense.

Today's radio has from one to five i.f. stages, depending mainly upon how much you paid for it. Each i.f. amplifying tube has an i.f. transformer, with both primary and secondary fixed-tuned on each side of it (Fig. 58). Each complete transformer is hidden in a *can* to shield it from stray electromagnetic fields, which might introduce a hum or cause the tube to oscillate. Two cans mean one stage of i.f., three cans mean two stages, etc.

Although the i.f. transformers are fixed-tuned, they are apt to get slightly out of tune, mainly from the effects of heat. For this reason they are made "semivariable." Each i.f. can has two holes through which the service man can poke a special tool, a nonmetallic screw driver, to "touch up" the circuits. Sometimes the eager home radio expert sees the little screws inside the cans and, noting they are loose, screws them down tight. This completely detunes the i.f. stages, greatly weakening the signal if not blocking it entirely. The radio service man has a term for these kitchen-table mechanics, but it is too technical for this book.

The superhet's task of reducing all the tuned-in frequencies to the intermediate frequency is not exactly a simple one; you can't, for example, use a brake on an oscillating current as you do on a phonograph turntable. In Greek, *heteros* means other, *dynamis* means power. Some "other power" is needed to change the frequency.

Strike middle C on the piano and you hear a frequency of 256 cycles per second (fundamental frequency). Strike the B just below it and the frequency heard is 240 cycles. Now strike both keys together. Blended with the piano's two notes is a third frequency of 16 cycles. Sixteen cycles is the difference between 256 and 240; it was created when the air waves of these two frequencies struck your ear drums simultaneously. There is also a frequency produced equal to the *sum* of 256 and 240 cycles.

Two alternating-current frequencies can also be combined in this way to produce a third or difference frequency, called a *beat note*. The technician thinks of one frequency "beating against" the other. Even the complex carrier frequency arriving at the radio receiver can be reduced by this method without damage, as can color television's carrier, which has been modulated by both brightness and color frequencies.

A second frequency, the "other power" mentioned above, is supplied by an oscillator tube, the same kind of oscillator found in every transmitter. This local frequency is mixed with the carrier frequency from the tuner (Fig. 57). Out of the mixture, which takes place inside a tube, the *mixer tube,* comes the difference frequency. It gets its name, intermediate frequency, from being between the audio and carrier frequencies.

As the frequency of each station on the dial is different, and the i.f. is always the same, the oscillator frequency must be variable. It has its own variable condenser mounted on the same shaft as the tuning condenser (or condensers), so that they all turn in unison.

The i.f. in many radio receivers is 456 kc. To keep the difference between the oscillator frequency and the tuned-in frequency always at 456 kc., the oscillator frequency can be either 456 kc. above or below it. It is always kept 456 kc. above the tuned-in frequency. For example, suppose you turn the dial to a station broadcasting on a frequency of 700 kc.; at the same time you are adjusting the oscillator frequency to 1,156 kc. (You can't help yourself, with both condensers mounted on the same shaft.) For 1,156 minus 700 equals 456.

The television frequencies in the ultrahigh band (300 to 3,000 megacycles) now coming into use, must be reduced before the older type of set can receive them. Heterodyning is the method used.

Most radio receivers, including all the small a.c.-d.c. sets, manage to do without a separate oscillator tube by using a tube that doubles as oscillator and mixer—usually called the *first detector.* It has four grids and is called a *pentagrid converter* (Fig. 58).

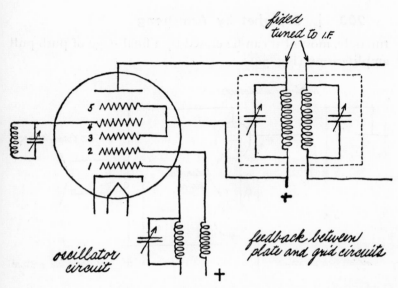

FIG. 58. Pentagrid converter, which functions both as oscillator and mixer in the superhet. No. 1 grid introduces the voltage from the oscillator. No. 2 grid is the *plate* of the oscillating circuit. Nos. 3 and 5 grids are both screen grids— they reduce feedback to the signal grid, No. 4. A single cathode, called a common cathode, supplies the electrons. Its electron stream is interrupted twice, once by the oscillator frequency on grid 1, and once by the signal frequency on grid 4. One result, in the plate circuit, is a frequency equal to the *difference* between them, which is the intermediate frequency (i.f.) (page 198). All the other frequencies are suppressed by the tuned plate circuit in the first i.f. section.

2

Most of us are familiar with the plaint of the young man struggling to master the trumpet: "I blow in so sweet but it comes out so sour." A similar unhappy transformation takes place inside the radio receiver: caused by distortion.

Changes in the tube's plate current never *exactly* conform to the grid-voltage rise and fall. Though this nonlinearity has its uses, it's an evil in audio amplifiers. It's called harmonic distortion, because it could be duplicated by adding harmonics to the fundamental (page 108). The most pronounced is the 2nd harmonic, double the fundamental. Fortunately, most of it can be erased by a final stage of push-pull amplification (Fig. 59).

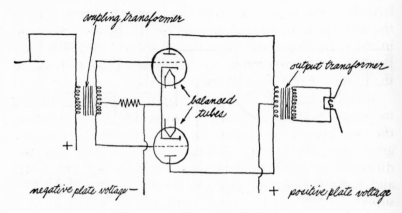

FIG. 59. Audio push-pull circuit.

Such an amplifier works like the double-button mike circuit of Fig. 36. Both have a split primary coil, though the amplifier, of course, has a pair of tubes instead of two mike buttons. The plate currents of the two tubes, each one passing through its own half of the primary coil, induce mutually aiding voltages in the secondary coil; with the exception, however, of the second harmonic frequency. In the secondary, one tube's second harmonic voltage is always rising while the other tube's is always falling, and vice versa, which tends to cancel them out. The same is true for all the even harmonics, fourth, sixth, etc., though it is usually only the second that is large enough to invite good riddance. Much power-supply hum is also canceled.

Nonlinearity also causes *intermodulation* distortion: one audio frequency modulates another. This means that the audio frequencies beat together to produce sum-and-difference frequencies (page 197). Like the added harmonics, they were not part of the sweet music blown into the set through the antenna.

Some frequency distortion occurs in the audio amplifier because the coupling condenser (C_7 in Fig. 55A) passes the higher audio frequencies better than the lower ones. But frequency distortion also takes place on the other side of the detector tube, in the intermediate frequency stages and in the radio frequency stages too, if any are used. It's a little difficult to understand. For a starter, we must return to the modulation process in the transmitter.

Modulation varies the power supply to the transmitter by means of the audio frequency. And strange as it may seem, the two frequencies, audio and radio, are also *mixed*. We get a heterodyning effect, from which emerge both sum and difference frequencies. It's the same as though the audio and radio frequencies were fed into the mixer stage of a superhet. This can be proved mathematically, though it is impossible to visualize. At least it is for me.

Suppose the transmitter's frequency is 1,000 kc., modu- lated by a 5,000-cycle note of some kind. Despite the big difference between 1,000,000 and 5,000 cycles, we still get sum-and-difference frequencies of 1,005 kc. and 995 kc. that are troublesome. For the transmitter isn't sending out a pure 1,000-kc. wave, but one with a frequency width of 10 kc. And note what happens when this *band* of frequen- cies reaches the intermediate frequency stages of the re- ceiver: the i.f. transformers, when tuned *sharply* to 456 kc., won't let through the 1,005-kc. and the 995-kc. part of the carrier. It cuts them off. As a result, you don't hear the 5,000-cycle note in the speaker. These sum-and-difference frequencies, on each side of the carrier frequency, are called the *side bands*. The side bands actually contain the audio frequencies of music and speech.

The solution would seem to be simple: use broadly tuned i.f. transformers that pass a wide-enough *band* of frequen- cies to let through all the musical notes in the orchestra. The fundamental frequency of even the highest musical note is under 5,000 cycles, though the important harmonics may go up to 10,000 cycles or higher. Consequently, a superhet's i.f. stages should pass all the side bands up to at least 10,-000 cycles on each side of the carrier frequency. Instead, even the best of them are capable of passing frequencies of only 5,000 on each side. And for a very good reason. If they were tuned more broadly, there would be too much interference from other stations. The standard broadcast band is limited, and the F.C.C. (Federal Communications Commission) has to crowd as many stations as possible into it, which means that station frequencies must be too close together for ideal tuning.

The i.f. stages in a cheap little table model may chop off all frequencies above 2,500 cycles or so. The lows will be completely lost, because of the speaker (page 209). However, the harmonics provide a sort of substitute for their fundamental. The ear unconsciously fills it in, in somewhat the same way that the light and dark in a painting fools the eye into seeing a third dimension. When even the expensive commercial radio, TV, or phonograph slights the lower frequencies, this lack of bass is also the fault of the loudspeaker.

The quality audio amplifier passes all the frequencies evenly enough for the crankiest hi-fi fan. Harmonic and intermodulation distortion are kept well below 2 percent at normal power rating. (Overloading greatly increases distortion.) With the more efficient pentodes, *negative feedback,* the opposite of regenerative feedback, is necessary. Some of the amplifier's output signal is *fed back* to mix with the input signal, 180 degrees out of phase. Distortion, caused by nonlinearity, is generated within the tube, so it isn't amplified in the output. The feedback voltage, with the distortion "in reverse," getting the same amplification as the distortionless input voltage, almost completely cancels the nonlinearity.

19

FM IS BEST

FROM the time that Marconi first started spraying his father's chestnut trees with Hertzian waves, radio's Enemy No. 1 has been static. I remember summer days cruising along the coast of Central America when static was so severe that one could open the door of the radio shack and throw the big brass key, with message attached, farther than the ship's 2,000-watt transmitter would carry. There was so much electricity coming down from the antenna that if the antenna switch was left a quarter of an inch or so from the connection to ground (the sea), an almost continuous stream of sparks would splutter and crackle between the electrodes. This was almost the identical arrangement used by D'Alibard, in 1752, to prove that lightning is electricity; but it was of no use to me in this respect because I had long been sold on B. Franklin's theory. Static seldom troubles radio listeners in or near the cities anymore, but it still shuts off around ten million listeners in outlying districts from regular broadcast service.

It is curious that the first wireless receiver was not designed to receive telegraph signals at all, but to pick up the electromagnetic waves generated by static, the waves that we have been vainly trying to keep out of our receivers ever since. I refer to the device built by the Russian, Alexander Stepanovitch Popoff, to warn him of approach of thunderstorms. As a storm approaches, the static usually increases; and Popoff had his receiver so set that after the static had built up to a critical level it operated a coherer, which permitted the current from a battery to flow. The battery current rang an electric bell.

Russia has recently dug up the Popoff experiments to prove that he, and not Marconi, invented wireless. But there were probably dozens of scientists, and not a few inventors, repeating and even extending the Hertz experiments at about the same time.

Galvani, the 18th-century anatomist of Marconi's home town, Bologna, received electromagnetic waves from a friction machine with his frog; later the frog responded to the waves from flashes of lightning. Any electric spark, man made or nature made, sends out trains of electromagnetic waves, modulated so we can hear them in our loudspeakers, or perhaps see them on our television screens. In addition to lightning, or even comparatively mild ethereal discharges that are not accompanied by a visible spark, our radio and television receivers pick up waves from leaky insulators on power lines, the sparking commutators of electric motors, and other electrical devices.

Some of the man-made static rides in on the 110-volt power line. A filter should be connected across the line at the device itself to suppress these frequencies; if not, one can be installed at the receiver. A small one that plugs in ahead of the cord, and sells for about a dollar, may help some.

Some static can be tuned out by means of very selective tuning circuits, but there is a limit to this because too much selectivity causes distortion; it cuts off the higher frequencies, mostly harmonics, by blocking the side bands (page 201).

Why hasn't the engineer-inventor, with all his genius for such things as television and radar, been able to silence static, say by some little gadget that traps it in a drawer which the housewife can empty when she dusts? The answer to this is that the static wave is too much like the radio wave itself to be successfully discriminated against. Radio men long felt that one might as well try to neutralize the law of gravitation.

The inventor who finally solved the problem had to use an entirely new kind of broadcasting to do it: FM. (FM stands for *frequency modulation*.) He was Major E. H. Armstrong, the Columbia professor who gave us the superheterodyne. Actually, Miss Frequency Modulation herself is older than De Forest's audion. However, the engineers saw no particular virtue in her and she was consistently ignored. Major "Pygmalion" Armstrong fished her out of the gutter, gave her some pretty clothes, and taught her the art of make-up. Today she not only moves with pride in high-frequency society, but she makes the old queen of modulation, AM, look drab and old-fashioned in comparison.

Modulation, you remember, is the process of combining the program's audio frequency with the much higher frequency of the carrier wave. When the audio frequency alters the *power* of the carrier frequency, thereby varying the carrier's amplitude in step with it, it is called *amplitude modulation,* abbreviated AM.

Frequency modulation, as the two words indicate, fastens the audio to the carrier by altering the carrier's *frequency*. Now at first blush this seems to make no sense at all; each station's wave should have a single frequency, otherwise how could you tune it in to the exclusion of all the other frequencies on the dial? There is no cause for panic. The audio frequency varies the carrier frequency over a range of 150,-000 cycles, or 75,000 on each side of the unmodulated frequency; the i.f. circuits in the receiver can easily be made to tune broadly enough to pass the entire 150,000 band.

There isn't room for such wide bands in the standard broadcast frequencies, which is one reason why FM was neglected. The FCC has assigned FM to the frequencies between 88 and 106 million cycles. (A million cycles is called a megacycle, abbreviated mc.)

Fig. 60 shows graphically how a carrier wave is frequency modulated. The audio frequency from the microphone is pictured above, the radio frequency below. One half cycle of the audio frequency increases the radio frequency; the other half cycle decreases it. (One of them is positive, the other negative.) The audio frequency, therefore, "extends" and "squeezes" the radio frequency, as if it were the bellows of an accordion. At least it looks that way when we picture it on paper.

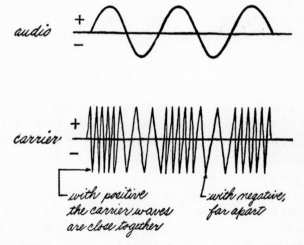

FIG. 60. With frequency modulation (FM) the audio frequency from the mike varies the carrier frequency.

The louder the sound the higher the audio frequency peaks rise and the more each half cycle varies the radio frequency. Thus the loudness of the sound determines the amount of the frequency change.

How a microphone's audio frequency can modulate a radio frequency is shown in Fig. 61.

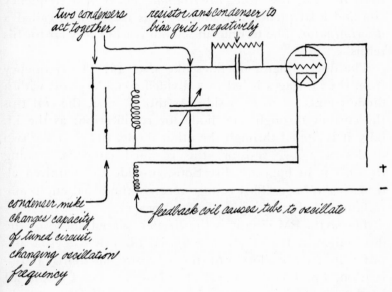

Two condensers act together

resistor and condenser to bias grid negatively

condenser mike changes capacity of tuned circuit, changing oscillation frequency

feedback coil causes tube to oscillate

+

−

FIG. 61. Simple method of frequency modulation. A two-plate condenser **in** a resonant circuit is also a microphone, one of its plates functioning as the diaphragm. As the diaphragm vibrates, it changes the condenser's capacitance, which varies the frequency of the resonant circuit in step with the sound waves.

This is not a practical method of frequency modulation, and it gives very poor quality. Armstrong found that it fails chiefly because the radio frequency isn't varied over a wide enough range.

A block diagram of the FM receiver is shown as part of Fig. 75. It is a conventional superhet except for one added circuit and a different kind of detector.

The loudspeaker's voice coil will not respond to a *frequency* change; it wants a *current* change, the up-hill-and-down-dale kind it gets from the detector of the old-type radio. The FM detector supplies it by converting an i.f. frequency increase to a current flow in one direction, an i.f. frequency decrease to a current flow in the opposite direction. It must, therefore, *discriminate* between a frequency rise and a frequency fall, and for this reason it is called a *discriminator*. The technician seldom reaches very far for his terms.

The discriminator operates like a seesaw. The frequency from the i.f. stages is fed to a divided secondary coil with a diode connected to each side. As the i.f. rises, the coil tips the current through one diode for rectification; as the i.f. falls, it is tipped through the other diode. Between the two diodes is a big resistor; the rectified currents, passing through it in opposite directions, provide the required alternating voltage. This voltage receives the usual audio amplification before going to the loudspeaker.

The extra FM circuit is the *limiter,* placed ahead of the discriminator. It consists of a special tube that doesn't amplify; in fact, it does just the opposite, it *limits* amplification. The FM signal peaks from the i.f. stages should all be the same height; if some have been amplified too much, the limiter slices them off, which does the signal no harm. At the same time, all *amplitude-modulated* peaks are eliminated. The wave trains of static are, for the most part, amplitude modulated; in other words, the carrier wave of a burst of static is just like the carrier wave of a standard broadcast signal. So most of whatever static is able to fight its way through the i.f. stages bites the dust in the limiter. Armstrong estimated that the FM receiver picks up from 1/500th to 1/1,000th as much static as the AM receiver.

Although Armstrong began courting FM because of her staticless character, he soon discovered that she had another virtue: high fidelity. The frequency distortion in the AM receiver that results from the lopping off of the side bands in the i.f. stages is not present in the FM set. FM's i.f. stages pass everything the station sends out. Please note, however, that the FM set is superior to the AM only in the matter of frequency distortion in the i.f. stages, and in the r.f. stages if any are used. There is nothing to prevent a distressing amount of either frequency or amplitude distortion in the audio end of a cheap FM receiver any more than there is in a cheap AM set. And then there's the loudspeaker, which may be the *main* stumbling block to good reproduction.

The smaller speakers neglect the bass notes more than the highs. A little 4-inch speaker may reproduce none of the frequencies below 200 cycles, and not very many above 3,500. The next larger speaker's frequency range may be between 150 and 4,000. However, in recent years the smaller speakers have been greatly improved by using new materials in the cone, changing the shape, improving suspension, etc. The so-called high-fidelity speaker should reproduce, with close to equal efficiency, everything between 30 and 15,000 cycles. The twin-cone type is popular, a small cone for the highs (*tweeter*) a large one for the lows (*woofer*). When both cones are mounted on the same axis it's called a *coaxial* speaker.

A big problem with the speaker is that the back of the cone radiates sound waves as well as the front. The two sets of waves are 180 degrees out of phase—one always rising while the other one is falling, and vice versa; thus, if the two meet in front of the cone they tend to cancel each other out. The *slower rising low frequencies* (30 to 200 cycles) do meet in the case of the average radio, which accounts for its lack of bass response and tinny sound.

The obvious way to eliminate bass cancellation is to prevent the front and back waves from meeting. For example, mount the speaker in the wall between two rooms. A less efficient way is to build a small wood wall and mount the speaker in it, off-center (Fig. 62A). Called a *flat baffle*, it should be at least 8 feet square to isolate front and back radiation effectively down to about 80 cycles. Few housewives would welcome this monstrosity in the living room.

The flat baffle can be made smaller by folding in its edges to form an open-back cabinet (Fig. 62B). Commercial radios, from table model to console, are of this type, though even the console is too small. A cabinet provides better bass response with its back closed tight and the inside padded to *absorb* back radiation. This is the *infinite baffle* cabinet (Fig. 62C).

Today's most popular speaker enclosure is the *bass reflex*. It is also a closed-back box, but with a difference: it has a second opening called a *port* (Fig. 62D). Size of port and cabinet are such that low-frequency back radiation emerges from the port *in step with* front radiation to build up bass response. Inside padding absorbs high and middle frequencies only. To the sound waves the air in the box acts like a capacitance, the port like an inductance. By means of the proper combination of box size and port size the bass reflex can be *tuned* to the speaker's resonant frequency. This extends the bass almost an octave below that frequency.

Any type of structure has a resonant frequency of its own which can cause distortion by accenting that frequency. Therefore, all cabinets should be as rigid as possible. Any *enclosure of air* also has a resonant frequency; the open-back console's natural rate of vibration, for example, produces a thumping bass at around 150 cycles that is *not* high fidelity, as many a salesman has let the novice assume.

Generally speaking, all enclosures should be as large as practicable, with 6 cubic feet the minimum. Speaker should always be matched to enclosure, with particular regard to the resonant frequency of each. Matching is easier and more effective when the bass range is confined to a speaker designed for it alone—a woofer. High and mid-range units can be coaxially, even triaxially, mounted, or separately mounted.

A superior, entirely different and more expensive way to increase bass response is by means of a bell-shaped (exponential) horn (page 119). The bass frequencies require such a large horn that manufacturers resort to the folded type; some utilize the room's corner walls as an extension of the horn.

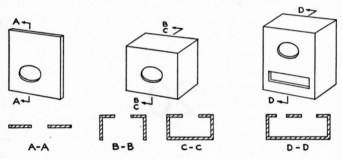

FIG. 62. (A-A) flat baffle, (B-B) open-backed enclosure, (C-C) infinite baffle, (D D) bass reflex enclosure.

Distortion is a major problem with speakers. A pronounced resonant frequency can cause *hangover* effect; the cone wants to keep on vibrating independently of the applied frequency. As a result, the voice coil can't respond smoothly to the rapid changes in current flow through it, and individual notes lack crispness. Nonlinearity occurs in speakers as well as in tubes. Its cause: mechanical movement of the voice coil doesn't correspond exactly to the rise and fall of applied voltage. It is more pronounced when the voice coil moves the farthest—with the bass frequencies. When nonlinearity changes a single bass tone, it's amplitude distortion; and when this changed tone combines with higher ones to create new frequencies (they sound harsh), it's intermodulation distortion.

After all, it's asking quite a lot of a combination of copper voice coil, paper cone, iron magnet, and wood baffle to reproduce, with complete faithfulness, a whole symphony.

20

OUR IONIC ROOF

THE frequency of the standard broadcast station is low, as radio frequencies go: between 550 kc. and 1600 kc. The wave of these low frequencies is called a *ground wave*, because it stays close to the earth, following its curvature as we humans must do, for the present at least, whether we go by bus, ship, train, plane, or horseback.

The standard broadcast transmitter uses a vertical antenna with one end grounded (Fig. 63). The electrons that are the antenna current, by reason of their electric (electrostatic) and magnetic fields, have a "grip" on the ether; as they move up and down the antenna they shake the ether as a man shakes a rope. The electromagnetic waves travel out in all directions.

Most of the energy goes out horizontally, though some of it streaks toward the sky. None goes straight up. The hori

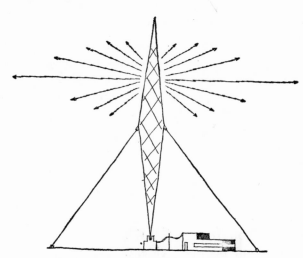

FIG. 63. Antenna of a standard broadcast transmitter. This vertical antenna radiates energy in all directions horizontally. The longer the arrow the greater the radiation in the direction indicated.

zontal radiation, hugging the earth, is good for a range of 100 miles or so in the daytime from the average transmitter.

The frequencies don't all act the same after they leave the antenna. They have a choice of three different routes, and we roughly classify them according to which one they customarily prefer. The *low frequencies,* which include the broadcast frequencies mentioned above, go up to three megacycles (mc.). The *high frequencies* go to 30 mc., the *very high frequencies* to 300 mc., the *ultra high frequencies* to 3,000 mc., and the *super high frequencies* stop at 30,000 mc.

During the early days of radio the low, earth-bound frequencies were believed to be the best. Ships talked with each other in their dot-and-dash language on a frequency of 500 kc. A frequency as high as 1,500 kc. was thought to have very little value, and in 1917, when our radio was first regulated by Washington, the government tossed it to the amateurs to play with. The "hams" had a lot of fun with it, too, while they were teaching the engineers a few things; some of them, like Major Armstrong, became engineers themselves.

The builders of the first powerful transoceanic transmitters put their faith in frequencies much lower than the ship-to-shore frequency of 500 kc. The Germans even tried a 10,000-cycle carrier wave, low enough to be heard by the human ear, so there was no need for modulation. Very large coils and condensers were necessary for such a low frequency. The experiment was a failure, though a French station had some success with a frequency of around 13,000 cycles. Much better results were had, however, with frequencies between 50,000 and 150,000 cycles.

After De Forest's little audion began to oscillate over such a wide range of frequencies, the virtues of the three-to-30-megacycle band became evident. And what travelers these high frequencies proved to be! A little 50-watt United States station could lay down a signal in Cape Town or Singapore with greater ease than a 100,000-watt low-frequency station. The principal reason for this is that the high-frequency wave travels up to the sky and down to earth again. Most of its energy is in a *sky wave*. Under normal conditions it has no ground wave.

As early as 1902, Britain's great physicist Oliver Heaviside wrote about the possible reflection of radio waves from the sky; and Dr. A. E. Kennelly of Harvard independently had the same idea. But the inventor sometimes lags far behind the scientist. Marconi, after discovering that he got much better reception of his wireless signals at night, concluded that sunlight weakened them in the daytime. What was happening, of course, was that some of the energy of the low frequencies was taking the sky route at night.

No flash bulletin is needed to tell us that all forms of life on this planet depend upon the sun. And without the sun we would have no sky wave, because the sun creates the *ionosphere* that sends the radio waves back to the earth again (Fig. 64).

Forming the ionosphere are several layers of ionized air

varying in height from 20 to 250 miles. Twenty miles up, there isn't enough atmosphere to keep a frog alive, and the air continues to get thinner the higher one goes; but even at from 200 to 250 miles there is enough oxygen and nitrogen to make effective ionization possible.

Ionization is created by radiation from the sun. Violet rays, high-speed electrons, or protons? All three? The scientists aren't sure yet, but the American and Russian satellites tell us that the *intensity* of this cosmic radiation is much more severe than suspected.

Whatever particles, or combination of particles, create the ionosphere, they are stopped by their own creation. The ionosphere stops showers of electrons from the sun, for example, and it lets only enough of the ultraviolet rays through to keep us in good health.

There are seasonal variations in the amount of ionization created, which means there are seasonal variations in the nature of the ionosphere. There is also an 11-year cycle. But the greatest changes are daily ones. During daylight hours, when the sun is shining directly on the earth, ionization is at its peak. As many as five layers may be created, one on top of the other. At this time, the *intensity* of ionization is also at a maximum. When night comes, the ionosphere doesn't vanish altogether; only the lower layers disappear. The two upper layers merge into one, raising our invisible roof. This drastically affects short-wave radio communication and broadcasting.

Fig. 64A shows an average condition of the ionosphere in the daytime, with ionization at its peak. Three layers (above the C layer) are shown, D, E and F_1. Fig 64B shows the ionosphere at night, with the upper layers merged into one, F_2. Now let's start with the low frequencies of standard radio broadcasting, and go on up the ladder to the super highs, noting how each one acts with relation to the day and night ionosphere.

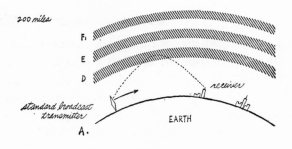

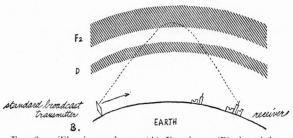

FIG. 64. The ionosphere. (A) Daytime. (B) At night.

In the daytime, some of the energy in the standard broadcast frequencies is reflected by the bottom two layers, D and E. But these layers are so close to the earth they don't get the signals out very far; and in addition they absorb considerable of the energy of the wave. (The ionosphere always absorbs *some* of the energy of any wave that it turns back.) Thus, in the daytime the radio fan relies upon the standard broadcast station's ground wave for his listening. Come nightfall, though, and it's another story.

At night the station doesn't *lose* its ground wave, but some of that part of its radiation that is beamed skyward is returned by the F_2 layer. Fig. 64B reveals how it is that this wave gets out so much further than the ground wave, which explains why your receiver starts picking up distant stations after the sun goes down. This is not always an unmixed blessing. Sometimes the F_2 layer funnels so many stations into your set that it sounds as though you've tuned in on an argument among some chirping, stuttering Martians. Your i.f. stages must be sharply tuned to keep out most of this interference, and too sharply tuned i.f. stages distort the music by lopping off the side bands that carry the higher audio frequencies.

Next, the high frequencies, ranging from three to 30 mc. (These are often called the short waves.) In the daytime, they pass through the ionosphere's lower layers to be returned by its top layer F_1; at night they are returned by the single F_2 layer. Thus your short-wave receiver picks up foreign broadcasts both day and night, though the greater height of the F_2 layer usually permits greater distance at night.

A wave can make two round trips between ionosphere and earth, called two-hop transmission. Three-hop and even four-hop transmissions are also used. It is even possible to detect waves that have twice circled the earth in this fashion—a distance, I suspect, slightly in excess of the "limit" dreamed of by Marconi and Preece on Salisbury Plain in 1897.

With all frequencies above 30 mc. we forget the ionosphere; if we beamed them skyward they would pass right through it, though there are exceptions, now being investigated, which hold promise for the future. These frequencies also lack a ground wave to tie them to the earth's curvature. For the present, at least, they are restricted to what we call *line of sight,* a range that is usually only about 40 miles, depending upon antenna height.

FM's home in the very high frequency band is between 88 and 108 mc. Television, which needs much wider channels than FM, has 12 of them in the very highs; half are under the FM frequencies, from 44 to 88 mc., the other half are above them, between 174 and 216 mc. The amateurs, the police, and the telephone company (for auto phones) have also been assigned slices of very high frequency.

The next rung in the frequency ladder takes us up to the ultra highs, from 300 to 3,000 mc. (All frequencies above 300 mc. are also called microwaves.) During the war many claims were staked out in this area of the spectrum, largely as a result of radar development. More recently, the FCC has set aside 70 channels in the ultra highs for television. These frequencies range from 470 to 890 megacycles. The FCC has assigned some of the ultra highs to the relay stations, now used in increasing numbers for moving television programs and telephone traffic cross country. The stations are installed in towers placed about 30 miles apart, high on a mountain-top if available. Reception and retransmission are completely automatic. No attendant is needed, except for weekly servicing. General Electric built the first one, for jumping programs from its New York studios to its television station near Schenectady. Frequency: 2,000 mc. Since September 4, 1951, the telephone company has been delivering television shows throughout the country from such a system, a 2,992-mile, 107-jump, cottontail express stretching from New York to San Francisco. Total cost of towers and equipment, 40 million dollars.

Perched on top of the frequency heap are the super highs, from 3,000 to 30,000 mc. Some government weather radars use 24,000 mc.; commercial radar frequencies are close to 3,000 and 10,000 mc. The radio relays use frequencies as high as 7,000 mc., the telephone company's New York to San Francisco system being in the 4,000-mc. range.

Above 30,000 mc., we come to the frontier of electronic communication engineering. The main problem is to build a tube that will oscillate at these frequencies of over 30 *billion* cycles per second. and at the same time deliver usable power. Experimental 510,000-mc. frequencies are in use.

Signal fading also belongs in this chapter, because of its connection with the ionosphere. What causes fading? The ionosphere may vary slightly in height and density from minute to minute, causing some variation in signal strength; but severe fading usually occurs when receiving a combination of ground and sky wave. Or, perhaps, a combination of two sky waves.

At night, at distances of upwards of 150 miles or so from the standard broadcast transmitter, the sky wave is usually returned to the earth. The ground wave may also be present. The sky wave has had the longer journey; suppose it has traveled just twice as far as the ground wave: then the two waves arrive at the receiver in step with each other, or *in phase,* as the expert says. The voltages of the two waves, rising and falling together in the antenna, are mutually aiding at all times. But suppose the sky wave has traveled a distance that results in an out-of-phase relationship with the ground wave; this could mean either some mutual aid or some mutual cancellation, even complete cancellation. Thus, any change in either the strength of the sky wave or the distance it travels can affect signal strength. Even a slight shift in the ionosphere's height, or a small change in the degree of absorption of the wave, can weaken or strengthen it.

The only easy remedy for fading is automatic volume control, abbreviated AVC. AVC doesn't bring up a weak signal, it merely cuts down a strong one; its leveling-off effect is only a partial remedy. AVC is a must in city radios, however, to keep the volume of nearby stations on the same level. Without this circuit, the dialer must keep one hand on the volume control as he tunes the set, or risk being suddenly blasted out of his chair by a strong signal.

Within certain limits, the higher the negative bias on an amplifier's grid, the less the tube amplifies. (Especially true of tubes built for AVC.) AVC reduces a too-strong signal by causing a rising signal current to increase this negative bias on one or more tubes.

The bias circuit of Fig. 103 is used, ordinarily in the diode detector circuit. The resistor's negative voltage, with proper values of resistor and condenser, rises and falls with signal average current $(E = IR)$. Connected to the grids of amplifiers ahead of it, as signal strength increases so does the negative voltage, and down comes amplification. The circuit shouldn't act too quickly, however, or it will cut down a *weak* signal, impairing the set's sensitivity. For this reason the designer often uses a second bias voltage, in series with and opposing the AVC voltage. The AVC voltage can't act until it rises higher than the second voltage. This is called *delayed* AVC.

Recently it has been found that the troposphere, the earth's atmosphere from 6 to 12 miles up, can even return energy to the earth from radio waves. This new method of communication, via the troposphere, is called *scattering,* or *forward scattering.* When very high and ultra high frequencies are beamed skyward, at an angle of around 45 degrees, countless blobs of air with a lower density, which means a slightly lower dielectric constant, serve as tiny refracting lenses. The blobs bend some of the energy around, sending it downward again. When high power is used, enough is available to operate sensitive receivers, and signals are being transmitted reliably over distances up to 400 miles. Frequencies range from 100 to 10,000 mc. Troposphere scattering is being used along the DEW line in the Arctic.

Even greater distances can be obtained by scattering via the ionosphere. For this, the best frequencies have proved to be between 30 and 50 mc. Distances up to 1200 miles have been covered satisfactorily. Ionosphere scattering holds promise for a global TV network. The U.S. Air Force is working on a series of scatter relay stations linking Washington and London.

TV, anyone? Okay, 20 chapters and 26 centuries away from amber, we have finally reached that magical plateau.

21

TELEVISION: THE CAMERA

In 1915, David Sarnoff, now Chairman of the Board of the Radio Corporation of America, was working for RCA's predecessor, the American Marconi Company. The first big radiophone station had just been built, and young Sarnoff sent a memo to his boss presenting a plan to "bring music into the home by wireless." A little "music box" on the parlor table would not only receive music, but even lectures, world news, and baseball scores. Sarnoff thought a range of 25 to 50 miles was possible.

With this auspicious start, followed since by many other instances of sound soothsaying, General Sarnoff has become the "official" forecaster for the industry. So when he stated, early in 1947, that television would play its first big role in the 1948 election, possibly revolutionizing the technique of that campaign to the same degree that radio broadcasting did the Coolidge-Davis campaign of 1924, few had any heart for doubting him. But this time the vision in his crystal ball failed to materialize. As the 1948 election approached, network television had a potential audience of millions of voters in some of the key states, but neither Truman's nor Dewey's face appeared on the glass screens. The greatest reversal of form since David took the measure of Goliath could not be explained by the influence of the new video.

Television did figure largely in the 1952 campaign. The difference between the Taft and Eisenhower smiles no doubt had much to do with the latter's triumph in the primaries. And although the final results indicated that the public had long before decided upon Ike, Stevenson's warm video personality, together with his wit and engaging candor, made a deep impression. By 1956, the novelty had worn off.

Compared with television, radio seems a simple affair, a conversion-reconversion job you could probably explain to a backward three-year-old dog, with a little patience and a few cases of Red Heart. But converting a *picture,* and a *moving* picture at that, to current waves (for modulating a carrier) and reconverting the current waves to a moving picture again in the receiver! Katie, bar the door! Can a reader without four years of college physics, one who is merely interested in how the thing works, find his way through this double metamorphosis? On the other hand, a glance at a television-circuit diagram reveals that it consists mostly of the same coils, condensers, tubes, etc. with which we are already familiar in the radio circuit. Give me your hand.

The late J. L. Baird, Britain's premier television inventor, was early in the field. His transmitter combined the phototube with a scanning disc that Paul Nipkow, a Russian, had patented in Berlin in 1886. Not only were Baird's pictures of poor quality, but the mechanical features of his system seemed to preclude much improvement. It seemed certain that if television was ever to become good enough to sell soap, it would have to be all electronic. As long ago as 1911, an Englishman, A. A. Campbell-Swinton, described how it could be done. The key device would be an electronic camera tube, based upon the Crookes tube. This device had already developed into a potentially practical instrument, largely in the hands of Germany's Ferdinand Braun; and DuMont in the United States later did significant work on it. Providing an electronic camera tube soon took on all the aspects of a race between two inventors in the United States, Russian-born Vladimir Kosma Zworykin on the east coast and Philo T. Farnsworth on the west coast.

Zworykin studied electrical engineering at the Technological Institute in Leningrad; from there he went to the Collège de France, where he conducted X-ray experiments under Paul Langevin. He responded to his country's call during World War I, and after this he emigrated to the United States. His talents first found employment with Westinghouse. Before 1926 he had a Ph.D. from the University of Pittsburgh and citizenship papers from the United States Government. He joined the research staff at RCA in 1929 to become director of electronic research.

Zworykin's long years of television research culminated in a camera tube he called the *iconoscope*. Like an ordinary camera, it uses lenses made of ground and polished chunks of optical glass. But in place of film, the image is focused on a screen called a *mosaic*. The dictionary says mosaic is a picture or design formed by small pieces of stone, glass, or wood. The iconoscope's mosaic consists of millions of tiny dots of *metal* on an insulator backing. Each dot is, theoretically, at least, separated from the others: and each is one plate of a condenser. The scene before the camera, then, is focused onto the plates of a few million tiny condensers. But what follows isn't all condenser action; it is also part *photoelectric*, which calls for some explaining.

In a radio tube, we get electrons by heating a filament. These are called *thermoelectrons* (from the Greek *therme* meaning heat). But it is also possible to liberate electrons by means of light: *photoelectrons*. The story of the relationship between light and electricity begins with Hertz, author of the Hertzian waves, who made the discovery while operating his laboratory wireless. He noticed that when an ultraviolet light was directed at the spark gap he got a fatter spark. A fellow German, Hallwachs, in a series of experiments with the electroscope, proved that electrons can be removed from zinc by means of ultraviolet rays. It was found later that even ordinary light rays have enough energy to remove electrons from the "alkali" metals, which cling to their electrons with less tenacity; these rare metals are lithium, sodium, potassium, rubidium, and caesium.

We have a small tube today with a caesium-coated cathode; instead of heating it to obtain electrons, we shine a light on it; the brighter the light the more photoelectrons are released. It is called a phototube (Fig. 97). In the motion-picture projector the phototube changes a light (shining through the sound track) to current for the loudspeaker, and it has many other uses. Caesium on the iconoscope's mosaic provides the *photoelectric* effect that makes the mosaic sensitive *(electrically* sensitive) to the scene before the camera. Suppose we take a nibble on Alice's size-reducing mushroom so we can crawl inside the iconoscope for a look around (Fig. 65).

This Wonderland needn't frighten us, for the iconoscope is basically a version of our old friend the Crookes tube, though with so many changes and additions that the two now enjoy the same kind of relationship as a Laundromat with a flat stone by the river. Start with the photosensitive mosaic: on it we would see, if our eyes were sharp enough, a few million tiny droplets of caesium-silver compound sprayed, or rather sort of "sneezed," on the mica dielectric so that each droplet is more or less insulated from the others. These photosensitive droplets are the plates of a million

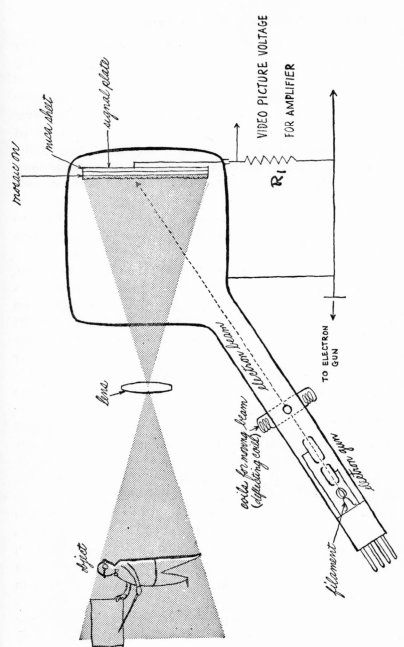

Fig. 65. Zworykin's camera tube, the iconoscope.

or so condensers. Peeking around the other side of the mica backing, we see a thin metal coating, the common second plate for the droplet condensers, and called the *signal plate*.

We note that the mosaic is placed directly behind the camera's lenses and that each individual caesium-silver droplet on the mosaic gets a different amount of reflected light (theoretically at least) from the scene before the camera. And as each droplet emits electrons in direct proportion to the amount (intensity) of the light striking it, each droplet is left with a different amount of positive charge. In other words, the light rays remove negative electrons to "etch" the scene (lights and shadows) on the mosaic with positive charges.

It is obvious that a "seeing" mosaic is only the first step. We must get a current flow from it to give us a changing picture voltage, comparable to the changing audio voltage from a microphone. Fig. 73 shows such a changing voltage. It represents one horizontal line across the mosaic. The mosaic is covered by 525 of these lines. (Try counting them on your television screen.) How does the iconoscope obtain these lines of rising and falling voltage? And, finally, how do the lines describe the scene on the mosaic?

In the neck of the diagram of Fig. 65 we see what is called an electron gun. Like any radio tube, it has a hot cathode that supplies electrons. The electrons are threaded through a tiny opening in the grid to form them into a narrow pencillike beam, and then focused so that the beam comes to a sharp point where it touches the mosaic. (Fully explained in the next chapter.) A high positive voltage, perhaps 10,000 volts, moves the beam electrons through the tube at high speed. Two rapidly changing fields (in this case they are magnetic) sweep the electron beam tip across the mosaic, an operation called *scanning*.

The beam tip scans the mosaic from top to bottom, 525 lines, each 1/30th of a second. Thirty complete pictures each second are necessary in order to give the appearance of movement that fools the eye. The beam's negative electrons fill up the "holes" in the mosaic; that is, they discharge the positive charges left on the tiny condensers by the light that strikes them; and as the amount of positive charge on each droplet varies in accordance with the amount of light it receives from the scene, the electron current in the circuit will fluctuate in accordance with the light and dark of the picture. This current fluctuation is picked up as a changing voltage across the resistor R_1. This is called the video voltage. Video means vision. The lighter the picture at any point on a line, the greater the current flow, and the higher the video voltage peak. Fig. 66 shows graphically how light and dark is converted to a rising and falling voltage.

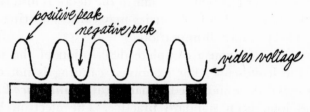

FIG. 66. Checkerboard shows relationship between light and dark of the picture and the rise and fall of the video voltage.

Television's receiver also has a cathode ray tube with an electron gun. But instead of scanning a mosaic, this gun's beam scans a screen that *releases* light. The beams in both tubes swing back and forth in perfect unison; at the same time, the video frequency controls the number of electrons in the receiving tube's beam. The higher the voltage of each video frequency peak the more electrons in the beam, and the more light released from the screen. Briefly, this is how the receiver reproduces the scene before the camera.

The video frequency is much higher than any audio frequency. Let's figure out just how high it might be. The mosaic is scanned by 525 lines each 1/30th of a second: a total of

15,750 lines per second. Suppose the beam tip is capable of noting 400 variations in each line. Then in scanning an image from a scene with considerable detail, such as a man in pepper-and-salt tweeds sitting a roan horse, there could be 6,300,000 variations per second (400 x 15,750= 6,300,000). As each variation is a half cycle of alternating current, this is a frequency of 3,150,000 cycles. When 3,150,000 cycles modulate the carrier, the side bands create a band width of 6,300,000 cycles (page 201), which hardly fits in the 6-mc.-wide channel with the sound carrier. However, one side band can be partially *suppressed,* without damage, and this is done at the transmitter. The transmitter normally sends out a video frequency of 4.75-mc. maximum width.

It is apparent from this that, if your receiver's amplifier blocks the higher frequencies, some of the detail is lost. Blocking of the lower video frequencies may cause smearing, and uneven background illumination.

I haven't given you a complete description of the workings of the iconoscope. For example, scanning is not quite so simple as I have indicated: what is called *interlaced scanning* has long been standard practice. The electron beam scans every other line, and then returns to fill in between. Thus, it covers the mosaic from top to bottom with 262½ lines in 1/60th of a second, and 60 of these "half pictures" go out each second. Interlaced scanning reduces flicker.

Zworykin applied for a patent on some of the basic ideas of his iconoscope in December 1923, and after some years of interference proceedings he was granted the patent in December 1938. In 1924, he showed Westinghouse officials a television picture of indifferent definition; Farnsworth, in 1927, also had a blurry image on a glass screen in his little laboratory on Green Street, in San Francisco. Good 441-line television was ready for the public in 1941, when it was sidetracked by preparations for defense. Shortly after the war's end, television of better quality was back on the main line again, with a green light from the FCC, fascinating a mushrooming audience.

Philo T. Farnsworth was born on August 19, 1906, in Beaver City, Utah, of Mormon parents. He has stated that before he was 12 years old he felt he "could be an inventor." Among the books on science that he found to stimulate him at high schools in Rigby, Idaho, and Provo, Utah, were several on the electron theory. After graduation he enrolled at Brigham Young University as a special student, but his father had died a short time before and lack of funds soon forced him out.

Farnsworth drifted about a bit, and then became a radio service man in Salt Lake City, operating his own shop. Business was bad, however, and he found a job with a community chest campaign in that city. There he met the two men who were running the show, Leslie Correl and George Everson. He tried to explain for them some ideas he had for a system of television. At that time (1926) even radio wasn't being taken too seriously, and as for television, what was that? Nevertheless, the 20-year-old youth fired the imagination of the money raisers, and through their efforts he was soon installed in a small laboratory, first in Hollywood and a few months later in San Francisco.

Farnsworth thought that $5,000 would be enough to put together the gear needed to prove the correctness of his television theory. Everson personally dug down into his pocket for the money. It wasn't long before he was out looking for more. But with all his practice in raising money for charity, he had no success drumming it up for science. Finally, after many rebuffs, he got the promise of a few thousand dollars from a group of San Francisco bankers. Thirteen years and one million dollars later, Farnsworth was able to demonstrate a complete system of television that produced an image of very good quality. The bankers stayed with him a long time, though many of them sold their stock to the public at a profit. The stock had lost most of its value by the time Capehart took over the company, when Farnsworth became vice president in charge of research for Capehart Farnsworth Corporation.

Farnsworth's camera tube is the *image dissector*. Its workings aren't quite as believable as those of the iconoscope. Instead of upon a mosaic photocathode, the scene is focused on a photocathode with a thin *coating* of photosensitive material. The light rays from the scene cause photoelectrons to be emitted from the photocathode, and the number of electrons leaving any point is in direct proportion to the intensity of the light striking it. Farnsworth uses these freed photoelectrons to obtain his video current; in fact, these photoelectrons *are* the video current. No condenser action is involved as in the iconoscope.

Farnsworth first got the idea for obtaining a video frequency from such a "cloud picture" of electrons when he was a 15-year-old student at Rigby High. It seemed a pretty quixotic scheme to the engineers who were later consulted as to its feasibility, though they all admitted that it was possible. The problem required, first, focusing the electrons. Farnsworth finally managed this by means of a coil, whose magnetic field moves the electron image down the tube toward a *scanning aperture*. And in the meantime, the image must be moved rapidly back and forth, and up more slowly, to enable the aperture to gobble up the electrons, line after line, until the entire image has been scanned. Two pairs of coils do this.

The perfected image dissector provides a good sharp picture, sharper than the iconoscope. However, it is not as sensitive as the iconoscope, and so requires more light on the scene before the camera. This explains why the first tube to be used extensively in television studios in this country was the iconoscope. The image dissector, however, has no filament to burn out, which may explain why the Diamond Power Specialty Corporation of Ohio early acquired it for their industrial television camera, the *Utiliscope*. (Since then, several other companies have entered the industrial television field.) The armed forces use it in television work, and part of it is found in the *Sniperscope*, developed during World War II, which puts an image of the enemy in the rifleman's sights in total darkness.

In developing a complete television system, Farnsworth obtained more than 100 patents. Many of these patents are basic to the television in use today, both in transmitter and receiver. RCA has acquired rights under certain patents from Farnsworth.

2

RCA's David Sarnoff Research Center persisted in camera research, developing a number of other camera tubes, including the image iconoscope, the orthicon, and finally the image orthicon. The image orthicon is today's standard camera tube. Its great superiority is in light sensitivity: it needs only about one tenth as much light as the iconoscope. Actors can work under ordinary lighting, instead of being subjected to the intense heat and glare from batteries of high-wattage lamps; and a football game televised in a snowstorm gives the viewer at least the equivalent of a seat on the 50-yard line down close to the field. The much cheaper iconoscope is still used, however, in televising film.

The mysterious workings of the image orthicon are revealed by the drawing of Fig. 67. Its large end houses the ordinary glass lenses, which pass the picture on to a photosensitive cathode; an electron gun is in the small end. The photocathode is coated with a caesium-silver compound, just as in Farnsworth's image dissector. However, this photocathode is *semitransparent,* with the coating on its inside surface, facing the electron gun. Thus the light rays cause the photo-electrons to be emitted into the tube in the direction of the electron gun.

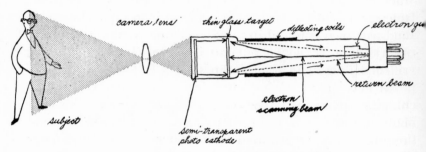

FIG. 67. The image orthicon camera tube.

The electron image, being essentially the same as the one in Farnsworth's image dissector, must also be focused by a coil at the same time that it is being moved away from the photocathode by a positive voltage. The positive voltage is placed upon what is called an *accelerator grid*.

The photoelectrons released by the image strike a thin glass disc called the *target*. They strike the target with enough force to knock other electrons out of it, called *secondary electrons*. (Secondary electrons are explained under Fig. 56.) This leaves the scene "etched" on the target with positive charges, just as it is on the iconoscope's mosaic. The positive charges stay put, preserving the picture, because the target disc is glass, an insulator.

And as in the iconoscope, the video frequency is obtained by scanning with an electron beam. But the electron beam is on the other side of the target; how, then, does the beam tip reach the charges? The glass target is so *extremely thin* that the positive charges also appear on its opposite surface.

The electron beam goes over the target twice in scanning it with the American standard of 525 lines each 1/30th of a second, using interlaced scanning. It is a low-velocity scanning beam. Close to the target is an electrostatic field that stops the electrons in the beam tip just in front of the target. With no picture being televised, all the electrons rebound from the field, returning to the electron-gun end of the tube. But with the camera in use, the number of returning electrons constantly fluctuates, depending upon the amount of variation in the size of the positive charges on the target opposite the beam tip: for each one of these tiny positive charges snatches from the beam the electrons it needs for neutralization. The beam electrons, with everything they should know about the picture in their fluctuations, become the current of the video frequency. Size of target, $7/8''$ x $1\frac{1}{4}''$.

The secondary electrons knocked out of the target by the photoelectrons are disposed of through a very fine mesh screen* placed close to the target, almost touching it; made two volts positive with respect to the target, the screen attracts the electrons and conducts them away. This mesh screen has 500 openings to the inch, and at the same time 50 percent of its area is open. The target disc is .0001 of an inch thick; 40 discs would be needed to make a stack as thick as a single page of this book. Figures like these help to give one an inkling of the magnitude of the engineering problems involved in the development of a tube like the image orthicon.

The price of the iconoscope is around $550; the image orthicon sells for $1,300. A price tag hasn't been placed on RCA's new color camera yet, but some idea of its probable cost may be had from the fact that not only is it more complex than the monochrome cameras but it contains *three* image orthicons.

RCA makes three different types of image orthicon. The 2P23 for outdoor work requires the least light. The 5655

* Not shown in picture.

is designed for studio programs, the 5769 for general use.

Radio tubes amplify voltages and power. It goes without saying that we could also make good use of an amplifier of *light*. How valuable it would be, for example, as an adjunct to the astronomer's telescope, the physician's fluoroscope, even the home owner's TV screen of the future that hangs on the wall! Light amplifiers have been developed by GE, Bendix, Westinghouse, RCA, and others.

Most employ secondary emission. The electrons emitted from a photocathode by the photons of light are directed (focused) to a special screen, where the impact of each individual electron releases many more secondary electrons. Several stages may be used. Focusing is by magnetic fields, acceleration by electric fields (Chapter 22). The final electrons strike a fluorescent screen, as in the TV picture tube, where the original image is greatly magnified.

The image orthicon has an *electron multiplier,* first used by Farnsworth in his image dissector, which uses secondary emission to amplify the stream of electrons returning from the target. Now it is being applied between the photocathode and the target in the form of one or more *intensifier screens.* The impact of each individual electron releases from ten to twenty electrons from one screen, as many as 300 from two screens.

The intensifier in an image orthicon makes it so sensitive it can literally "see" in the dark of the moon. After Ireland gets around to television we'll find out what a leprechaun really looks like.

The *Nautilus,* during its historic journey under the North Pole, had one of these supersensitive cameras mounted next to the conning tower, offering the crew a continuous view of the bottom side of the Arctic ice. The infinite variety must have been more fun to watch than a soap opera.

22

TELEVISION: THE RECEIVER

Iт тоок the inventors many years
of patient effort to tame the photo and thermoelectrons
in the bottle we call a camera tube. Thanks to their triumphs,
today's television technician manages these electrical particles with all the confidence and dexterity—if not the aplomb
—of the late great W. C. Fields juggling his cigar boxes.

The receiver's cathode ray tube is much closer to the old
Crookes experimental job than the camera tube. It is com-
monly called a *picture tube;* its RCA name is kinescope
(Fig. 68).

The neck of this funnel-shaped tube houses the electron
gun, the opposite end *is* the television screen. Modern
pumping techniques remove the air so completely that the
pressure on the glass screen is upwards of 500 pounds, starting with the smallest tube. The slightly convex screen aids in
preventing collapse of the tube. Which reminds me that

such tubes should be handled with extreme care; the flying glass from an *imploding* tube is dangerous.

The screen is *fluorescent:* coated with a chemical that releases light when struck by the electrons. As the electron beam scans the screen, its flying tip releases light in horizontal lines. To reproduce an image that closely resembles the one before the camera, the receiver must fulfill two conditions. First, the beam tip must release more light the greater the rise (higher the voltage) of the video frequency. Second, the electron beams in both camera and picture tubes must scan their respective targets in unison, line after line, from top to bottom.

To fulfill the first condition we place the video frequency on a *control grid* in the picture tube. The more positive the grid, the more electrons it passes; and as the brightness of the screen increases with the number of electrons in the beam, the more positive the video voltage the brighter the screen.

The second condition is fulfilled by using the same scanning-beam frequency in both camera and picture tubes; and at the same time inserting special pulses in the carrier wave that "lock together" the back-and-forth movements of the two beams.

Fig. 68A shows most of the controls of a picture tube. High positive voltages for pulling the electrons away from the hot cathode are placed upon anodes (plates) No. 1 and 2, with No. 2 getting the highest: the newer 21- to 27-inch tubes take a voltage of around 17,000. The anode voltages also serve to focus the electrons so that the beam comes to a sharp point at the screen.

Note that the anode voltages must pull the electrons through the control grid, which is cylindrical in shape, like the first anode. (The second anode may be a metallic coating on the inside of the glass tube.) The control grid has a baffle inside that would block the electrons completely but

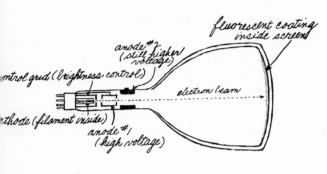

A.

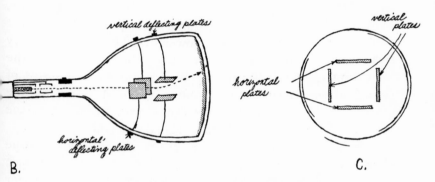

B.   C.

FIG. 68. Television's picture tube, the kinescope.

for a tiny hole in its center, which acts as a door. A positive
voltage opens it, a negative voltage closes it. In most picture tubes, 63 volts negative is enough to shut the door tight
on the electrons. A negative voltage is kept on the control
grid at all times—a bias voltage—which is *variable*. You vary
it by a knob on the front panel attached to a resistor.

The video frequency, with its positive and negative peaks
(Fig. 73), is picked up by the receiver, and the signal amplified and sent to the control grid, landing right on top of
the negative grid bias. The steady variable bias is already
determining how light the screen is before the signal arrives.
In other words, the negative bias resistor functions as a
brightness or *brilliance* control.

Try turning the brightness control to the left; this increases the negative bias. Perhaps you can cut off the electron beam completely, blacking out the screen; and then the peak positive video voltages might not be strong enough to get any electrons through the grid. Turning this control to the right, you may be able to cut down the negative bias enough to light up the screen to the point where even the peak negative video voltages are unable to darken it to any extent. So what are we doing when we twist the brightness-control knob? We're changing the *average background illumination*.

Many television sets have just one other picture control to adjust after switching on the power. Marked "contrast," it is attached to a resistor that controls the amount of amplification of the video signal. In a radio, the amount of amplification determines the volume of sound; but amplifying a video voltage increases the difference between the positive and negative peaks of the signal, as you can see by glancing at Fig. 73. As the positive peaks brighten the screen, and the negative peaks darken it, increased amplification means increased contrast between the light and dark areas of the image.

The contrast control is often helpful, though too much contrast causes distortion. More contrast is usually demanded in a well-lighted room. If either the brightness or contrast control is changed, the other one should also be adjusted, for they react on each other. In an effort to simplify operation, some manufacturers today are eliminating one or the other of these controls. The discarded control may sometimes be found, together with some others, beneath the name plate on the front of the panel.

Chemicals that emit light aren't anything new. The alchemist of three centuries ago noted that white barite rock absorbs daylight and emits a feeble blue light at night. It is said to be *phosphorescent,* because it absorbs energy, in the form of light, and emits it later. Fireflies and glowworms are *bioluminescent*. The fluorescent material on the picture tube's screen differs from the white barite rock in this respect: it emits light only so long as it is receiving energy from the impinging electrons, or only for an instant longer. The light should persist for 1/60th of a second after the electrons strike it, to provide maximum brightness. If the light persists for longer than 1/60th of a second, which is the time required for the beam to scan the screen once (interlaced scanning), a double image results.

The light from fluorescence or phosphorescence is called a "cold light," because the light rays are not accompanied by heat rays. The chemicals, either fluorescent or phosphorescent, are called *phosphors*.

There are dozens of phosphors, many of them zinc compounds, though they are not common in nature. Different phosphors can be made to glow with all the colors of the rainbow, a fact not overlooked by color-television inventors. Zinc orthosilicate gives off a green light, cadmium tungstate a blue light, cadmium borate a red light. Zinc sulphide combined with silver provides the white light for black-and-white television. A. R. B. Wehnelt, in 1904, was the first to coat a cathode ray tube with a phosphor.

2

This section contains some more details about (1) how the electron beam is focused, (2) how the beam is moved back and forth in scanning, and (3) how the receiver's beam is disciplined so that it stays in step with the camera tube's beam.

After passing through the first anode, the electron beam must be focused so that its tip is sharpened. In the tube shown, the anode voltages also act as lenses. Faraday's electrostatic lines of force explain how a charge exerts force at a distance; steady voltages applied to grid and anode give a certain "shape" to their surrounding electrostatic fields; in other words, the electrostatic force is so distributed around them that the electrons hurrying through the fields are moved to converge at a *cross-over point*. A second lens system moves the electrons gradually in toward the axis of the tube, so that the electrons come to another cross-over point at the surface of the screen (Fig. 69). At that point the beam is narrowest and, because the screen chops it off there, *pointed*.

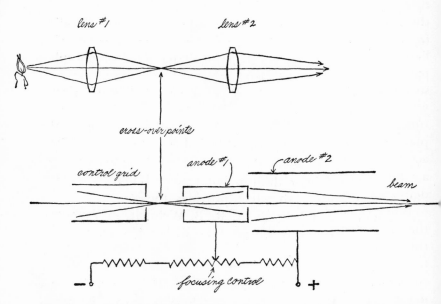

FIG. 69. Focusing of the beam in a picture tube by means of voltages, called electrostatic focusing, compared with focusing of light.

We see from this that if either cross-over point should move backwards or forwards, the beam tip would increase in size. A larger tip defocuses the beam, lending the picture a fuzzy look. It is also apparent that the screen must be concave to the beam tip; if it were flat, the further the tip moved from the screen's center the longer the beam and the larger the tip—which would also cause defocusing, making the picture fuzzy around the edges.

Focusing the electron beam *magnetically* calls for an alnico-core coil slipped over the neck of the tube. The first cross-power point is still obtained electrostatically, and a second high anode voltage to accelerate the electrons is also needed. The early picture tubes used electrostatic focusing, though most of today's tubes are focused magnetically.

Now for scanning. Note the two pairs of plates inside the tube of Fig. 68B. I don't know what J. J. Thomson called the plates he used back in 1898, but these are called *deflecting plates*. They look like our plates attached to the storage battery in Fig. 7B. And they are also condensers. Take the pair of *horizontal deflecting plates* in the figure; put a steady voltage on them and the strong field between them will move the negative electron beam to one side of the tube, the positive plate attracting the beam, the negative plate repelling it. Of course, in practice the beam must move across the tube many times each second, and this calls for a rising and a falling voltage. We get it from a large condenser outside the tube.

When discussing the filter circuit on page 187, we learned that a condenser takes a little time to charge or discharge; the larger the condenser the more time it takes. If we want to increase the charging time we charge the condenser through a resistor.* By selecting the proper values of condenser and resistor, we can get a charging voltage that rises just fast enough to pull the electron beam across the tube at the required speed. The beam must return to the other side of the tube in a much bigger hurry, which calls for a much faster discharge of the condenser—so we discharge it *around the resistor*. On paper, such a slowly rising, quickly falling

---

* The mathematics: $T = RC$. R is the resistance in ohms, C is the capacitance in farads, T is the time in seconds required to charge the condenser to 63.2% of maximum. Same applies to discharge. This equation and the one for impedance match are perhaps more often used than any other in electronics.

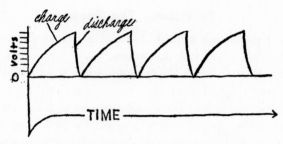

Fig. 70. Graph of a saw-tooth voltage, used to move electron beam back and forth in a cathode ray tube.

voltage looks like the teeth of a saw, which inspired the name, *saw-tooth voltage* (Fig. 70). A simple vacuum-tube circuit for producing this kind of voltage is shown in Fig. 71.

The pair of *vertical deflecting plates* has its own saw-tooth circuit. Suppose we switch on the two deflecting systems and watch what happens. We start with the beam tip's dot of light in the upper left-hand corner of the screen, held there by steady positive voltages on two of the plates. The saw-tooth voltage on the horizontal plates, as it rises from zero, pulls the dot across the screen, reaching its peak at the instant the dot arrives at the right-hand edge of the screen. At this instant, the voltage quickly drops to zero again, allowing the dot to return to its starting point. The dot moves so fast that all one sees is a line of light. This line of light is called a *trace* (Fig. 72).

Meanwhile a much more slowly increasing saw-tooth voltage on the vertical deflecting plates is pulling the beam tip *down the screen*. The steady downward pressure on the beam causes the horizontal traces to slant a little to the right. And so it is that, when the second horizontal trace starts, its starting point is a little lower, the third has dropped a bit further, etc., until the screen has been completely scanned.

The vertical deflecting saw-tooth voltage increases at a rate that permits just 262½ horizontal traces on the screen before it reaches its peak; then it discharges, returning the dot to the top of the screen again. The 262½ lines constitute a *field*. Two fields, the lines interlaced, constitute a *frame*.

A total of 262½ lines each 1/60th of a second adds up to

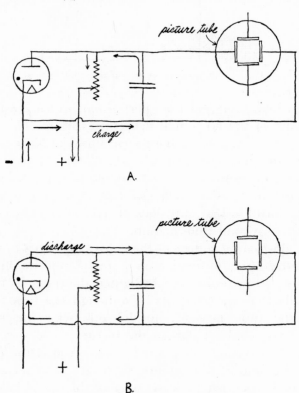

picture tube

charge

A.

discharge

picture tube

B.

FIG. 71. Simple circuit for generating a saw-tooth voltage. (A) The charging voltage is across the condenser, with a resistor in series. As the condenser takes its charge, through the resistor, the rising voltage also appears on the two deflecting plates, which move the electron beam across the tube. At the instant the beam reaches the right edge of the screen, the charging voltage is high enough to break down the resistance of the tube, which is gas filled (indicated by the dot). (B) The condenser then discharges through the tube. Rate of discharge is much faster because the discharge is *around* the resistor. A little neon gas bulb will also work in this circuit.

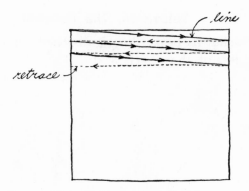

FIG. 72. Trace and retrace on television screen.

a grand total of 15,750 lines per *second*, which must be the frequency of the horizontal deflecting voltage. The vertical deflecting voltage, as we have seen, must be 60 per second.

With our dot scampering back and forth across the picture screen, forming a rectangular block of light, let's tune in a program. First, though, we had better adjust the brilliance control so that our block of light is a light gray. This is our background illumination.

The fluctuating voltage of the video signal goes to the grid to control (the technician says *modulate*) the brilliance of the trace; its positive peaks lighten the trace, its negative peaks darken it. (Incidentally, although the tube's face is gray, the tube is black inside; otherwise the negative video peaks couldn't darken the picture when they reduce the number of electrons in the beam.) And if the electron beams in camera and picture tubes are always exactly in step, an image that at least *suggests* the scene before the camera can't help but appear on the fluorescent screen. The closeness of the resemblance is governed by many factors. A few of them are (1) the number of scanning lines per frame—the more lines the greater the detail, (2) sharpness of beam tip in picture and camera tubes, (3) quality of the receiver's amplifying circuits, and receiver's proper adjustment, (4) the amount of interference from electrical disturbances of various sorts or from other signals, such as FM broadcasts.

Now we come to the matter of hitching together the electron beams in camera and picture tubes—synchronization, the expert calls it, though he prefers the abbreviation *sync*, pronounced as though it had kitchen in front of it. That should be good enough for us too.

Fig. 73A shows two of the pulses that are inserted in the signal at the transmitter—one at the end of each horizontal line. Each looks something like one of Junior's sand castles turned upside down. It's a negative pulse, and when it reaches the grid of the picture tube it drives the grid so far negative that the door is slammed shut on the electrons, completely darkening the screen. Because it comes right at

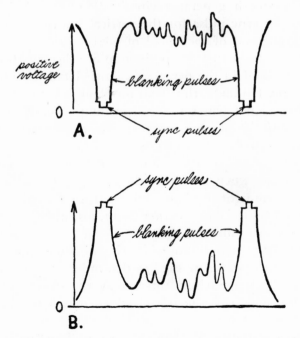

FIG. 73. One line of video signal voltage, between blanking and sync pulses. (A) Positive picture phase. (B) Negative picture phase.

the end of each horizontal line, the screen is *blanked out* during the instant the beam tip is returning to the left-hand side of the screen. This is absolutely necessary in order to prevent the horizontal return trace, called the *retrace,* from being visible on the screen. If you see the retrace, it means that the set isn't adjusted properly to enable the blanking pulse completely to darken the screen. As there must be a blanking pulse at the end of each line, the pulses come at a frequency of 15,750 per second.

Note also, perched on top of the blanking pulse—or perhaps I had better say, clinging to its bottom—the little pill box. As you see, it is even more negative than the blanking pulse. It is the synchronizing, pardon me, the *sync* pulse. A tube, called the clipper, slices it off and sends it to the horizontal saw-tooth generator circuit (Fig. 74). A blanking pulse and a sync pulse for the vertical saw-tooth generator come at the end of each field of 262½ lines.

The sync pulse must be positive to fire the *thyratron* tube of Fig. 74, and in the paragraph above I talk about a negative pulse. However, this is no problem, because each time the video signal passes through an amplifier, it is turned over; positive peaks become negative, negative peaks positive. The *negative phase* of the television signal is shown in Fig. 73B. The video signal must always be in its positive picture phase when it reaches the grid of the picture tube; otherwise the light portions of the picture would show dark on the screen, the dark portions light, a situation that could spell ruin to a minstrel show.

The amount of resistance in series with the condenser in the saw-tooth circuit of Fig. 74 determines the speed with which the voltage rises; this resistance, therefore, determines the length of the traces, which means the width of the image. In the case of the vertical system, it determines the height of the image. Now, it's a simple matter to make part of this resistance *variable,* in order to provide a means

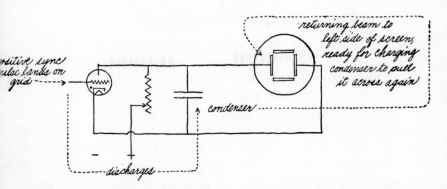

*positive sync
pulse lands on
grid* - - - - →

*returning beam to
left side of screen,
ready for charging
condenser to pull
it across again*

condenser - - - - - - -

- - - - *discharges* - - - - - -

FIG. 74. Sawtooth generator for horizontal deflection. Functions same as circuit of Fig. 71, except that it is controlled by a synchronizing pulse sent out
by the transmitter. The sync pulse lands on the tube's grid at the end of each
horizontal line (Fig. 73).

for correcting image width and height. *Width* and *height*
variable resistors are usually placed on the rear of the
chassis, handy to the service man. For 15 cents you can
buy a screwdriver and go to work on the image yourself,
squeezing and expanding it to fit the screen. Be sure, though,
that the *centering* controls, horizontal and vertical, are properly adjusted first. The *focusing* control, which sharpens the
beam tip, seldom needs to be touched, except on some of the
cheaper sets that don't have voltage regulators. If there are no
adjustment screws for centering, this probably is accomplished by a mechanical adjustment of the focus coil on the
neck of the tube.

Not only must the saw-tooth waves be of the proper length
for width and height of image; they must also be *linear*. In
other words, they shouldn't bend too far over to the right
as they rise (Fig. 70). A resistor-condenser combination for
adjusting the grid bias of the amplifying tube in each sawtooth system corrects this tendency. Its variable resistor gives
us a *linearity control*. Egg-shaped "circles" on the screen invite attention to either the *horizontal* or *vertical* linearity
controls, which are also usually found on the rear of the
chassis.

I regret to say that the thyratron tube of Fig. 74 is no longer used to discharge the saw-tooth condenser in TV sets; it has long since been replaced by a vacuum tube that *oscillates* at the required frequency—15,750 for horizontal deflection, and 60 for vertical deflection. You must forgive me for having used it as an illustration: its action is easier to follow than the action of the oscillator. The latter discharges the saw-tooth condenser once each cycle, at the instant its plate circuit starts to conduct, whether a satisfactory sync pulse arrives or not, which has its advantages. Of course, the sync pulse is still needed to prevent the oscillator frequency from wandering off the "beat," as it were. In earlier systems, a positive sync pulse, landing on the oscillator-tube grid, forced the plate circuit to conduct, thereby discharging the saw-tooth condenser at a point in the cycle just before it would normally conduct all by itself without any prompting. But suppose a heavy burst of static arrives and takes over the sync pulse's job! Such a series of premature discharges of the horizontal condenser could *tear* the picture. Because of this, and for other reasons, the engineers devised circuits that automatically control the frequency of the oscillator through the sync pulse. Most of the static may be neutralized in this *automatic frequency control* circuit (AFC) or ahead of it. For explanation of tear, see page 255.

When a TV set is sold, its automatic frequency control should be working perfectly. But after some time has passed it may tend to wander off the "beat," due to tube aging, which justifies correction controls. These are called *vertical hold* and *horizontal hold*. You know that the former needs adjusting when the complete picture starts moving up, as if it were on a turning drum. It's called picture slippage. The horizontal hold control needs attention when the picture looks as if sections have been "torn away," or it is badly distorted and appears to slip horizontally. If the hold controls are on the rear of the chassis, you can place a mirror on a chair in front of the screen while making corrections. This applies to adjustment of the other controls also. Sometimes most of the controls are under a removable shield on the front of the set.

In the larger picture tubes (over 10 inches) magnetic deflection of the electron beam has replaced electrostatic deflection, just described. With magnetic deflection, two pairs of coils outside the tube replace the inside deflecting plates. They are mounted in a single unit called a deflection *yoke,* which slips over the neck of the tube, just ahead of the smaller focus coil.

The coils require a saw-tooth current in place of a saw-tooth voltage. A saw-tooth generator circuit, essentially the same, is used. Magnetic deflection has a number of advantages: among them, the tube is cheaper to make, power requirements are reduced, and the tube can be shorter, making possible a correspondingly smaller cabinet.

I have omitted several circuits, most important of which are automatic brightness control (direct-current restoration) and automatic gain control (AGC) which is the same as AVC in radio. You will find details for these circuits in standard textbooks on television servicing. There is also an ion trap, a magnet either permanent or coil, on the neck of the cathode ray tube, for capturing negative ions that would otherwise create a brown spot on the screen's center. (Not necessary with electrostatic deflection.) It is found near the base of the tube, next to the focus coil.

The sound signal accompanies the video signal and is transmitted from, as well as received on, the same antenna. Both signals are kept within a band width of six megacycles, and your receiving antenna must tune broad enough to cover not only this band but usually several other stations besides. The sound signal is frequency modulated (FM), while the video signal uses amplitude modulation (AM). An FM video signal would have more trouble with "ghosts" and synchronizing action, besides requiring greater band width.

Fig. 75 shows a block diagram of a television receiver. You see that both sound and video carriers stay together through one stage of amplification, a radio-frequency stage. Both enter the mixer tube (first detector) together, where the oscillator frequency cuts them down to their intermediate frequencies. Then they part company, the sound i.f. going into a conventional FM set, the video i.f. into its own amplifier. After detection, the video frequency gets one or two stages of amplification, corresponding to the audio amplification in a radio, before going to the picture tube.

3

The diameter of the round television screen ranges from three to 30 inches. Choice of screen size is closely integrated to one's bankroll: the bigger the thicker. A large Eskimo family in its igloo or a small American family in a one-room apartment might be quite happy with a little seven-inch tube. The image is sharp (has good *resolution*), even if it isn't much larger than the picture of you in curls in Aunt Gussie's locket. (Long obsolete, this approximately 4 x 5-inch screen has returned in desk sets for "busy" executives.) For a long time the 12-inch screen seemed to most people a miracle of science. It was followed by the 17-inch tube, which lasted until along about 1953 or 1954. After that, the advertising trade made it impossible for a man to hold his head at optimum height in the community with anything smaller than 21 inches of screen in a console.

Early in 1950, the American Structural Products Company found a way to manufacture economically a picture tube with a rectangular screen. With no waste space, as on the round screen, tube dimensions are smaller, permitting a smaller cabinet, which means a lower price, which sells more

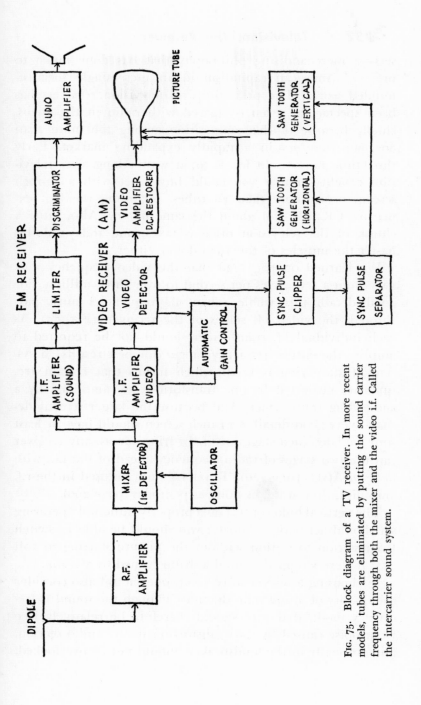

FIG. 75. Block diagram of a TV receiver. In more recent models, tubes are eliminated by putting the sound carrier frequency through both the mixer and the video i.f. Called the intercarrier sound system.

sets—a merchandising philosophy that has done much to preserve American capitalism in an increasingly socialist-minded world. The price drop on television receivers has been spectacular, even compared with radio in the 1920s, chiefly because of the competition among the more than 80 manufacturers in a rapidly expanding market. Early three-tube radios sold for $250; it wasn't long after television caught on that you could buy a set with a 12-inch screen, using more than 20 tubes, including the big, expensive CR tube, for about the same money. Also, quite a chunk of the television price is taxes, and today's dollar hasn't the muscles of the 1920 dollar either.

We learned on page 228 that the video frequency may vary from a few cycles per second to over three million. For good detail, this whole range of frequencies must pass through the video i.f. stages of the receiver (Fig. 75). As each individual i.f. transformer should not be required to amplify the entire frequency range (for best results), a system of staggering is used: which means that certain frequencies neglected by one transformer are amplified by a succeeding transformer. And because the larger screens demand very good detail, a 21-inch screen should have at least four well-designed stages of i.f. In fringe areas, any receiver can use two stages of radio frequency ahead of the i.f., with *delayed* AGC (page 220). Triodes should be used in the r.f. amplifier: they aren't as noisy as pentodes (page 290).

The vertical hold control on a properly built and operating set should act with *authority;* you should be able to switch from station to station without the picture starting to roll as if it were wrapped around a drum turned by a crank.

In choosing a television receiver, one should also consider the quality of sound reproduction. Though the sound is frequency modulated, and should therefore be relatively free from noise caused by static, distortion in the audio section, and especially in the loudspeaker, should not be overlooked.

In the table model, the big cathode ray tube doesn't leave much space for a loudspeaker: perhaps only enough for a five-incher, with its restricted audio range. And the speaker must be placed in the *side* of the cabinet. Some table models have two small speakers.

The i.f. circuits of many sets now use printed wiring (page 293). Some dispense with the power transformer by rectifying and filtering the 120-volt a.c. power supply for the plates and heating the cathodes with filaments in series (page 67). The 17,000 volts or so needed for pulling the electron beam through the tube has long been obtained from the 15,750-cycle frequency of the horizontal deflecting current, whose voltage is raised by a transformer, rectified, filtered, and applied to the second anode. A good 15-tube set can now be built, though not for fringe areas; these usually require two stages of good, low-noise, r.f. amplification, described on page 268.

One way to improve picture quality would be to increase the number of lines. This probably will never be done because color TV provides a good picture with 525 lines, and it is likely that new tubes that don't use the lines at all will be perfected. Great Britain gets good results with only 405 lines, using 50 frames to our 60 (wobbling the lines with an oscillator helps some). France uses 819 lines. Russia's numerous transmitters enable viewers before two million sets to follow a 635-line picture. The early receivers all had 4 x 5-inch screens, many with a plastic magnifying lens, but bigger screens are common now.

There are black-and-white picture tubes in the laboratory stage that operate a little differently from the old ones. They are made flat, to hang on the living-room wall like a picture. The receiver for this type of display device, with transistors replacing tubes, need be no larger than a shoe box. Today's big, bulky TV may some day be as obsolete as the bookcase.

23

TELEVISION: THE ANTENNA

On the day that De Forest inserted the grid in the diode for the first time, a pair of *gremlins* suddenly appeared, probably from spontaneous generation. These tiny, invisible devils have since multiplied like rabbits. The one aim of their existence is to harass the technician. They joyfully detune circuits, burn out tubes, mess with wiring, puncture condensers, introduce distortion, and they have even been known to gang up and throw a switch during the lunch hour.

Gremlins are especially clever at creating frequency distortion in video receiver circuits. When they cut off the higher frequencies, detail is rubbed out in the horizontal lines, and when they cut off the lower frequencies a smearing of the picture results.

Sometimes the gremlins are able to interfere enough with TV circuits, usually of the cheaper receivers, to cause a "blizzard" on the screen. The technician appropriately calls it *snow*. More often, however, snow is caused by static, or by the "noise" that is inherent in any electronic circuit. Bursts of static can even discharge the horizontal saw-tooth condenser, interrupting the scanning process. This causes sections of the picture to disappear as if they had been torn away, a type of defect aptly called a *tear*.

You remember how Armstrong invented the superheterodyne, trying to tune in the waves from the spark plugs of German bombers. One of television's problems is the signal from automobile spark-plug broadcasts, together with the one from leaky power insulators and various kinds of electrical machines. Whether the static is made by nature or by man, we attack it through the antenna installation. Except under very unusual conditions, the right kind of antenna job can always reduce static to the point where it is no longer troublesome.

Another problem with television is double images, called *ghosts*. Ghosts are much more prevalent in the big cities than in the surrounding country. The country viewer's main problem is more often a weak signal because of his greater distance from the transmitter. Both problems must also be attacked through the antenna installation. Suppose we take a good look at this television antenna that is so vital to good reception.

In contrast to the "any-length-of-wire," draped over Van Gogh's "Bridge at Arles," that usually works well enough for radio reception, a television antenna system is a precision device. In the first place, it must be *tuned*. The type of tuned antenna used with television is the half-wave dipole of Hertz, or a variation of it.

The half-wave dipole is tuned by varying its length. Imagine a straight piece of aluminum wire of infinitely small diameter, floating around in space way up above the stratosphere. Its length is exactly 14.28 feet; this means that our hypothetical wire is *tuned* to a television carrier frequency whose wave length is 14.28 feet: because a frequency of that wave length *fits right on it.*

If we cut the wire in two halves, each 7.14-foot length will also be tuned to the wave, because *half* of the wave will fit right on it; and we'll have a half-wave dipole.

However, it can't be any shorter than 7.14 feet and function as a tuned antenna for the 14.28-foot wave. It can be longer—if we jump a full half wave each time. For the 14.28 wave, an antenna 21.42 feet long would function as a 1½-wave antenna; one 28.56 feet long would function as a 2-wave antenna.

It is customary to refer to the wave length in meters instead of feet. The 14.28-foot wave is 4.35 meters long; and 4.35 meters means a frequency of 69 megacycles.

Now let's pull down our half-wave aluminum antenna from the sky and anchor it to the roof. To do this, we must give it diameter to make it self-supporting. And because it now has body and is close to earth and surrounding objects, it acquires both inductance and capacitance (page 99). The effect of inductance and capacitance is to slow down the velocity at which the wave travels along its length. The same wave won't quite fit our antenna now, unless we make it a trifle shorter. About 90 percent of its former length of 7.14 feet, or 6.8 feet, will do very nicely.

We really needn't go to all this figuring to determine the correct length for a half-wave rooftop dipole. There is a simple formula, $L = 468/\text{mc}$. Length is in feet, mc. is for megacycles. Thus, for our 69-mc. wave, $L = 468/69$. $L = 6.8$ feet.

You may have concluded from all this that it is necessary to have a separate half-wave dipole cut to the exact resonant length for each station's wave. This might be ideal, but it's seldom necessary, because a compromise can almost always be made that works well enough. There is room for five stations on television's lower frequencies, from 54 to 88 mc.

These are channels 2, 3, 4, 5, and 6. However, the FCC assigns only three channels on these frequencies to any single locality, in order to prevent interference as much as possible. An antenna cut to resonance at a frequency close to that of the middle station usually receives all three stations well enough. This might be the 69 mc. of the antenna we have been discussing, which is channel 4.

On the higher television frequencies, between 174 and 216 mc., there are seven channels, seven to 13 inclusive, of which the FCC never assigns more than four to a single locality. A higher frequency means a shorter wave length, and the shortest antenna you see on the popular twin-antenna installation is for them (Fig. 77G).

Under good conditions, a single antenna can be used to receive all the stations on both the high and the low television frequencies, ranging between 54 and 216 mc. In this case, the half-wave dipole is cut for a station near the middle of the low frequencies. For the stations on the high frequencies, this antenna is approximately 1½ wave lengths long; so, for these stations it functions as a 1½-wave antenna.

Before we go any further into antenna installation we should pause to consider the wires that connect it to the set.

The *lead-in* wire for the radio receiver is part of the antenna; in fact, you might say that the short length of wire commonly used with the city radio is both antenna and lead-in, there being no overhead installation with it. Not so with television's dipole lead-in, which is a critical link between the antenna and the receiver. Because it transmits the waves from antenna to receiver, it is called a *transmission line*. It must be engineered to the demands of both dipole and receiver.

One solution to the problem of the transmission line would be to tune it, like the antenna. This would involve cutting it to just the proper length for one or more quarter waves to fit on it. (Quarter waves can be used as units of resonance for a transmission line.) But a resonant transmission line for television receiver jobs is difficult to deal with, and what is called a *nonresonant line* is used.

The nonresonant line is said to have a certain *impedance,* called *characteristic impedance* or *surge impedance.* Impedance is another term for resistance and is also measured in ohms. I wish I could explain this transmission line impedance in a few well-chosen words. But I can't, so I suggest we just try to accept it without knowing what it is. After all, we have plenty of precedent for this; every day we talk confidently of such things as vitamins, hormones, aeons, and complexes, and who *knows* what *they* are?

The antenna has an impedance, the input to the receiver has an impedance; to prevent the transmission line from greatly weakening the signal, one end should have the same impedance as the antenna; the other end should also be *impedance matched* to the receiver.

Of course, even a perfect impedance match at both ends wouldn't eliminate all loss in the line: some of the energy is always converted to heat in the wires and in the insulation. This loss is figured per foot of line, and must be kept in mind when selecting the type of line for an installation. Fig. 76 pictures the most popular types of transmission line used with television receivers.

Can you open a window and draw a bead with a rifle on the antenna of your favorite station or stations? If so, you're lucky. A built-in antenna or a rabbit-ears antenna on a pedestal would give you a good picture. You might even get by with no antenna at all. Signal strength would always be high enough to override snow-causing static, unless it was exceptionally severe.

Starting with the little portable dipole mentioned above (Fig. 77A), we shall now run a series of tests with various types of antenna to see what happens. We shall assume that the set's input impedance is 300 ohms, which has become

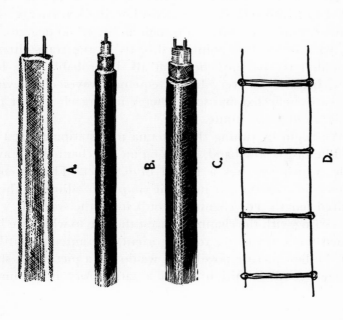

Fig. 76. Four most commonly used types of transmission line. (A) Plastic strip. Two wires embedded in the outer edge of a polyethylene strip, ⅜ inch wide. Simple to install—just tack it down inside the house. Impedance, 300 ohms. Signal loss not too high for vast majority of installations. Cheapest type, about 5 cents per foot. (B) Coaxial cable. This type of line is widely used between cities by the telephone company. One conductor is a metal tube, the other a wire in its exact center. Flexible type for TV receivers has the center wire molded in plastic, the outer conductor being braided copper. Grounding the outer conductor shields the line from static and other interference, though not perfectly. (The signal current travels on the outer conductor's *inside surface*, known as *skin effect*.) Impedance, 72 ohms, though other impedances available. Price largely determined by quality. (C) Twin-pair, surrounded by third conductor, which is grounded to shield the line from snow-causing static. Impedances, 150 and 300 ohms. Signal strength losses higher than for coax, but usually easier to match. Rather expensive. (D) Ladder line. With no solid plastic between its two conductors to eat up energy, this type has relatively low loss. Often mandatory in areas close to the ocean where conducting salt collects on the plastic-strip line, changing its impedance and weakening the signal. Impedance, 300 ohms and 400 ohms. There is less leakage across the wider separators of the latter. Medium priced among impedance lines.

pretty much standard. (An exception was the DuMont receiver, with an impedance of 72 ohms.) Thus the set asks for a 300-ohm line. This is quite a mismatch at the antenna, whose impedance is 72 ohms at its *center*. But the center impedance is 72 ohms at resonance only; the impedance increases some when receiving stations with frequencies above or below resonance. The mismatch may be a good thing for this reason. Although the antenna itself isn't so sensitive to the frequencies above and below resonance, these frequencies get an improved impedance match, which tends to average matters out; in other words, tends to broaden the installation's frequency response. We must remember that *each channel* is six mc. wide, and there may be three or four channels on each of the bands. Of course, a broader frequency response is obtained at the expense of sensitivity, just as with any tuned circuit (Fig. 40). TV-antenna installation is largely a matter of trading; more compromise goes on than in the cloakrooms of Congress.

The half-wave dipole receives best when placed *broadside* to the transmitter. It receives less and less energy as we turn it from this position through an arc of 90 degrees; until, with either end pointing directly at the transmitter, it shouldn't receive any energy at all. It probably will, however, because the very high frequency waves of television are easily reflected and some energy may reach it after traveling a circuitous route.

We begin by tuning the antenna to a station nearest the middle of the low band, say to 69 mc., if channel 4 is available, which requires a length of 6.8 feet. The antenna's telescopic construction makes it simple to adjust to the required length. For channel 4, pull it all the way out.

Starting with the channel nearest the one to which we have tuned the antenna, we rotate (orient) the antenna until we get the best picture possible, if we do get a picture. A sharp image (good definition), with a satisfactory minimum of snow, means we can try the other channels on the low band; and if results continue good, the channels on the high band are in order. Though on the high band our half-wave dipole will function as a 1½-wave antenna as is, it is usually best to use it as a half-wave antenna by telescoping the two elements to one-third their former length. The antenna should be oriented for best results on each station. We can also try moving the antenna around the room; often it will receive best up close to a window.

Our little indoor portable dipole will fail us if: (1) We aren't picking up enough signal strength to override the static; the heavier the static the greater the signal strength required. A too-weak signal can mean we are too far from the transmitter, or that there are intervening buildings or hills that block the waves, creating what is called a shadow; (2) large objects, such as steel buildings or bridges, reflect the waves, causing ghosts. In any case, we shall now climb to the roof, though in actual practice an attic antenna, or one fastened to the building outside a window, might be improvement enough.

On the roof we'll start with the simple dipole with a center impedance at resonance of approximately 72 ohms (Fig. 77B). The antenna should be kept as far as possible from galvanized-iron flues, metal gutters, guy wires, etc. Stand-off insulators are used to separate the transmission line from mast and building. Often a brick chimney makes a good anchor for the antenna mast.

For the time being, let's stick to the cheap, easy-to-install, 300-ohm, two-wire plastic strip line. If we twist it about half a turn per foot, it picks up less interference, though this doesn't apply to the shielded type of line, B and C in Fig. 76. As we have seen, a 300-ohm line connected to the center of a 72-ohm antenna is quite a mismatch, though it may be a good thing because it gives a better over-all frequency response. (In case a closer match is necessary, it can be had by connecting the line to the antenna at two points a short distance from each side of the center tap, where the impedance is higher. The impedance is always highest at the two ends of a dipole, lowest at its center.)

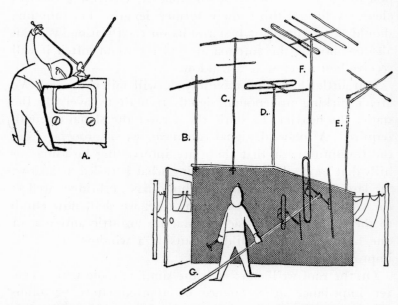

FIG. 77. TV receiving antennas. (A) Portable dipole. (B) Simple Hertz dipole on mast. (C) Single simple dipole for each of high and low bands. Sometimes mounted on same level with shorter dipole (higher frequency) in front. (D) Folded dipole, with reflector. (E) Double-V dipole. (F) Folded dipole with one reflector, three directors. Called a Yagi. (G) Folded dipoles with reflectors, for high and low bands.

As before, we tune the antenna to the middle of the low band by adjusting its length. Then comes the all-important and often difficult job of orientation: turning the antenna till it's as closely broadside as possible to all the transmitters. This can be quite a problem with several transmitters, all in different directions. We might be forced to settle for a compromise position that picks up a fair signal from all of them, though not too good a signal from any one. Even this may be impossible. Using a single dipole, we have two strikes on us; so let's add a second dipole for the higher frequency 7 to 13 channels (Fig. 77C). Now we can orient each dipole separately. Antenna installation is greatly simplified when all the transmitters are in a single location. In New York City the upper stories of the Empire State Building house seven television transmitters; from them, transmission lines go to their antennas on a 220-foot steel tower atop the building. The seven antennas are mounted one above the other, suggesting a giant totem pole. The building itself is 1,250 feet high. In Southern California, the rookery for telecasters is Mount Wilson, 5,000 feet above Hollywood. Nine television transmitters are roosting there, including two in the ultra high frequency band, together with the telephone company's transmitters and receivers for its mobile service.

A 5,000-foot antenna has a range of around 100 miles when the receiving antenna is 100 feet high, and even further with a superior type of receiving antenna.*

A higher receiving antenna not only feeds the set a stronger signal, it also picks up less man-made static. However, we must bear in mind that the transmission line, if unshielded, picks up static. Also, the longer the transmission line the greater its signal-strength losses. But back to our job on the roof.

Suppose we find that even our *pair* of dipoles, each one oriented separately, isn't good enough; because a compromise position that favors one or more stations slights the others too much. For one thing, these simple dipoles tune

---

* A simple formula for figuring range, based on antenna heights, is $d = 1.23 \ (\sqrt{h_t} + \sqrt{h_r})$; d is for distance in miles, h_t is transmitter antenna height in feet, h_r is receiver antenna height in feet. The Mount Wilson figures in this formula give us $d = 1.23 \ (\sqrt{5,000} + \sqrt{100})$; $d = 1.23 \times 70 + 10$; $d = 1.23 \times 80$; $d = 98.4$ miles.

pretty sharp, and it should help some to replace them with antennas having a flatter resonance curve.

The folded dipole of Fig. 77D, which is, in effect, two simple dipoles in parallel, has a flatter resonance curve. (Disregard second element for the moment.) The conical dipole of Fig. 77E also has a broader frequency response. Both antennas have a center impedance at resonance of 300 ohms, the same as our line and set, which solves our matching problems. Or perhaps it doesn't, for our district may shelter some electronic apparatus, such as X-ray or diathermy machines made before 1947 that harass us with interference; and to clear up the screen we must install a shielded transmission line. We are on easy street if we can use the shielded two-wire line of 300 ohms impedance (Fig. 76C). But because of its high losses, it can be used only with a strong signal, and perhaps a distance between antenna and set of not over 75 feet. Otherwise we shall have to resort to the 72-ohm coaxial cable, good for greater lengths, providing it is *high-quality* cable. With the coax, we must match a 72-ohm line to a 300-ohm antenna. This can be done by means of what is called a *matching section:* a piece of 150-ohm transmission line, about half the length of the antenna, placed between line and antenna. At the receiver, simply ground one side of the input.

It is quite possible, especially in the city, to be getting satisfactory signal strength and still be bothered by double images: ghosts! The transmitted wave, dividing some of its energy, arrives at the receiver by two different routes (Fig. 78). One, popularized 2,200 years ago by Euclid because of its shortness, and still a specialty of the bee and the crow, follows a straight line to the receiver. The other route is roundabout, in this case by way of two steel buildings. Both waves produce images on the screen. But the reflected wave, having farther to go, arrives a few microseconds later; and by that time the traces on the screen have

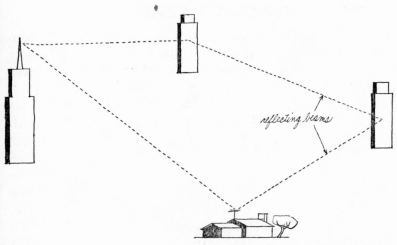

Fig. 78. Principal cause of "ghosts." Energy from the transmitter, reflected by the two buildings, arrives at the receiver later than the direct wave. The late arrival creates a second image a little to the right of the first.

moved a fraction of an inch or so to the right (Fig. 79). As a result of this *time lag*, the reflected wave puts its image on the screen a little to the right of Euclid's. (A microsecond is one millionth of a second; it is widely used in electronics as a division of time, and we shall encounter it again when we tackle radar.)

I have said that mismatching a 300-ohm line to the sharply tuning 72-ohm dipole may be good because it broadens the

Fig. 79. "Ghost" on screen.

over-all frequency response. However, with a broadly tuning antenna, such as the folded dipole, as close an antenna
match as possible is desirable. The match to the receiver
should always be perfect, in any case. A serious mismatch
here can even cause ghosts. The remedy for this type of
ghosts is obvious; the remedy for ghosts caused by multi-
path reception (Fig. 78) is to use a sharply directional
antenna. This type of antenna should either eliminate or
greatly reduce the signal strength of the reflected wave. In
the unlikely event the reflected wave is the stronger, because
of a shadow, we can discriminate against the direct wave.
Any of our varieties of dipole can be made more directional
by adding a *reflector* (Fig 77D).

The reflector not only increases directivity; it has other
advantages too. A dipole receives equally well from both
sides, rejecting only those signals that arrive from the directions in which its two ends are pointing. The reflector causes
it to reject most of the signal that approaches from the reflector's side. This serves to eliminate most of the interference from that direction, such as nature's static. An antenna
with a reflector also picks up more signal strength, because
some energy is "reflected back" to the dipole. It also has a
lower center impedance. As mentioned before (page 261),
a higher impedance for matching to the transmission line
may be had a short distance from each side of the center.
Most television antennas have connections for matching to
a 300-ohm line.

It probably has occurred to you that an antenna with
greater directivity complicates the problem of orientation.
A solution for this is to rotate the antenna by means of an
electric motor controlled by a switch at the receiver, so it
can be freshly oriented for each channel. This may not be
necessary, however, unless the stations are in all different
directions, and we are perhaps obtaining greater directivity
by means of a third element, called a *director* (Fig. 77F).

The director also further reduces the amount of interference picked up from the reflector side and provides the antenna with still more signal strength. Center impedance is lower too. Several directors may be added, as shown.

The most popular television antenna in most localities is either the folded twin dipole (or the conical), equipped with reflector and using the 300-ohm plastic-tape transmission line (Fig. 77G). Properly installed and oriented, it provides good reception for the majority of set owners. It usually fails, however, in what is called the fringe area, between 20 and 50 miles from a transmitter, or possibly in a shadow area.

To combat the earth's curvature, the fringe area wants an antenna as high as possible. This means a long transmission line, which should therefore be the low-loss (Fig. 76) ladder line, though the plastic tape is frequently used. A weak signal asks for an antenna with reflector and one or more directors. This type of antenna, by the way, is called the *yagi,* after its inventor, a Japanese physicist by that name. (During the war we used it with our mobile radar against Japan.) The yagi for television reception has a band width of only about six megacycles, which means that a separate antenna is necessary for each station. Were it tuned any sharper it would cut off the side bands, killing the higher video frequencies to erase detail in the horizontal lines; but if it did this, it would also cut off the sound carrier, and the owner would find himself back in the silent-picture days. Each antenna should have its own transmission line to prevent interaction between antennas. For an exceptionally weak signal two yagis can be used, one on top of the other, when they are said to be *stacked.* (Any of the antennas I have mentioned can be stacked.)

The commercial variety of antenna usually comes with connections for a 300-ohm line. If cost is no deterrent, it is often possible to erect an antenna that will bring in a signal from a transmitter as far as 250 miles away. A good r.f. amplifier that generates a minimum of *noise* (causing snow) is necessary. This noise, explained on page 290, is less severe in a triode than in a pentode because of the fewer positive elements in the triode. However, its *gain* is much less than that of a pentode. A new type of low-noise r.f. amplifier, called the *cascode amplifier,* compensates for this by using two triodes connected in *series.* The plate circuit of the first triode goes direct to the cathode of the second. The amount of current through the two tubes is governed by the bias on the grid on the first tube, which must be neutralized by some negative feedback to keep it from oscillating (page 190). Output is taken from the plate circuit of the second tube. Any up-to-date book on television will furnish the details of this new circuit.

A *wave trap* (quarter-wave length of transmission line) is often used to block interference, such as an FM signal. The *r.f. booster,* a separate amplifier for shadows or fringe areas, was more popular before the cascode amplifier.

A lightning arrester must be placed in each side of the transmission line, connected to the ground; though a shielded type of line, being itself grounded, makes this unnecessary. The metal antenna mast should also be grounded. Grounding wire should be size 14 or larger, insulated, and connected to a metal pipe or rod driven a couple of feet into the earth. All this extra fuss is of no help to the picture, but it will please the National Board of Fire Underwriters no end.

Before leaving the television antenna, here is a hint that may possibly save you considerable expense. If your transmission line is the plastic-strip variety (Fig. 76A) and you start getting a weak signal, try wiping the line (outside the house) with a rag soaked in alcohol or carbon tetrachloride.

24

TELEVISION: IN COLOR

On December 16, 1953, the Federal Communications Commission, figuratively speaking, dropped a red, blue, and green flag, and the entries in the color-TV race were off and running, turtlelike. Three years later, even the leader with the patents for rent, RCA, was a long way from the finish line of volume sales. The poor time can be laid to two things, high price and a color tube difficult to keep adjusted.

A color signal on the air does not mean that your old black-and-white screen will suddenly blossom in technicolor, like the bouquet of flowers that springs from a vase under the stage magician's wand. But you will still have your black-and-white pictures, perhaps with a little better definition than before; which means that the color signal is *compatible*.

Can your old set be converted to color? This is possible, in many instances, but not practicable, because of the high cost. It would be cheaper to buy a new one. The first color sets, with their tiny screens, sold for around $1,000. In June 1956 RCA announced a table model with a big 21-inch screen for $495. The public reacted with remarkable restraint. With time, of course, reliability will rise as cost and service fees fall, perhaps when the color tubes from other manufacturers appear.

Color-television development has been handicapped because the black-and-white version was perfected first. Twenty-three million, two hundred thousand households (October 1953) had been equipped with the monochrome screen, and so extra obstacles were placed in the path of the inventors. For a compatible system demands that both the black-and-white signal and the color signal be kept within the present 6-mc.-wide channel. Thirty frames per second and 525 lines per frame must also be preserved so that circuit changes will not have to be made in the old sets.

Before we describe a color-TV system that embodies the standards approved by the FCC, suppose we first outline a more simple system. It is not compatible, and would require a channel wider than 6 mc.

Three colors whose combinations will produce almost all the other colors (white also) are red, blue, and green. Our color camera contains three image orthicons. One of them has a filter in front of its lens that passes only red light, so that its photocathode yields a video voltage only when a red area is before the camera; the other two tubes are similarly equipped to respond to blue and green light respectively. The video voltage from each camera tube modulates a separate carrier frequency. Standard amplitude modulation is used.

The receiver has three picture tubes, each with a different type of phosphor: one produces red light under electron bombardment, one blue, the third green. After detection (demodulation), each video voltage is directed to its appropriate picture tube. At this point we have three pictures, each of a different primary color. For the final picture they must be superimposed. This is done by projecting them onto a viewing screen by way of suitable lenses and mirrors. The three should blend into a full color picture of good resolution and fidelity. However, three carrier frequencies demand too wide a channel for use today; and a home receiver with 3 CR tubes and a projection system would be too costly for mass distribution. This type of receiver can also be used with a more advanced system, and it will possibly be available in the future as a luxury set for those who want a color screen larger than can be had on a single CR color tube.

One virtue of the system I have just described is that it is completely *simultaneous:* all three primary color signals are both transmitted and applied to the viewing screen simultaneously. The alternative to this method is the *sequential* system, in which the video voltages of first one color, then another, and finally the third, are strung out on a single carrier frequency like wash on the line. For a time it seemed that sequential transmission, with a single carrier, might be the only solution to the difficult problem of staying within the 6-mc. band width.

In the sequential receiver, the electron beam tip "dabs" on one color at a time, but at such a fast rate of repetition that our persistence of vision prevents us from detecting the subterfuge. The color can appear in a sequence of dots, lines, fields, or frames. Several years ago CBS climaxed ten years of research with a very acceptable *field* sequential system, and after competitive tests with Color Television, Inc., and RCA, it was approved by the FCC. This was October 1950. A year later the government stopped all color-TV activity, in the interests of national defense, and the system has since been abandoned for telecasting, though it is now used by industry with closed circuits.

This CBS system is comparatively simple. The camera lens

looks through a rapidly turning scanning disc with red, blue, and green filters arranged in sequence. While a red filter is in front of the lens, the electron beam in the camera scans a complete field of 202½ lines. (A field is a half picture, the alternate lines scanned.) The same for each of the blue and green filters. To prevent flicker, the number of fields per second had to be raised from 60 to 144. The receiver must also have a scanning disc, synchronized with the camera's. The eye looks at a red field, then a blue, then a green, each one lasting 1/144th of a second; but it *sees* a picture in which all three colors are combined.

The CBS system produced no monochrome signal for the old sets. However, it did enable owners of the smaller receivers to convert them to color by mounting a color wheel in front of the screen, making a few changes in the scanning circuits, and adding a sync circuit for the motor. Many objected to the mechanical feature of the scanning wheel, which also limited the size of the screen. It may even prove practicable to use the wheel as a cheap means of conversion to the present system of color, though picture quality would probably be inferior. For one thing, the color signals that are broadcast simultaneously must be applied to the screen in sequence, so they synchronize with the color wheel; and for this reason the picture will lack the brilliance of a regular color tube.

RCA has been more than active in color TV down through the years. After having spent $50 million on black and white, the company has poured another $25 million into color development. Extensive experimentation was carried out on several different systems that showed promise. At the 1950 tests for the FCC, RCA demonstrated a dot-sequential system. Since then, company research has been largely concentrated on simultaneous transmission of a three-color signal. Engineers have recently staged a number of very successful demonstrations of the results of this research for the press. Conforming with the NTSC's specifications, now approved by the FCC, the system uses but a single carrier frequency in the 6-mc.-wide channel to carry both a compatible black-and-white signal and a color signal.

As with black and white, it's the *camera* that makes the mare go: a three-image orthicon job, one for generating red video voltages, one for blue, and one for green. A single optical system, consisting of the usual combination of lenses, provides an image for all three of the tubes. The real image reaches the tubes' photocathodes via a system of four special mirrors, which are also filters. These are *dichroic* mirrors: each reflects light of one color only, passing all the others. For the future, RCA also has a single-tube color-TV camera in development. Details are lacking on the new CBS-Hytron color camera.

First of all, this camera must provide a *luminance* or *brightness* signal for the black-and-white sets. (This signal is also necessary for both color and black and white in color receivers.) The best brightness signal is a mixture of 30 percent of the red, 59 percent of the green, and 11 percent of the blue. This provides a good white, and also better contrast between the grays, even better than the monochrome camera, which is more sensitive to the blue-greens than to the reds.

As this is a simultaneous system, both the brightness and the *chrominance* or color signals must modulate the carrier frequency at the same time. One problem has been to crowd the brightness signal and the *chrominance* or color signals into the narrow 6-mc. channel without causing interference. For instance, the color signals can't interfere with the picture on the black-and-white sets. A big help has been the fact that the eye, when viewing color, fails to distinguish fine detail. Tie red, green, and blue toy balloons together and watch them float away; after they shrink to a certain size the color disappears. As you know, fine detail is carried by the higher video frequencies, and since color is not distinguishable in fine detail, only the lower frequencies are necessary. For some colors, 1.3 mc. is adequate; others may require no more than .4 mc. Partial side-band suppression is also used to reduce further the color-band width (page 228).

The transmitter generates a local frequency of approximately 3,580,000 cycles. The three-color (video) frequencies, none higher than 1.3 mc., modulate this subcarrier. A type of modulation we haven't considered before in this book is used, called *phase* modulation. The color voltages change the phase of the subcarrier, relative to its unmodulated frequency—each color changing it by a different amount. At the same time, the shade of the color, called color *saturation*, varies the amplitude of the subcarrier. So what we have, at this point, is a 3,580,000-cycle subcarrier, phase modulated for color (hue), and amplitude modulated for saturation.

The subcarrier, in turn, modulates the transmitter's carrier frequency, together with the 60-cycle to 4-mc. brightness signal, taken from all the colors. Heterodyning produces a great many other frequencies in this mixture too, but these can be filtered out.

The above is a short-cut version of how the brightness and chrominance signals are contained within the 6-mc. channel. In practice, both subtraction and addition of brightness and color frequencies take place (in transmitter *and* receiver) a complex maneuver that simplifies the problem.

In the receiver, after r.f. and i.f. amplification, the brightness signal and the subcarrier are separated; then the color signals are separated from the subcarrier. The latter requires *phase-detection* circuits, new to us. In order to determine the amount of phase difference, the phase detector must also generate the subcarrier frequency of 3,580,000 cycles. A quartz crystal oscillator is used (Fig. 103). This local frequency must always be exactly in phase with the unmodulated subcarrier in the camera, making synchronization necessary. For this, each horizontal blanking pulse carries a "burst" of eight cycles. Comparison of the local frequency with the incoming *modulated* subcarrier reveals an amount of phase difference, which identifies the color. The *amplitude* of the subcarrier frequency at any instant is a measure of color saturation. How the picture tube uses the three reclaimed color voltages to reproduce the picture will become apparent after our discussion of display tubes that follows.

The cost of tomorrow's color set will depend largely upon how cheaply the big color picture tube can be mass produced. RCA's shadow-mask tube will have competition. Engineers have been struggling for years to get the bugs out of the *Chromatron,* invented in 1946 by the University of California's Ernest O. Lawrence of Cyclotron fame. Then there's CBS-Hytron's *Colortron,* and tubes from Philco and GE, not to mention the flat color tubes. One of the flat type, now pretty far along, combines patents of Dr. D. Gabor of London and W. Ross Aiken of the Kaiser Aircraft and Electronics Corporation, Oakland, Calif.

The Chromatron, owned by Paramount Pictures, will be manufactured for home sets by the Allen B. DuMont Laboratories, Inc. A single electron beam activates red, blue, and green phosphor stripes, painted vertically on the inside surface of the rectangular glass screen. Two separate grids of fine wires are built into the tube just behind the color stripes and parallel to them. Instantaneous voltages applied to the grid wires switch the beam to the correct color stripe during scanning, which is horizontal.

General Electric's entry has the same vertical red, blue, and green color stripes with horizontal scanning. It also uses a parallel wire grid for focusing. (Electric fields function as a lens for electrons. See Fig. 69.) However, unlike the Chromatron, three beams from three separate guns are used. Each beam tip is guided to its color stripe by the combined lens effect and the angle at which the electrons pass between the grid wires.

Philco's color tube also has red, blue, and green vertical phosphor stripes on the inside surface of the rectangular screen. Like GE's, it is a 22-incher. But even though it has but a single electron gun, no wire grid is required. Instead, it has a novel indexing system. The electrons from the gun are split into two beams: a writing and a marker beam. Behind each green stripe is a magnesium-oxide marker stripe which releases secondary electrons when the marker beam crosses it. These electrons, attracted to a positive voltage on the tube, provide an index frequency. The time difference, the phase difference, between the two beams crossing the green and marker stripe, and the other two stripes, reveals where the writing beam is at any instant. Between green and blue there are 120 degrees, between green and red 240 degrees. Between green and green 360 degrees—no phase difference.

RCA uses the checkerboard or dot distribution of the phosphors in its three-beam, shadow-mask kinescope. The viewing screen is a flat glass plate. The phosphors are distributed in groups of three dots, one red, one blue, one green. There are 195,000 groups, making a total of 595,000

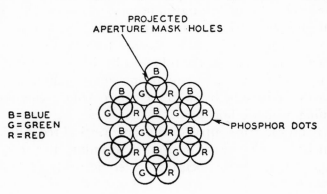

VIEWED FROM GUN END

Fig. 80. Orientation of the mask holes with the phosphor dots in the RCA tricolor kinescope. (Diagram by courtesy of RCA.)

dots. The latest model is the round type for a 21-inch picture.

Just inside the phosphor-dot plate, and parallel to it, is the shadow mask or aperture mask (Fig. 81). This is a metal plate with 195,000 holes, one for each group of phosphor dots. The holes are placed in relation to the dots as shown in Fig. 80. The electron beams are directed so that each one arrives at the mask at a different angle, and as the beams sweep across the plate, each beam tip finds its own row of color dots. The holes in the mask provide color separation by *shadowing* two of the three-color dots in each group from the wrong two beams.

The electron beams are focused to the glass plate electrostatically (Fig. 69). All three beams must also *converge* at each shadow-mask hole, as indicated in Fig. 81, and this is also done electrostatically. Deflection of the three beams, in unison, is accomplished electromagnetically by means of a deflection yoke more complex than the one on the black-and-white kinescope. An extra pair of coils for alignment of the

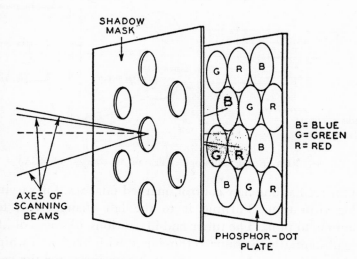

Fig. 81 Relation of scanning beam, shadow mask, and phosphor-dot plate. (Diagram by courtesy of RCA.)

beam, called a *purity yoke,* is also needed. Fig. 82 shows where all three controls are mounted on the neck of the tube.

CBS-Hytron has succeeded in putting the color dots directly on the inside surface of the spherical glass plate of its *Colortron,* using a spherical shadow mask. Without the flat glass plate, the tube is simpler, lighter, and cheaper to make. And other advantages are claimed for it, such as better contrast and simplified focusing. The shadow mask was invented by Dr. Alfred H. Goldsmith in 1940. Dr. A. B. DuMont has patents on the triad grouping of the color phosphors.

As I write, most of the leading manufacturers of standard television sets are building experimental color receivers. When the final versions are arrived at, they won't all be the same; there are usually several ways to accomplish the same result in a piece of electronic apparatus. Therefore, the color receiver described below is a purely hypothetical one.

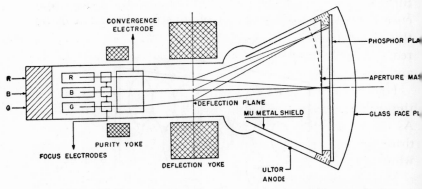

Fig. 82. RCA tricolor kinescope. (Diagram by courtesy of RCA.)

Our set has one new control, marked CHROMA, for varying color saturation. Turning it to the left changes red, for example, to pink. The tuner and i.f. sections (6 stages of i.f.) are substantially the same as those used with black and white. Provision is made for a 300-ohm antenna input for the very high frequency stations, and a 75-ohm input for the ultra high. There are extra circuits for separating the brightness signal from the chrominance. The brightness signal controls all three grids together; each of the three color signals goes to a single grid, enabling it to control its own electron beam independently.

Let's imagine the color camera trained upon the White House. High on our receiver screen, Old Glory waves in true red, white, and blue. The white? All three camera tubes pick up a signal from the white, and their three video voltages, applied to the three grids of the kinescope simultaneously (by the brightness signal), fluoresce the red, blue, and green phosphors. The three colors obligingly blend into white for us. A black area, of course, produces no signal, in which case we see the screen, which looks black in contrast to the white.

Colors between the primaries are also color composites. For example, yellow causes both the red and green camera tubes to generate video voltages. The resulting phase difference is between that of red or green alone. In the receiver, this phase difference directs voltages to the grids of both the red and green scanning beams simultaneously: and the red and green phosphors, lit together, produce yellow.

For telecasts in black and white, operation is restricted to the brightness signal, derived from all three primary colors. As this signal goes to all three grids together, it lights the three phosphors simultaneously in varying degree: fully lit, white, partially lit, gray.

Most people aren't bothered much by small imperfections in the black-and-white picture: a little horizontal non-linearity, for example, or poor low-frequency response. These individuals are going to be more finicky when it comes to color. Color reproduction will have to be well-nigh perfect. This demands very high standards of performance by both transmitter and receiver. Some of the elements in the receiver must be of higher quality, tolerances closer, adjustments finer, inspection better, servicing more expert. But when this chain of quality is unbroken, the grand payoff can be such diverting, lifelike pictures as to generate a sharp rise in blood pressure in the entire family. In fact, until the novelty wears off, which should require at least three days, there should be very little cooking done around the house, less sleeping, and no reading at all, even of books like this one, that try to add something to the enjoyment by revealing how the trick is done.

The Russian bureaucracy has promised its minions color TV by the end of 1959, at a price not much higher, if any, than black and white. Both color camera and color receiving CR tube have been "adapted" from RCA models.

25

DID RADAR WIN THE WAR?

Dᴜʀɪɴɢ the First World War, the British experimented with sea lions as submarine locators. Sea lions have very sensitive ears, and by placing food near a submarine propeller the British hoped the animals would develop the proper conditioned reflexes to swim toward an enemy sub with all the alacrity of field hands responding to the dinner bell. The navy, of course, would be there with a submarine destroyer in hot pursuit. But the animals proved too slow—about 4½ miles per hour—and too temperamental, for they were easily diverted from the hunt by sounds from other sources.

During the next world war, Britain and America used Hertzian waves to locate submarines. The waves are not only much faster than a sea lion, they are also more reliable; for their speed is always the same, close to 300,000,000 meters per second, regardless of location, temperature, altitude, humidity, or underwater noises. In fact, Einstein assures us that the speed of electromagnetic radiation, from radio waves to gamma rays, is the only completely reliable thing in our universe; it's an *absolute,* a starting point for all our figuring.*

When the waves from a radar transmitter strike a conducting surface, such as a steel ship, some of them are reflected straight back to their source, just as sound waves are returned from a canyon wall. Hertz amply demonstrated this in 1882.† If the echo is not too feeble to be picked up by the radar receiver, which is remarkably sensitive, the time required for the waves' round trip is automatically calculated by electronic circuits. This, I think, is the astounding feature of radar: that 186,282-miles-per-second waves can be so accurately *timed,* even with the aid of the electron. However, compared with the tasks this mighty particle performs for television, it's really quite simple.

Radar's basic tool is television's cathode ray tube, with its beam of electrons controlled by saw-tooth voltages. Used to show voltages, it's an *oscilloscope,* or *scope,* for short. The tip of the electron beam forms a dot of light, bottom center on the screen. The voltage from a single saw-tooth generator is connected to the vertical deflecting plates; the instant this voltage starts to rise, the radar transmitter sends out a burst of radio waves. While the waves are racing out into space— and back again if there is an echo—the saw-tooth voltage is moving the dot of light from the bottom to the top of the screen, forming a *trace,* or line of light.

The speed of the climbing dot is such that the burst of radio waves has time to go a certain distance and return before the trace reaches the top of the screen. Any echo is

---

* Energy, for example, is related to the speed of light in the formula $E = mc^2$, the m for mass and the c^2 for the speed of light in centimeters per second squared.

† His reflectors can be seen today at the Deutsches Museum, in Munich (American zone)—if a bomb guided by Hertzian waves didn't find them during the war.

amplified and fed to the tube; the echo voltage goes to plates that momentarily pull the beam out of its path, forming a V (Fig. 83A). And the time it takes the trace to rise to the V is the time it takes the radio waves to go and return. Knowing how fast the trace is rising, as well as the speed of the waves, makes it an easy matter to calculate the target's distance away. The V may be called a peak, a pip, or a blip.

A radar transmitter sends out hundreds of "bursts" of radio waves each second. Each burst is called a *pulse*. A trace is always started at the instant each pulse leaves the transmitter. The barrage of returning echoes keeps the pip hanging on the screen like a firefly.

The transmitted pulse is also allowed to put a pip on the screen as it *leaves* the radar (Fig. 83A). This is an essential check: it assures the operator that the pulse is leaving the antenna at the same instant the electron beam starts its trace on the screen.

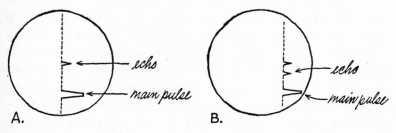

FIG. 83. Radar receiver screens. (A) Pulse and echo's blip on the time base line. (B) Time base line that moves with revolving antenna shows target at 45-degree angle from plane's heading.

In some radars a horizontal trace is used. Radar men call the trace, whether horizontal or vertical, the *time base line*.

On a five-inch-diameter screen, the pulse waves travel a distance of 5, 10, 25 miles and back, whatever is the range, while the beam tip moves only five inches. At 186,282 m.p.s. the waves travel 984 feet each *microsecond*. (When you are driving your car at 60 miles per hour, 947 microseconds pass while you are moving ahead just one inch.) Suppose a radar screen to be calibrated in microseconds; and while each pulse goes out to the target and returns, the trace moves across the screen for 54.5 microseconds. This places the target about five miles away: for 54.5 x 984 = 53,628 feet, or over ten miles out and back. Wartime radar was often accurate to within a few yards over this distance, through darkness or fog. Like the finger of fate that reaches out from your draft board, there is no dodging it.

A very early type of radar, useful on the seashore to spot enemy ships, or subs that had surfaced, had a manually operated antenna. The operator would swing it back and forth as he swept the area to seaward. When he had located a target, the distance of the pip from the screen's bottom told him its range (distance away); and whichever direction the antenna was pointing when the pip was brightest revealed its bearing. A British improvement upon this rig used two antennas, side by side, like the eyes in your head. The signal went out simultaneously from both antennas. The two echo signals from the target were mixed in the receiver in such a way that they could cancel each other out. They canceled out completely, however, only when they were of equal strength (Fig. 41). They would not be of equal strength if the antennas were turned so that either one was aimed more directly at the target than the other one. Equal strength and complete cancellation occurred only when both antennas together bore directly on the target; this is the so-called *null point,* when the pip on the screen fades out.

This general type of radar has been widely used for locating enemy aircraft from the ground. The radar is often mobile, mounted on a truck or trailer. But a search radar is better if it is automatic, and this is absolutely necessary for fighter-plane radar. A fairly early type of automatic airborne radar uses an antenna that is constantly on the move.

To determine the angle of the target to the right or left,

called the *azimuth,* the antenna turns on its vertical axis, like the earth, making one complete revolution about once each second. As it turns, a rising voltage on a pair of horizontal plates pulls the *whole vertical time base line* across the screen. Antenna bearing and time base line are synchronized. Suppose, for instance, the antenna is pointing to the right of the pilot at an angle of 45 degrees when it picks up a target; then the moving time base line will have reached the position seen in Fig. 83B, halfway between the screen's center and its right-hand edge; and the pip will, of course, appear on this line. Height of pip still indicates range. During the time the revolving antenna is facing toward the rear of the plane, the radar automatically blanks out.

Even with this improvement, the pilot would still miss any planes that were very far below or above him. To rectify this, the antenna is made to move up and down (the way you nod your head) at the same time that it continues to turn on its vertical axis. This *angle of elevation* can't be shown on the same screen with azimuth and range, and it calls for a second scope. Elevation and azimuth appear on one, range on the other. But two scopes complicate things. One airborne radar manages with a single scope for azimuth and angle of elevation, and also for range, which is revealed by the *size* of the pip: the closer the target the stronger the signals and the larger the pip. When an enemy target puts a "firefly" on the screen, the pilot maneuvers his craft until he has stopped its flight dead center on the glass. Then he knows he is flying straight toward the enemy. As he closes in, the firefly starts to grow, and when it is just wide enough to touch two vertical lines drawn on the glass (Fig. 84) the rattle of machine guns suddenly drowns out the roar of the engines. Or the guns can be fired manually.

The antenna of Fig. 85A is the half-wave dipole, used also for short wave, FM, and television. As the frequencies are high, the wave length is short, and so must be the antenna.

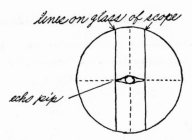

lines on glass of scope

echo pip

FIG. 84. Radar scope shows fighter plane flying directly toward target.

A frequency of 3,000 mc., for example, means a wave length of 1/10th of a meter. 300,000,000/3,000,000,000 = 1/10). Half of this is 1/20th of a meter, which is less than two inches. The Hertz *parabolic reflector* in which it rests beams the energy as a headlight reflector beams light rays (Fig. 85B). The radio astronomers now use giant versions of this wartime "flying dishpan" to tune in the stars and planets.

Another variety of radar antenna is the yagi (page 267). A third type, employing a great many dipoles arranged on a framework, is called the *bedspring antenna* (Fig. 85C). Because of the distance apart of the individual dipoles, all the waves going straight out are *in phase* and mutually aiding; the waves going out in other directions are out of phase and cancel each other. The bedspring antenna, therefore, also concentrates its energy in a narrow beam. This type of antenna is very efficient, though it is not always practicable, or even possible, for radar to use it. The many dipoles give it what is known as *high gain;* which means that for a given power input, the radiated power is many times what it would be for a single dipole. It works the same way when connected to the receiver, picking up much more voltage than a single dipole.

It has probably occurred to you that there is nothing to prevent a friendly target from forming a pip on the radar screen. The experts' answer to that was a device called IFF (Identification Friend or Foe). When a radar beam swept over one of our ships or planes equipped with IFF, the re-

ceived waves triggered a small transmitter, which sent back
a signal that showed on the scope, right next to the pip, saying in effect, *"Lay off, brother."*

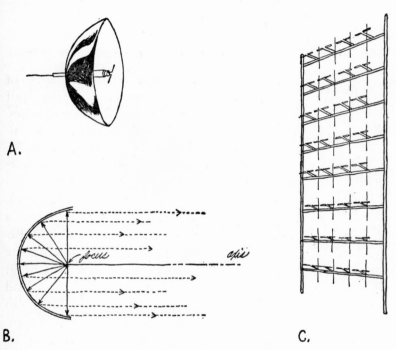

A.

B.   C.

FIG. 85. Radar antennas. (A) Tiny dipole in parabolic reflector. (B) How
the beam is focused. (C) Bedspring antenna.

2

Between pulses the radar transmitter shuts down. This enables the receiver to pick up the echoes, for no receiver could
function with a powerful transmitter operating right next to
it. It also permits the use of the same antenna with both transmitter and receiver, which is common practice. Both the
duration of each pulse and the time between pulses are important. Let me try to explain this by means of examples.

Suppose the transmitter's pulse lasts for five microseconds. During those five microseconds, the radio wave has time to go and return from a target that is almost half a mile away. (5 x 984 = 4920; 4920/2 = 2460 feet.) During this transmitting period the receiver is inoperative, waiting for the pulse to finish. So half a mile would be the minimum distance for this radar; for a closer target the pulse would have to be shorter.

Suppose the time *between* pulses is 428 microseconds. This allows each pulse time to travel out to a target 40 miles away and back again before the next pulse starts. But 40 miles is the *maximum* distance, because an echo from a target a little farther away would find the transmitter going again when it returned, blotting out the receiver; so more time between would be required to locate a more distant target. One-quarter-microsecond pulses, spaced 428 microseconds apart, will take care of what might be a complete range, from 150 feet or so to 40 miles.

The long-distance radar record is to the moon and back, hung up by United States Signal Corps engineers on February 4, 1946. Length of each pulse, 250,000 to 500,000 microseconds; interval between pulses, 2½ seconds; frequency of wave, 111.6 mc.; power, 50 kw.; antenna, bedspring. The echo's pip *proved* the moon to be 238,000 miles away, no surprise to the astronomers.

Since then the use of the moon to return the "line of sight" frequencies has become quite commonplace. In 1951, the Bureau of Standards sent a message from Cedar Rapids, Iowa, to Sterling, Virginia, via the moon, on 418 mc., using 20 kw., the same power with which Marconi spanned the Atlantic 50 years before. In 1958, Fort Huachuca, Arizona, relayed a teletype message to Encino, New Mexico, by way of the moon with only 10 kw. of power, on 810 mc. Research at the University of Michigan's Engineering Research Institute indicates the moon may soon be our most important relay station for trans-world communications. Around 800 mc. has proved the best frequency for transmission of voice.

When locating targets in the earth's atmosphere with radar, 300 miles is about the limit. On the earth's surface, with the radar set on the same level, maximum distance, as with television, is normally restricted by the earth's curvature to less than 50 miles. And even if, as Einstein tells us, the waves that shoot off into space return some day, after circumnavigating the universe, they can hardly be of any help to our generation; because the time required for their grand tour, says the professor, is 300,000,000 years.

Fig. 86 shows a block diagram of a radar set. The *keyer,* or *timer,* is the "brain" of the set: it measures out the pulses in microseconds; starts the process that triggers the power tube for each series of pulses, and starts the trace across the screen the instant the pulse leaves the antenna. The keyer uses the same kind of tubes found in radio and television

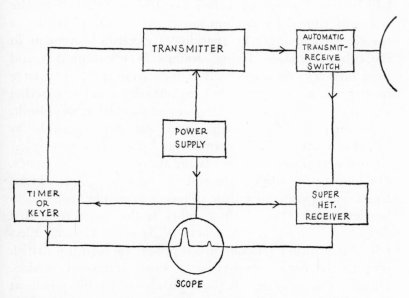

FIG. 86. Block diagram of pulse radar set. FM and Doppler radars are now coming into use.

sets, and for essentially the same purposes: amplification, clipping, oscillation, and generating little "fingers" of voltage, like television's sync pulses, for triggering tubes. Radar's single antenna makes necessary automatic electronic switches to keep the transmitter's power out of the receiver and prevent the received signal from passing into the transmitter.

The amount of energy returned by the echo is only an infinitesimal part of the energy sent out, even when the target is large and close by; and it was quite a problem to "squeeze" enough voltage out of it to get a good pip on the scope. The inventor-scientists attacked the problem in both receiver and transmitter, making the former as sensitive as possible, the latter as powerful.

Sensitivity of a receiver depends mainly upon the amount of amplification but, unfortunately, amplifying stages can't be added without limit. If the received voltage is too weak to make a fair impression on the first tube, the signal level will be too close to this tube's so-called *noise level*. (Noise is mostly caused by random movement of the electrons in the circuit and slight fluctuations of electron movement in the tube; it causes "frying" sounds in a loudspeaker and snow on a television screen. The technician speaks of a satisfactory *signal-to-noise ratio*.) Nevertheless, radar superhet receivers with ten or more stages of amplification were built.

In the transmitter, high power was made possible by utilizing what might be termed the "pile-driver principle." An ordinary triode stops oscillating above a certain frequency. For most of the ultra highs and all the super highs, special tubes that operate on a little different principle have had to be developed. One of these tubes is the *magnetron,* first described in 1921 by Dr. Albert W. Hull, of General Electric. But it didn't generate much power. In 1940 the British sent us the *cavity magnetron,* a vastly improved version. Dubbed the "maggie," it packs an almost cosmic punch at the superhigh frequencies necessary in most radars. Neither the Germans nor the Japanese succeeded in developing any comparable oscillator.

Granted that the magnetron can convert a direct current to radar pulses with a terrific wallop, where is the d.c. power to come from, for example, in a plane? Simple. Each individual pulse is short, compared with the time between pulses; so a million watts of power can be poured into each pulse, just as a pile driver's power is concentrated in each blow. No power being needed between pulses, the *average* power consumed can be relatively small, small enough to come from a few large storage batteries. Battery power accumulates in a large condenser between pulses, just as in the old spark transmitters (Fig. 42).

Perhaps we should yield some space here to a description of the method used for transmitting radar power from magnetron to antenna. The higher frequencies, especially those above 3,000 mc., are subject to a very high loss in the transmission lines shown in Fig. 76. The loss is much lower when the waves are merely *guided* to their destination by sending them through a hollow metal tube (usually copper or brass), much as sound waves travel through a speaking tube. They can also be guided by a solid dielectric cylinder, though this method is less efficient. The metal wave guide may be circular, square, or rectangular; it may be air filled, gas filled, or evacuated. Its size is determined by the size of the wave —its wave *length*; the rectangular guide is slightly more than a half wave length wide. The countervoltage induced in the metal pipe by the wave prevents its escape. Bell Labs is developing a round, flexible wave guide of thin copper wire, tightly coiled, to replace coaxial cable. It should carry tens of thousands of phone conversations with lower losses.

At the antenna, the energy spills into a parabolic reflector, which directs it to the target. When functioning as a receiver, the reflector picks up the wave and directs it to the guide. Any type of antenna will always receive best the wave that it transmits.

The usefulness of war-developed radar by no means ended with merely locating the enemy. I have told how the guns in fighter planes were automatically fired by radar. We also have a *gun-laying radar,* for use with anti-aircraft guns. Once this radar has an enemy plane caught in its beam, it continues to track the plane, pinning the echo to its scope. Of course, the gun can't aim where the radar is aiming: by the time the shell arrived the plane would be someplace else. An electromechanical *gun director* tells how far ahead to aim, once a dial is set for the plane's speed; and it also makes the necessary corrections for temperature, wind velocity, air density, etc. At first, the director's information had to be fed to the gun manually; later the whole operation was made automatic. The later, supersecret 1953 model, the 315-tube Skysweeper, detects aircraft out to 15 miles, automatically starts firing 75-mm. shells, 45 per minute, when the target comes within its four-mile range. Cost, $300,000. It was a combination of radar and gun director that aimed the guns that brought down 76 percent of the Nazi buzz bombs (V-1s) near the end of the war. All such shells are equipped with the proximity fuse.

A British idea, according to Churchill, the proximity fuse was developed in America, under the direction of Dr. Merle A. Tuve. (Tuve and Gregory Breit pioneered in radar technique in this country in connection with measuring the height and density of the ionosphere; this was in the early 1920's). No bigger than a can of tomato sauce, it rides in the nose of the anti-aircraft shell. The fuse transmits radar pulses from a miniature transmitter. The closer the shell approaches to the plane the greater the energy in the echo signal returned to the fuse. When the shell is from 10 to 70 feet from the plane, the echo's energy causes a voltage pulse to trigger a thyratron tube, just as the sync pulse is shown triggering it in Fig. 74. The sudden flow of current through the thyratron heats a length of resistance wire, igniting some explosive, which sets off a firing charge that detonates the shell. The circuit uses five miniature tubes and what is called a *printed circuit,* which substitutes silver lines drawn on plastic sheets for wires, coils, and condenser plates.

3

The *conductivity* of an object is the main factor in determining how much energy it returns to the radar receiver. A large conducting object returns a stronger echo than a small one; a battleship can be located much farther away than a sub's periscope.

The *angle* at which the radio waves meet the object is also important. Even though the sea is a good conductor, the waves from the radar all tend to scatter away from the ship. There can be a return, however, when the surface of the water is ruffled by waves, especially close to the ship.

Because of the variable amounts of energy returned, it was possible to design a type of radar that displays a "live map" of the area scanned. This is the PPI (plan position indicator) developed during World War II. Fig. 87 shows a section of New York harbor on a PPI scope. The water, returning no echoes, shows up black. Shore line, steel buildings, other ships, buoys, etc. return good energy to light the scope.

A glance at Fig. 88A reveals the difference between a ship's PPI and the other types of radar I have described. Instead of a vertical or a horizontal time base line all the way across the screen, the PPI scope uses one that starts at the screen's center and moves out to the edge, like the spokes of a wheel. A revolving antenna (Fig. 88B) is synchronized with the direction of the time base line, making it certain that the antenna is always transmitting in the direction the line is moving out from the screen's center; thus, any echo that

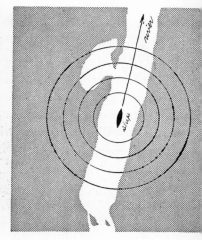

A.   B.

FIG. 87. New York harbor on plan position indicator (PPI) scope.

forms a pip is seen on the screen in its relative bearing from
the ship. So many pulses go out each second that the time
base lines are very close together, which has the effect of combining the pips so they form a map of the area covered. However, an individual object very far away must be quite large
to reveal its shape; a ship usually shows up as just a speck of
light. De Forest patented radial scanning in 1941.

The antenna makes, say, five complete revolutions per minute. You may be puzzled how a complete map is shown with
such a slowly moving antenna. The answer to this is the glass
screen's fluorescent coating: it is a type that holds the light
for one-fifth of a minute, which prevents the picture from
fading out before the time base line has returned to provide
a new one.

During the war the active warship's PPI was constantly in
use, day and night. It was called a search radar, its range the
usual 40 miles or so, which is twice as far as a battleship's
18-inchers can shoot. After locating an enemy vessel, if it is
within gun range, a second scope is switched on that covers
only a couple of thousand yards around it. "Spotlighting"

the target in this fashion makes possible a more accurate determination of range and bearing. The information is electrically fed to the computers.

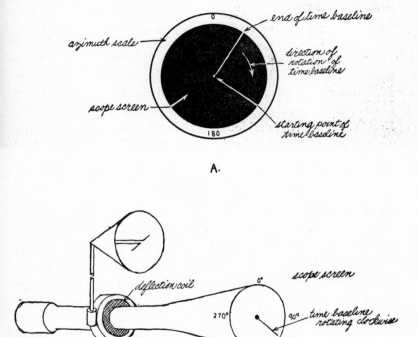

A.

B.

FIG. 88. (A) PPI scope, showing rotating time base line. (B) The revolving antenna is synchronized with the scope's rotating time base line.

This is usually a signal for the gremlins to go to work. By slipping some very slight error into the computations, they can cause the first shell to land a short distance from the target. More electrons to the rescue! The splash made by the misdirected shell appears as a blip on the scope of another radar, also trained on the target. This new information enables the necessary corrections to be made; and as salvo follows salvo, the spot of light formed by echoing waves from the enemy warship slowly dissolves, until the big guns are silent once more.

4

The United States' great wartime "hotbed" of radar research was the Radiation Laboratory, established in 1940 at the Massachusetts Institute of Technology. Here the scientists were turned loose on invention under the direction of Dr. Karl T. Compton, president of the Institute. They met the almost constant demand for different types of radar to operate under new conditions with a stream of rugged "miracle" instruments for use on land and sea and in the air. (Scientists at M.I.T. have recently designed ultrasensitive equipment, wholly new in concept, for the new Arctic radar network.)

In the same year we began to exchange technical data with Great Britain, and we learned that her researchers had independently arrived at very similar circuits and frequencies. IFF (Identification Friend or Foe) was a British development, improved by us.

British research scientists, under the direction of Robert Watson-Watt, since made Sir Robert, began investigating the possibilities of Radio Location early in 1930. By the fall of 1935, Britain had a station that could detect airplanes at 50 miles. By 1938 she had completed a chain of stations along her southeast coast, and soon after the outbreak of the war she had the rest of her coastline radar protected.

Early British radar used a frequency too low to detect low-flying aircraft (30 mc.). The higher the frequency the sharper the beam, the more energy returned to the receiver, and the brighter the pip. A second chain of stations, using a higher frequency, was established, and IFF put into operation. This was the radar curtain that met Hitler's waves of bombers in 1940, and was such a vital factor in enabling the "so few"

British fighter pilots to hand him his first defeat. If the radar report of the unidentified planes approaching Pearl Harbor on December 7, 1941, had had better luck, the war with Japan might possibly have been over before it was necessary to atomize two of her cities.

Japanese wartime radar was vastly inferior to our own. Their coast radar, for example, failed to locate objects very close to the water. Having captured some of their equipment, we knew this, and we took advantage of it. After General Doolittle's intrepid pilots lifted their bombers from the deck of the *Hornet* for their famous raid on Tokyo, they dropped down to within 50 feet of the sea and stayed there all the way to the target. Bombs were falling on Tokyo while the defending fighter pilots were still sitting at their card games.

Radar countermeasures were an important factor in the war. One of these is the business of crippling the enemy's radar by sending out powerful signals on its own frequency to *jam* his receiver. German submarines jammed our radar receivers early in the war when we were still using the lower frequencies. Later we sent special planes, called *Ferrets,* over Germany. They were equipped with both sensitive receivers and powerful transmitters. Tuning in a German radar signal enabled the operator to determine its frequency, after which his transmitter could put it out of action as neatly as flipping a turtle over on its back.

Another effective radar countermeasure, from the Radio Research Laboratory at Harvard, was known as *window*. Bundles of metal foil were dropped in the sky over the continent during a bomber mission. As the bundles came apart, the thousands of strips of foil slowly drifting toward the earth returned so many echoes to the German radar scopes they lit up like a fire in a paint factory.

26

RADAR IN PEACETIME

A<small>N</small> IMPORTANT wartime radar chore that I didn't mention in the last chapter was bringing planes safely in for blind landings, either in bad weather or at night when it wasn't safe to light up the airfield. The radar installation was on the ground. All the plane itself needed was an ordinary radio receiver so that the radar operators, watching the plane as a dot of light on their scopes, could "talk" the pilot down to the runway. This radar is called GCA (ground controlled approach).

GCA proved itself spectacularly during "Operation Vittles" to Berlin in 1948-1949. Installed at the three Berlin airports in December 1948, it doubled the tonnage flowing in daily within a very short time. On some days it brought in the big C-54s on an average of one every minute.

A surveillance radar (search scope with a 100-mile range) was used to pick up incoming planes from a considerable distance out. This radar could enlarge its pattern close in by switching to a 20-mile radius, though it was seldom used.

Each field had its own approach and landing system. After instructions from the surveillance radar operator, the pilot was contacted by an approach operator, whose precision scope, with an eight-mile range, had a line on the glass marked *direction*. He talked to the pilot somewhat like this: "Fly at two thousand feet; steer right, one zero six," and so on. When he had the plane in line with the field's glide path, the pilot heard the voice of a third operator on the landing control.

The landing control also used a precision scope. The operator might say, "You are five miles from the runway; your present heading is okay. Start losing altitude at 300 feet per minute." And so long as the little dot of light moving slowly across the radar screen stayed on the line marked (on the glass) "glide path," the plane was coming in for a safe landing, perhaps between rows of tall buildings. Meanwhile, the pilot, hanging onto every word, eyes riveted to his instruments, held his breath until he could see to set his plane down gently on the concrete strip.

The first GCA system for commercial planes was installed at the Pan-American World Airways airport at Gander, Newfoundland, in December 1946. Early in 1947, the CAA (Civil Aeronautics Administration) sanctioned its use after a period of training had elapsed. Planes were soon permitted to use it with a 300-foot ceiling and a visibility of three fourths of a mile. GCAs now show both azimuth and elevation on the same scope (Fig. 89). The idea of radar landings originated with Luis Alvarez, nuclear scientist, during World War II.

Specialized radars have been developed, such as height-finding radars, three-dimensional radars, and a high-resolution type for presenting a view of all surface traffic on the runways and taxiways of an airport. Surveillance radars now aid the control tower in tracking planes coming in for a landing as they pass over specific geographic locations or "fixes." Most of these radars are of the pulse type.

The CAA's air-modernization plan, to be carried out under the Federal Aviation Authority (FAA), calls for several

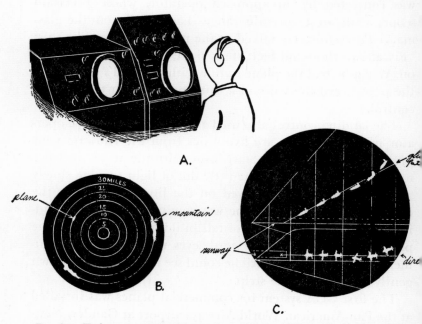

FIG. 89. Twin-scope ground control approach (GCA). (A) Single operator watches both scopes. (B) Screen of search scope. (C) Single scope showing both azimuth and elevation of plane as it approaches runway.

hundred air-route-surveillance radars between cities, 200–300 miles apart, to aid in aircraft control. The CAA hopes to have all planes that are at altitudes above 15,000 feet, throughout the entire three million square miles of the U.S., under positive control on "highways in the sky" by 1962. Whether even the 3-D radar scope will supply enough information for this task must still be determined.

Older than GCA is ILS (instrument landing system), developed by Federal Telecommunication Laboratories before the recent war. More than 100 of our commercial airports had ILS by 1950, at which time the minimum ceiling was 200 feet, visibility half a mile, at most fields.

ILS sends out four beams from a pair of mobile transmitters lined up with the runway. Two of the beams are round, two are elliptical. As Fig. 90A shows, the four beams overlap to create a pathway down their center. Having picked up the path about 15 miles out, the pilot watches two needles on a dial as he coasts in (Fig. 90B). As long as the two needles cross at right angles, there's no cause for worry; he is on the pathway; but if the horizontal needle drops below the center line (Fig. 90C), he is coming in too high; if it rises above the center line he is flying too low. Similarly, the vertical needle warns him if he is straying too far to the right or left (Fig. 90D).

The last few seconds before the touchdown is the big hurdle. The pilot who has just landed blind through a last, foggy 500 feet over the strip can sympathize with the man who stepped into an elevator shaft at the foot of some stairs: from

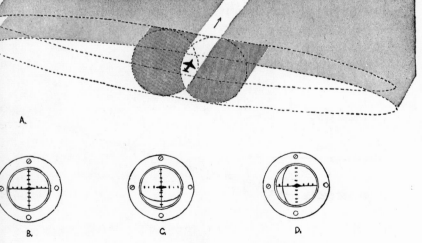

FIG. 90. Instrument landing system (ILS) for planes.

the bottom of the shaft he called back to his companion, "Look out for that last step, she's a dandy." If necessary, GCA may check an ILS landing, and some airports even add fog-piercing krypton lights. Bell Aircraft and Minneapolis-Honeywell are experimenting with automatic landing systems for setting a plane down safely and gently even on the rolling, pitching deck of a carrier.

2

The problem of all-weather landings, though perhaps the most important, isn't the only one that plagues civil aviation. All-weather navigation is another.

Since the late '20s, four-course *radio ranges* have been guiding aircraft between airports. The radio ranges were the first to use the overlapping beams later borrowed by ILS. Each pair of beams transmits complementary signals, one sending out the letter *a* (· —), the other one the letter *n* (— ·). The two signals interlace, they mesh, to produce a steady tone. But this only happens when the dot-dash and the dash-dot are of equal intensity, in which case the pilot is midway between the two beams and on course. A dot-dash means he's on *one* side of the pathway, a dash-dot on the *other*. But he

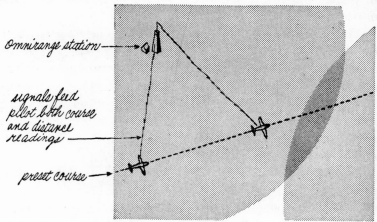

Omnirange station —

signals feed pilot both course and distance readings —

preset course —

FIG. 91. Omnirange system for positioning planes in flight.

must fly directly from field to field, and the beams don't reveal distance from destination. A newer system, VOR (very high frequency omnidirectional range), or Omnirange, remedies these defects and adds some virtues of its own (Fig. 91).

Omnirange signals go out in *all* directions from the transmitter. This enables aircraft to fly toward the airfield (or away from it) on any bearing desired. The range of VOR's very high frequencies (108 to 122 mc.) is restricted by the earth's curvature. At 500 feet, maximum range is only 30 miles, but this increases with height to 200 miles at 20,000 feet. However, most of the noisy static which can restrict the radio ranges so drastically is absent on the very highs.

VOR transmits two signals, both modulated by a 30-cycle sine-wave frequency (Fig. 41B). One, called the reference signal, goes out in all directions: the other one swings around in a circle like a revolving light. It's the difference in time between the rise and fall of the two sine waves, a phase difference in the receiver, that reveals the aircraft's bearing from the station. Suppose the revolving frequency is transmitting due north when its peak intensity synchronizes with the reference frequency's peak. Then both signals reach the receiver in phase, and the plane is some place on a line extending north from the station.

The pilot tunes in the VOR station at his destination, then twists the dial on an omni-bearing-selector, which is really a phase shifter. This brings the two signals into a phase relationship that produces zero current in a meter, and the needle is vertical. So long as the needle stays vertical, he's flying toward his VOR station; but if he wanders to either side, the phase relationship changes, current flows, and the needle moves off center. This is "flying the needle."

The plane can also carry DME (distance-measuring equipment) with its VOR. A small transmitter-receiver in the aircraft (an *interrogator*) sends out pairs of pulses which trigger a similar device at the Omnirange station (a *transponder*).

The elapsed time between departure and arrival of the pulses, traveling 984 feet per second, is translated into a current flow that operates an indicator which reads in miles. Both distance from the station and miles-per-hour speed can be shown. DME frequencies are between 960 and 1215 mc. As many as 100 aircraft can get answers from a single transponder simultaneously.

Another airborne radar device is the *absolute altimeter*. In contrast to the old barometer, which measures height above sea level, this radar measures above ground height. The most accurate type for low altitudes is an FM radar. The energy transmitted straight down toward the earth is frequency modulated—its frequency changes at a uniform rate. Consequently, the echo frequency is always different from the transmitted frequency.

Suppose the transmitted frequency to be increasing, just long enough for the maximum altitude registered, or 50,000 feet. The echo is mixed with the transmitted frequency in a receiver to obtain a difference frequency. If the plane is close to the ground, this difference frequency will be small. It will increase with the plane's height.

Converted to positive pulses, the difference frequency is used to charge a condenser, which slowly discharges through a resistor. The positive terminal of the resistor goes to the control grid of an indicator tube, which has an ammeter in its plate circuit. It's like the house that Jack built. The higher the difference frequency the more pulses per second, the greater the average charge on the condenser, the more positive the grid voltage on the tube, the more current through its plate circuit and meter, and the higher the plane. The meter is calibrated in feet.

3

Another war-born development similar to radar that also employs the Kilroy of the particles is *loran*, which stands for long-range navigation. Loran is operated in peacetime by the United States Coast Guard, as it was during the war. It gives a ship, or a plane over the ocean, its position within a radius of about 900 miles from shore. Nighttime may extend this range to 1,500 miles.

The first electronic direction finder was the radio compass, developed before 1920 to help ships find their way safely into port. The ship's radio officer asks for bearings from two or more shore stations, which they obtain from his radio signals. The navigating officer plots the bearings on a chart, the crossing lines pinpointing the ship's position. These shore-side compass stations have long been popular with everybody on the ship except the radio officer, who has too often been routed out of bed in the middle of the night to "take a bearing" to be enthusiastic about them.

Most ships now have a radio compass on board, enabling them to take their own bearings from any shore station, such as a broadcast station, that is operating. The compass can also prove extremely helpful in locating a vessel that is sending out distress calls.

Loran borrows from both radar and the radio compass. It uses radar's scope for timing pulses, and like the compass it relies upon signals sent from other stations. Its scope *times* pulses from stations on shore. But how, when there is no way of knowing when the pulses left the shore transmitters? This needs some explaining.

There must be four shore transmitters, working in pairs. Each pair comprises a master and slave station. Master and slave transmit the same kind of pulse, but the master is in control; that is, the master triggers the slave; it triggers the slave a short interval after it has sent its own signal. (A master can operate two slaves.) A loran receiver, tuned to both stations, always receives the slave's pulse later; though the interval between the two pulses will vary with the receiver's position. The loran scope measures this time difference, and

the amount of the difference places the ship or plane someplace on a line, a line with the shape of a hyperbola. The
navigator has special charts showing a hyperbola for each
time difference (Fig. 93).

This is easier to understand if we consider a simplified
version of loran (Fig. 92). These master and slave stations
transmit simultaneously. If both signals arrive at the receiver
together, the navigator's position will be *someplace* on the

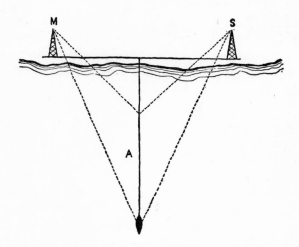

Fig. 92. Simplified version of loran. Both signals being transmitted at the
same instant, if they arrive together the navigator knows he is *someplace* on
line A, halfway between the two transmitters.

straight line marked *a,* which is equidistant from both stations. However, if the master station's signal arrives first, his
position will be on a line to the left of *a;* if the slave station's
signal is first, his position will be on a line to the right of *a.*
In practice, it is only practicable to operate the two transmitters with a time lag.

However, knowing that he's someplace on a hyperbola is
scant comfort to a navigator, so he tunes in the second master and slave. Their time difference places him on a second

hyperbola, which always crosses the first one to pinpoint his position (Fig. 93).

The average accuracy of loran positioning is within three miles, which is considered very good compared with the old method of celestial observation. Loran is not a cure-all for the problem of ocean navigation, valuable as it has prove to be.

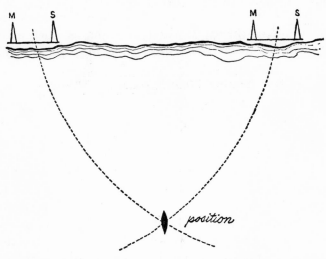

FIG. 93. Loran's master and slave transmitters place ship or plane on two hyperbolas; point where they cross reveals position.

Loran pulses are all 80 microseconds long; though the time between for each of the four stations is different, which enables the receiver to separate them. It's a matter of filtering.

To get its long daytime range, loran must use the low frequencies that have a ground wave and so hug the sea instead of bounding off into space; they're close to two mc., just above the broadcast band. The greater nighttime distances are explained by the fact that some of the energy takes the F_2 route to the ionosphere and back (Fig. 64).

The loran navigator sees two blips on the screen, separated from each other because one is a later arrival. He twists knobs attached to a time-delay circuit, until the two blips are brought together. The knobs change the numbers on a dial which refer to the lines on his charts. More recent loran models even relieve the navigator of dial twisting. They employ automatic time-delay circuits which operate on the feed-back principle.

As for the famous war-developed PPI scope, described in the previous chapter, it is ideally adaptable to peacetime use, in the air and on the sea. It will soon be just as much standard equipment on our merchant ships as the bilge pumps and the captain's copy of *Five Acres and Independence*. The Moore-McCormack Lines President, Albert V. Moore, having recently circled South America in one of his ships, had this to say: "With radar and all the other modern navigational aids, our skipper made it through the Strait of Magellan and Smyth Channel [inside passage along the Chilean coast] in 36 hours, at an average speed of 17½ knots. Why, in the old days, ships took weeks to thread through, if they got through at all."

The PPI scope is not only of great help when navigating close to shore, revealing shore line, buoys, rocks, other vessels, etc.; it is indispensable anyplace at sea in rain, mist, or fog. Even in a fog so thick one could, if there was a market for it, tamp it in barrels and stow it in the hold, the skipper can order full speed ahead, confident of his vessel's safety. As the radar antenna turns, making perhaps eight revolutions per minute, the revealing shapes of menacing objects form on the glass screen as if put there by a brush dipped in light and guided by the cunning wrist of a Fu Manchu. A congressional committee reported, following the tragedy of the *Andrea Doria* and the *Stockholm*, that the crash could have been averted if crewmen had "properly used" their radars.

One of the problems has been to build a merchant-ship radar that works close to the ship. The engineers now have them with a minimum of 50 yards or less. This short distance demands a pulse that lasts for only one-third of a microsec ond; actually the pulses are one-fourth or even one-fifth of a microsecond long. The Raytheon Company's newest radar has six different range scales, up to one, two, four, eight, twenty, and forty miles. The screen is an easy one to read; it is a 16-incher, four inches larger than most. General Electric's "Bi-Focal" radar includes an extra, safety scope, seven inches in diameter, permanently set for a two-mile range. Sperry, RCA, and Westinghouse also manufacture good, commercial, sea-going radars, differing only in details.

Merchant ships have a choice of two different radar-frequency bands: around 3,000 mc. (10 centimeters) and around 9,000 mc. (3.2 centimeters). The higher of these frequency bands can be more sharply focused, and therefore returns a better echo from a small target. This has one disadvantage: echoes are often returned from nearby waves and ripples on the water, even from rain drops. The unwanted echoes light up the screen with what is aptly called *clutter*. Reducing the amplification in the receiver (there is a switch for this) usually rubs out the clutter without disturbing evidence of vital targets, which in most cases return a much stronger echo.

One of these radars, using around 70 tubes, costs a steamship company close to $10,000, though the installation, complete with special mast, may tack another $15,000 to the bill. An ocean liner may need to save only a few days' running time in bad weather for the owners to recoup the full amount. Thanks to radar, the Matson Company now operates the luxury ship *Lurline* between Honolulu and San Francisco on a schedule so precise it is the envy of the New York Central.

During the recent war it was discovered that sometimes a blob of light on a plane's radar screen was the echo from a rainstorm; which gave radar its start as a meteorological aid, a bit more reliable than a rheumatic joint. After much re search, at least two firms, RCA and Bendix, are marketing airborne weather-radar units. Panagra was first to install the device, followed by Trans World, United, Pan American, American, National, and Continental. A rotating, dishpan antenna, 22 inches in diameter, is mounted in the nose of the plane, behind a plastic cover which is "transparent" to the radio waves. The antenna must be stabilized against roll and pitch. It can be tilted downward, when desired, at an angle of about 15 degrees, giving the pilot a "look-see" at the terrain under the nose and ahead of the plane. However, it's no help in avoiding collisions with other planes.

4

Many an American fighting man, as he gazed with admiration upon the newest-model radar, *must* have made the now traditional remark: "If you could only cook!" Radar has even learned to do just that.

General Electric's electronic oven is designed for heating precooked frozen foods in commercial eating places. The Raytheon Company sells its *Radarange* for electronic cooking. Ultrahigh-frequency (2450 mc.) energy from radar's magnetron tube is beamed at the food, and the rumpus kicked up by the waves among the molecules creates the heat. Food cooks in a matter of seconds! Frankfurters grill in from eight to ten seconds; biscuits bake in 29 seconds; and hamburgers, complete with sliced onions in a precooked roll, are ready in 35 seconds.

Otto Bismark, executive chef of the steamship *America,* of the United States Lines, has reported enthusiastically on the Raytheon Radarange. He has prepared Lobster American, two three-inch steaks, and baked potatoes, all in five minutes. A whole chicken, he says, cooks in four minutes. Not only is the Radarange fast, avers Otto, but the rapid cooking prevents loss of natural oils, juices, and flavoring, and there is no grease, smoke, odor, or heat. Missing are brown crusts on bread and crispy outsides on roasts.

Then what is the housewife waiting for? A lower price, for one thing. No price is available on the Westinghouse electronic cooking center, which includes surface units as well as an oven, but the Tappan and Hotpoint ranges, with Raytheon units, sell for around $1,400. And for that kind of money the American housewife expects a gadget that not only cooks dinner in a hurry but washes the dishes afterward, tunes in television, and opens up into a bed at night.

27

TIME-CLOCK ELECTRON

THE industrial revolution began by substituting machinery for muscle; it continues by substituting electrons for brains. It's a rare plant or factory today without some combination of electronic tubes to heat, count, compute, sort, divert, measure, control, analyze, protect, or inspect. If we ever achieve the 20-hour week, the educated electron will undoubtedly have more to do with it than the C.I.O. *Automation,* they call it. Total electronic sales in this country are now close to 10 billion yearly.

Industrial electronics has little theory that is new to us; it merely uses our four basic tubes for a different variety of tasks. These are the diode that Fleming, back in 1904, hoped would make a good wireless detector; De Forest's triode, which not only is a very sensitive detector because it also amplifies, but oscillates and modulates as well; the phototube that converts light to electricity, and the sophisticated member of the family, the cathode ray tube or oscilloscope, which converts electricity to light.

The diode can't do anything to the electrons except rectify them, which is to make them all move in the same direction. This may annoy the electrons, but it has smoothed the way for a tremendous amount of progress in industry. Both aluminum and magnesium, for example, are separated by means of an electrolytic process which entails passing large amounts of direct current through a liquid. Westinghouse developed the *ignitron* (from igniter, the device that starts it), a big steel-tank diode, for rectifying standard alternating current for this purpose (Fig. 94). A current of 50,000 amperes may be needed for each furnace, called a pot.

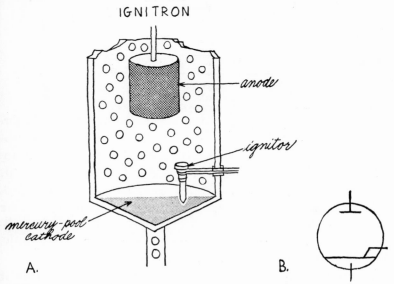

IGNITRON

anode

ignitor

mercury-pool cathode

A.

B.

Fig. 94. The heavy-duty ignitron. The pool of mercury is the cathode. Dipping into the mercury is the igniter. Its surface is rough, making poor contact with the mercury: and minute arcs or sparks appear when a positive voltage is applied, vaporizing a little of the mercury to release some electrons. On the positive half of the cycle, when the anode goes positive, it attracts these electrons, which, banging into atoms of mercury, create further ionization. The positive mercury ions, moving in the opposite direction to the electrons, strike the mercury pool cathode to create "hot spots," which release many more electrons. The tube rectifies, like any diode, by refusing to conduct on the negative half of the cycle.

A very much smaller type of ignitron is used for resistance welding. The process can be made entirely automatic by controlling the ignitron, so that it passes the proper amount of current for each weld, by means of the thyratron, a gas-filled triode. The circuit is similar to the one of Fig. 74.

Since 1922, when the X-ray machine was made powerful enough to penetrate metal, this diode has also been punching the time clock for industry. Two-million-volt machines are common, and General Electric's ten-million-volt betatron operating at the Naval Ordnance Laboratory, White Oak,

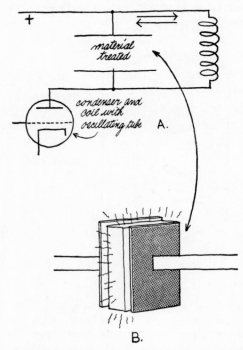

material treated

condenser and coil with oscillating tube   A.

B.

FIG. 95. Dielectric heating circuit. (B) Material treated is placed between the two plates of a condenser that is part of an oscillating circuit, as shown at A. The frequency generated may vary from one to 100 megacycles, which means that the voltages between the plates are reversed that many times each second, pulling the molecules in the material back and forth each time. The "molecular friction" creates the heat.

Maryland, will make a picture through a 10-inch wall of steel after from 30 to 60 minutes of exposure, revealing such imperfections as a crack or a blowhole.

2

If you have any furniture in your home made of plywood, and it would be strange if you haven't, you may have benefited from a branch of industrial electronics called *dielectric heating*. This type of heat is produced in an entirely different way from the heat of resistance welding; the material to be heated substitutes for the dielectric (insulation) between the two plates of a condenser. The plates are connected to a coil which takes a high-frequency current of millions of cycles per second from a triode oscillator (Fig. 95).

Dielectric heat is also used for curing and drying sponge rubber, roasting coffee, gluing wood on the job in furniture factories, and for hardening plastics.

The method has a twin sister, *induction heating*, which is used when metals are involved (Fig. 96). Here we have a

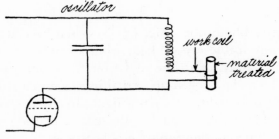

FIG. 96. Induction heating circuit.

transformer instead of a condenser. With the induction furnace, for example, the ore, alloy, or whatever requires melting is placed in a crucible that rests inside a coil of wire. The coil is merely the primary of a transformer, the crucible the secondary. Enough current is *induced* in the crucible to heat it to the required degree. Frequency is not high, perhaps around 200,000 cycles. Induction heating is also useful for annealing, brazing, and soldering.

A very good example of the superiority of induction heating over ordinary heating is in casehardening gears. The gear is placed inside the coil, which may consist of only a few turns of liquid-cooled tubing. A frequency of around half a megacycle is fed into the coil from an oscillating triode. Now, high-frequency current always flows near the *surface* of a conductor; the higher the frequency the closer it stays to the surface. So the currents (called *eddy currents*) induced in the gear do not go very deep. In a matter of seconds, the surface of the gear is red hot; and before the heat has had time to penetrate to the interior, current flow is stopped and water sprayed on the gear to cool it. Thus, only the surface of the gear, the part that gets the wear, is casehardened; the inside remains as it was, relatively tough and ductile and so less likely to break. This trick should have the old village blacksmith sitting up in his grave rubbing his smoke-reddened eyes.

3

The little phototube (Fig. 97) is so sensitive it will respond to the feeble rays of light from a candle a couple of dozen miles away, or to the rays from a distant star in the heavens. It can be hooked up so that it goes into action when it receives some light, or when a light already reaching it is removed. The latter method is illustrated in the circuit of Fig. 98, designed to shoot squirrels electronically.

As long as the light shines on the cathode of the phototube, there will be a current flow through it, the electrons going to the positive plate. This current flow must pass through the resistor, R, which is also in the grid circuit of the amplifying tube. The direction of the current flow is such that the end of the resistor connected to the grid is negative. The negative grid voltage prevents any current

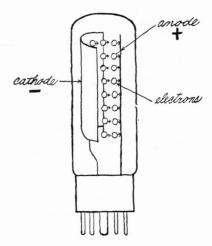

FIG. 97. The phototube.

flow through the amplifier. But let a squirrel blunder into the path of the light beam, shutting it off, and look what happens: current through the phototube stops, which removes the negative voltage from the amplifier grid, which allows current to flow through its plate circuit; the current energizes the electromagnet in the plate circuit, pulling the arm away from the tension of the steel spring; the arm is attached to the trigger of the gun, and if the gun is accurately aimed at the spot where the squirrel must be in order to shut off the light—well, there will hardly be time for any last-minute pardon from the Governor.

This device is called a relay system, more specifically a photoelectric relay system. It uses the tiny voltage from a phototube to "trigger" a flow of current, which does the work. A number of amplifiers may be added, if necessary, as in a radio receiver.

A current flow started by a phototube, controlling mechanical power through one of Joseph Henry's electromagnets, or perhaps through an electric motor, is by no means limited to opening expositions or pulling a trigger on defenseless rodents. It can, for example, operate a counter

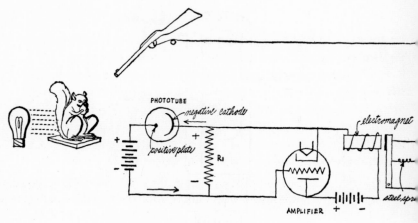

FIG. 98. A photoelectric relay system.

with the same facility as a baseball umpire and considerable less fallibility; it can turn on a fire alarm, shut down a machine, discard a bottle of pop containing foreign matter, toss out a defective vegetable, fruit, or nut, and consummate a thousand other similar tasks.

The squirrel exterminator illustrates perhaps the most common application of the phototube to industry, called the *obstruction method*. Another example is the door that opens when one walks into the light beam or drives a truck into it. Still another is the counting of moving objects on a conveyor belt; as each object momentarily obstructs the beam, current flows through a relay that operates a counter.

There is also the *intensity method* for using the phototube, illustrated by the phototube that "watches" the fire in a furnace or kiln, communicating any slight variation in light to a relay that regulates the heating current. The University of California has built a machine that sorts and sizes lemons by this method. As the fruit passes the phototube it casts a shadow; depending upon the size of the shadow the tube energizes one of five relays that opens one of five doors. The phototube also grades the lemons according to ripeness by noting the intensity of the light reflection. Handling five lemons per second, the machine replaces four women.

Finally there is the *reflection method,* and as you would suspect, it's "done with mirrors." A good example is the small mirror attached to a shaft, with a light shining on it. A phototube receives a flash of light for each complete revolution, which it communicates to a relay system whose dial registers the number of revolutions per minute.

From all this it becomes evident that the little phototube "sees" better than a Mexican eagle toting binoculars. It can also discern colors. Certain types of photoemissive coatings on its cathode make it more sensitive to certain colors than to others; potassium causes it to react more strongly to the blues and violets, caesium makes it more partial to the reds at the other end of the spectrum. The *alcometer,* a machine used by the police to test for intoxication, employs this type of phototube. The suspect breathes through a tube into a chamber containing iodine pentoxide. This chemical, when contacted by alcohol, releases iodine. The iodine is piped to a solution of starch, turning it blue. The more alcohol in the breath the bluer the starch. The bluer the starch the larger the current flow through the phototube. The current flow is registered on the dial of a simple ammeter. A challenge to the inventor is now a companion electronic device that walks the drunk around the block till he sobers up.

4

Diode, triode, phototube, and now finally the cathode ray tube or oscilloscope. The scope's usefulness is by no means confined to television receivers, radar gear, and the like; it is as standard a tool for engineers and technicians as the pipe wrench for the plumber. It is used for servicing almost every kind of electronic equipment. At its simplest it functions as an alternating-current voltmeter. Put an alternating voltage on either of its pairs of plates, and the length of the trace indicates the full (peak) voltage. But the scope can also *picture* the complete cycle of an alternating voltage, simply by connecting it to the vertical plates, if there is also a saw-tooth voltage connected to the horizontal plates.

The saw-tooth voltage, generated inside the scope, is called the *sweep voltage;* it rises at an even rate and alone causes the beam tip to trace a horizontal line on the screen.

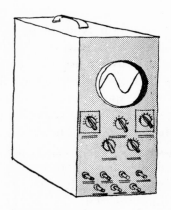

Fig. 99.   The oscilloscope used for testing.

But add a rising and falling voltage to the vertical plates and: the rising vertical voltage pulls the beam up, *at the same time* that the sweep voltage is moving it horizontally, the falling vertical voltage pulls the beam down while it is still being moved horizontally. In either case the two simultaneous movements of the beam cause its tip to trace the alternating voltage on the screen. The beam is almost like a pencil; you make the same motion with a pencil when you draw the a.c. cycle shown on the scope of Fig. 99. First you are moving the pencil up, at the same time that you are moving it horizontally across the paper; then you are pulling it down while still moving it horizontally. Try it.

28

DOCTOR ELECTRON

A MAN in pain, perhaps close to death, can ill afford the luxury of a critical frame of mind toward his doctor. Faith in the doctor's medicine is a must. There is no alternative. The medical man, rational and witch, has not always been above taking advantage of this situation; and he has, at various times, pushed almost every kind of substance on earth down the poor patient's throat. The remedies he has introduced into the sick chamber have ranged from incantations to insulin, and from bloodletting to plasma. So it would be strange indeed if magnetism and electricity had escaped his little black bag.

Magnetism was a popular remedy during the Dark Ages. Gout, headache, and the nervous breakdown were a few of the ailments people believed would yield to it, merely by their clutching a piece of lodestone in the hand. It was in fashion for centuries. Years after Columbus discovered a new world, we find the noted Swiss physician, Paracelsus, recommending powdered lodestone as a remedy for stab wounds; though our old friend Gilbert, in his book on magnetism, was contemptuous of the "lousy doctors and apothecaries" who prescribed it.

Although electricity hasn't as long a medical history as magnetism, its record is more impressive. It began in the 18th century, when the electric shock from the new friction machines was used to treat paralysis and other ailments. Next the luminous glass globe, evacuated by Von Guericke's pump and lit up by the voltage from a friction machine, was a "tranquilizer" for people with nervous disorders.

Galvani's theory of animal electricity, stemming from his twitching frog leg, inspired Yale graduate Dr. Elisha Perkins' *tractors*, patented in 1796. A pair of dissimilar metals, drawn over the skin of the patient, effected seemingly miraculous cures.

Dr. Laird C. Wilson, McGill University, has recently inserted a pair of "tractors" in a boy's leg bone that was shorter than the other. One tractor was of copper, the other of a nickel-copper alloy. The potential from this "buried battery" successfully stimulated bone growth. *Inducing* Galvani's "animal electricity" in the body (to be covered later) has been used by Professor André Djourno, of the Faculty of Medicine, Paris, to attack deafness. The tiny secondary coil of a transformer, made of fine silver wire, polyethylene insulated, and wound on an iron core, was inserted in the inner ear of a patient who had competely lost his hearing from an operation. One of the coil's terminals contacted the auditory nerve. The exterior, primary coil was attached to a microphone. What the man now hears is different from speech, but after a period of practice he has learned to understand it.

When the great cholera epidemic of 1849 struck, the telegraph wires had the Northeast pretty well laced with the feeble currents from voltaic batteries; and the newspapers started a rumor that this electricity was responsible for the epidemic. Other local philosophers developed an opposite theory: that electricity in the air would soon stop the spread of the disease. A machine was devised for indicating the presence of atmospheric electricity, and when electricity was detected, hopes for relief rose sharply. And please don't laugh. Engineers working at the Stanford University Medical School have only recently discovered a correlation between the amount of electricity in a room and human health and comfort. Tests have indicated that, for animals at least, negative ions in the air benefit the organism, positive ions being harmful. Both types of ions lose their charges to dust particles and drops of moisture, which is another argument for ridding some of our large cities of the smog that envelops them.

Medicine, ahead of everything else, was the first to benefit from electronics. Very soon after Roentgen discovered X-rays in 1895, the doctors were using them to "photograph" under the skin of both the Colonel's lady and Judy O'Grady. Roentgen himself in 1896 made a *radiograph* of a fellow professor's hand.

Cathode rays were first observed by the German, Pucker, in 1859. Hertz in 1892 made some experiments that convinced him the cathode stream could be made to pass through the glass walls of the tube. After his death, Lenard, who had been his pupil, got the electrons out of the tube through a small aluminum window; and he noted that they would fog a photographer's plate. Geissler and Hittorf made important contributions. But it remained for an obscure physics professor at the University of Wurzburg, Bavaria, Wilhelm Konrad Roentgen, to make the great discovery that the electrons, when stopped by the glass of the tube, released a much more penetrating ray. Roentgen detected the ray by means of a plate coated with the fluorescent zinc sulphide. He named it the X-ray, the X for mystery.

Because the first X-ray tubes had a cold cathode, a little gas had to be left in the tube. Small variations in gas pressure (caused by absorption of gas by the hot electrodes) made the early X-ray tube as temperamental as a helicopter in a hurricane, and twice as difficult to manage. After De Forest's audion with its heated cathode appeared, it was only natural that the X-ray tube would soon adopt it. William D. Coolidge of General Electric engineered the task. With the need for gas gone, an extremely high vacuum could be used, which in turn made possible a much higher plate voltage for giving the electrons more energy. The Coolidge X-ray tube was introduced in 1913 (Fig. 100).

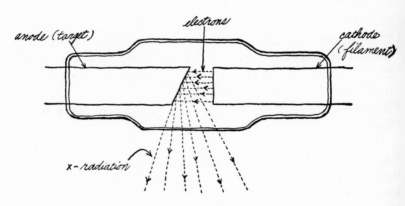

FIG. 100. An X-ray tube.

X-rays cover a *band* of frequencies, the higher the frequency the greater their energy. A higher frequency is obtained by increasing the speed of the electrons through the tube, which means higher voltages.

Roentgen had replaced the glass wall of the tube with platinum as a target for the electrons. Coolidge found that ductile tungsten is superior, and it is still used. It was Cool idge's discovery that tungsten can be made ductile.

The X-rays are universally used to diagnose tuberculosis, ulcerated teeth, and bone fractures; also silicosis, arthritis, gallstones, kidney stones, bladder stones, stomach ulcers (the patient first drinks barium sulphate) and, according to recent evidence, cancer of the breast. But the rays are by no means confined to diagnosis. Dr. Emil Grubbe, still practicing in Chicago, used them to treat a tumor in January 1896. Thirty-three years later the American College of Surgeons recognized the technique. If discovered early enough, cancer will usually yield to X-ray treatment. The rays are used against tumors, ulcers, sinus trouble, and about 80 different skin infections. They may also relieve the pain from bursitis and arthritis.

For diagnosis, and for treating skin infections, low-voltage machines of less than 100,000 volts are adequate. These machines generate rays of relatively low frequencies, called soft X-rays. But for attacking malignant growths inside the body, the more penetrating rays of higher frequency are often mandatory. These can only be had from machines in which a potential of upwards of one million volts speeds the electrons on their way to the target.

Dr. D. R. Kerst, of the University of Illinois, developed the betatron as a tool for the nuclear physicist. It uses a doughnut-shaped tube that whirls the electrons in a circle, getting them up to speeds only one millionth part less than the speed of light. Striking a suitable target, the electrons release extremely penetrating X-rays. A 22-million-volt betatron has been installed at the University's Chicago Medical Center for treatment of cancer. Dr. Kerst explains that its high-velocity X-rays have their maximum effect one and one half inches beneath the point of penetration, where X-rays of lower velocities dissipate much of their energy.

More recently, the University of California Hospital at

San Francisco has installed a half-million-dollar General Electric Synchrotron, a machine that combines some of the features of both cyclotron and betatron. It accelerates the electrons even more effectively than the latter machine; the X-rays released when the electrons strike the target have their maximum effect four inches below the surface.

There are only about a dozen one-million-volt X-ray machines in our hospitals today; most machines used for therapy are in the 250,000-volt category, and one of these costs around $18,000. However, Stanford University researchers have succeeded in building a simplified version of the linear-accelerator atom-smashing machine that produces a six-million-volt X-ray beam, and will soon sell for about the same price. Even two-million-volt X-rays are equivalent in quantity and quality to 5,000 grams of radium bromide, costing one hundred million dollars if it were available.

Since the nuclear bombs have focused world-wide attention upon the effects of radiation on the human organism, it has been found that even small amounts of X-ray radiation can harm us, at least to some extent.

2

The medicinal value of common, ordinary heat is well known to anyone who has ever applied a hot-water bottle to a rebellious midriff. Electronics provides for the sick room the same kind of heat that it does for industry: quick, concentrated, penetrating, controllable, and uniform. Even the methods for generating the heat are the same. Incidentally, the doctors were first with the idea.

When the ailing portion of the patient's anatomy replaces the plastic of industry, and becomes a dielectric between the two plates of a condenser, the process is called *diathermy*. When the heat is produced by the *electromagnetic* field, a more recent development, it is called *inductothermy*. (Both methods are popularly known as diathermy.) A high-frequency current of from 12 to 15 mc. in a coil placed near the body induces a flow of current in the blood stream; the blood stream is actually the secondary circuit, the same as the electronic crucible of industry. The heat produced is more effective than by the electrostatic-field method; and the high voltage of the latter, with its tendency to test the patient's fortitude with an occasional spark, is absent. But the newest way to generate heat for healing is to beam *radar frequency waves* at the affected area. The Mayo Foundation, which pioneered the technique over a period of years, has reported that the wave-delivered energy creates an extremely penetrating heat, and without developing high skin temperatures. After five minutes, blood flow in the arm increased eight percent; after 30 minutes the gain was 65 percent. Frequency: 2,450 megacycles. The Mayos found it very effective against arthritis and bursitis—just plain rheumatism to most of us. A radar heat treater costs about the same as a diathermy machine, around $750. The latter hasn't been replaced, by any means; for one thing, it diffuses heat over a wider area.

3

The human body is as alive with electricity as a switchboard; and though we don't generate sufficient power to plug a hearing aid into our anatomy, the voltages are high enough to interest the medical researcher. The heart, as it involuntarily contracts about 70 times per minute, generates a voltage that can be detected by connecting an electronic machine, the *electrocardiograph,* to the body's extremities. After our previous safaris through radio and television circuits, the insides of this machine needn't mystify us (Fig. 101). It is merely a detector with two stages of audio-frequency amplification—you can think of the body as the detector tube. The large resistor (10 million ohms) in series with the body passes the voltages on to the amplifier. The amplified current, instead of activating a speaker's voice coil as in a radio, moves the coil of a galvanometer in unison with the heart's voltages. A tiny mirror attached to the galvanometer coil flashes a spot of light onto a moving film, producing the kind of writing shown in Fig. 101, intelligible only to the specialist.

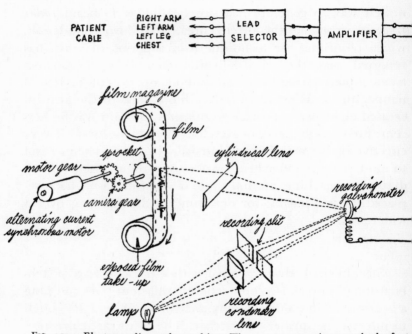

FIG. 101. Electrocardiograph machine. The more convenient method of attaching a pen to the coil, for writing on a moving paper tape, is now standard practice.

The brain is also a dynamo. With its 10 billion nerve cells, it is the "central" of the body's nervous system. When you reach the bottom of the page opposite some telephoning will be necessary before you turn it. First your eyes must phone the brain that the page is finished; your brain must then okay the turning, and here mysterious memory has its say: from the evidence it may have an alternative, such as lobbing the book into the waste basket; if not, your arm gets the go-ahead signal. Total human brain power: 20 watts.

Brain messages travel along the nerve fibers. It is an electrochemical reaction; there is both a chemical change in the nerve and a current of electricity through it. In 1929 a German neurologist named Hans Berger placed electrodes against the scalp and registered on an electronic machine the voltages of the nerve currents that start in the brain. The potentials, though only 30 *millionths* of a volt, were in wave form, proving that the brain has a beat, like the heart. Average rate was 10 beats per second. It is now known as the *alpha rhythm* and is associated with vision, its rate increasing with excitement. Later, less pronounced rhythms were discovered, the *beta, delta, kappa, theta.* Each person's peculiar combination of frequencies, or "brain wave," is as individual as handwriting. Today, as many as 8 or more graphs are taken from different areas of the head, the electrical rhythms converted to parallel wavy lines on paper tape by the *electroencephalograph,* a machine that operates basically like the one of Fig. 101.

Slow delta and theta rhythms (4 to 7 cycles), peculiar to infants and children, reappear in an adult who has acquired a childish personality. Certain types of epilepsy produce enormous slow waves, and it is often possible to pinpoint their origin in the brain. The waves may also reveal brain tumor, lesions, abscesses, mental disorders, and concussions. Some boxing commissions demand electroencephalograms of the fighters before a match.

The waves intrigue the psychologist as well as the doctor. When the image of an elephant appears on your eye's retina, the optic nerve automatically projects it onto a section of the brain cortex. That's how you *see.* But to *think* about the elephant, the image on the cortex must be transferred to billions of other brain cells. But how, since physical links between them seem highly improbable? The machine suggests it's done by *scanning*. The alpha rhythm may be the one that wipes out the cortex image, just as TV's 60-cycle frequency clears the screen for a new picture.

4

In America we make a specialty of taking a European invention and improving it out of all recognizability. A "primitive" electron microscope was assembled in 1932 by two German physicists. In 1937, at the University of Toronto, James Hillier and Albert F. Prebus produced one in which the electrons magnified an object 7,000 times. Three years later Hillier came to RCA's Zworykin at its Princeton, New Jersey, research center and with him developed the first commercial model. Today, RCA, General Electric, and Phillips market electron microscopes for around $12,000.

In Chapter 11 we discussed the Dr. Jekyll and Mr. Hyde character of light. Light both travels in wave form and consists of bursts of particles called photons. Photons aren't material particles; they are particles of pure energy, if you can imagine such a thing. They travel at a single speed, 186,282 miles per second, and if you stop them they are absorbed and disappear. Nevertheless, it could follow that if the photons have a wave form, so should any moving particle, an hypothesis that can be confirmed by experiment. A stream of electrons acts like *wave* after *wave* of electrons. Even a bullet, which is a pretty big particle, has a wave length. This doesn't jibe with common sense, but those who kneel at the shrine of common sense had best stay away from physics today. In fact, common sense has always been at war with the results, although not with the philosophy and methods, of physical science.

So we see there is logic in replacing light waves with a stream of electrons for purposes of magnification. The electron beam will magnify objects 200 times smaller than is possible with light. It can resolve objects down to about one half of a ten millionth of an inch (5×10^{-8} inches).

Focusing the electrons is done in the same way as in your television tube: magnetic fields direct the beam in such a way that the electrons come to a cross-over point at the object examined, from where they mushroom out to provide amplification. The shadow picture forms on a fluorescent screen, or a photographic plate may be used.

The machine has photographed cancer cells, the complex molecules called viruses, and bacteria in the process of decaying a tooth. Even more dramatic, perhaps, has been the photographing of those minute particles that theoretically are the unit carriers of hereditary characteristics such as red hair and blue eyes, and are called *genes*. University of Southern California scientists found them in slices of the dry salivary gland of the Drosophila fly, 1/250,000th of an inch thick. The genes are present in the nucleus of the cell. The nucleus is surrounded by the cytoplasm. As the organism grows, the genes must keep it under control. But how do the genes get their messages into the cytoplasm? Columbia University scientists may have found the answer in electron microscope pictures of slices of frog's eggs. The slices were one millionth of an inch thick; with this microscope one of the problems is to slice the specimen thin enough to prevent the electrons from literally burning it up. The pictures show rodlike fibers between nucleus and cytoplasm, indicating that some sort of material is continuous between them.

29

GRAB BAG

‎ **I** HAVE neglected a great many very important electronic devices, because they didn't fit neatly into our story as it unfolded, nor did they belong in the chapters on electronics in industry or medicine. Here are perhaps the most important of them, *lumped,* as the technician says of a coil's inductance or a condenser's capacitance, in our final chapter. Some are so common now that we tend to take them for granted, others are either still in the developmental stage or fresh from the laboratory, or both, as is the case with the little transistor. In the order of their appearance: telephoto system, fluorescent lamp, photography's strobe lamp, phonograph, lie detector, talking pictures, tape recorder, electronic calculator, transistor, and Ultrafax. I shall give each of them as much space as the limits of this book allow.

Before our Civil War, F. C. Bakewell, in London, was

drawing pictures with insulating ink on a thin copper sheet wrapped around a cylinder. A metal contact rested on the sheet as it slowly revolved and at the same time moved slowly along its axis. A battery current passed from contact to cylinder, and over wires to a similar arrangement at the receiver. The contact, moving alternately over conducting metal and insulating ink as it scanned the copper sheet, converted the smoothly flowing battery current to a fluctuating current. A chemically treated paper on the receiving cylinder was darkened in direct proportion to the amount of current passing through it. With the two cylinders synchronized, a negative of the picture appeared on the paper. Bakewell's wirephoto system failed—because the materials weren't equal to his idea. In 1873, when an Irish cable operator named May discovered that the resistance of selenium could be changed by shining a light on it—the stronger the light the less its resistance—it was thought that wirephoto was just around the corner; and in 1904, Arthur Korn used it to send a photograph from Munich to Nuremberg. But selenium proved sluggish in action, and it wasn't until the arrival of the radio tube, the phototube, and advanced methods of photography that the materials were at hand for a practical telephoto system.

RCA's first practical telephoto test was made in 1924, when pictures were sent from London to New York. Today the New York office accepts a picture (maximum size, $7\frac{1}{2}$ x 8 inches) for transmission to London, at a charge of $134. The picture is clipped to a modern version of Bakewell's rotating drum, and a beam of light focused to a point on it. As the drum revolves, the tip of the light beam moves slowly along it. The light reflected from this *scanning* beam contains all the required information about the picture in its *fluctuations:* because it rises and falls in direct proportion to the amount of light and dark in the picture at any instant. The reflected light is directed to a photocell, whose job it is to convert the light changes to a voltage, the picture frequency. After amplification, the frequency may be transmitted over wires or used to modulate a radio carrier wave in the conventional way. In the receiver, the picture frequency actuates a modulator glow lamp* which changes it back to a fluctuating light. The light is focused to a tiny dot on a film wrapped around a second drum synchronized with the first; and from positive to negative the speed of transmission is such that even the fastest carrier pigeon could never hope to compete, thus dooming another group of skilled workers to technological unemployment.

The gas-filled fluorescent lamp was introduced in 1932. Compared with the conventional lamp, it is as complicated as a slot machine, though much more generous in dividends; it returns about two and one-half times more light for the same power (wattage), because so much more of the power is converted to light, so much less to heat. Like the ignitron of industry, it contains mercury vapor, which must also be ionized. However, ionized mercury vapor produces mostly ultraviolet rays, which are just above the visible rays in the spectrum. The ultraviolet rays bombard a fluorescent coating on the glass walls to release the flood of visible light. It's the same as in a television picture tube, except that a shower of ultraviolet rays replaces the beam of electrons.

The complicated part of the fluorescent lamp is its starting mechanism, which partly explains its relatively high cost. The device comprises an automatic switch and a coil. When the lamp is turned on, current flows through the two filaments, one at each end of the tube, and through the switch.

---

* The glow lamp is a simple little diode containing a gas, usually neon or helium at low pressure. A small voltage ionizes the gas, causing the lamp to glow brightly. Brightness varies widely with small changes in the applied voltage, which makes it a good device for converting a changing voltage to a fluctuating light. The neon electric sign is really a glow lamp, as is the little night light that burns without much effect on either your sleep or the meter.

The heated filaments do two things: they release some electrons and they vaporize a drop of mercury. After a few seconds the automatic switch opens, breaking the circuit through the filaments; this leaves the lamp just a bottle of gas with a connection at each end, like the old Crookes tube (Fig. 1). The 110 volts isn't enough to ionize the mercury vapor, however, and here is where the coil goes to work; opening the switch stops the current flow, collapsing the current's magnetic field on the coil, which induces a voltage several times greater than 110 (page 99), enough to ionize the gas. The coil is more than a "self-starter"; it stays in the circuit to limit the current flow through the low-resistance lamp. In other words, it acts as a *choke coil* (page 188). The electrons and ions, dragged back and forth by the 60-cycle current, strike the filaments to keep them hot.

Another gas-filled lamp is the *strobotron,* now widely used by the photographer. The lamp gives him so *much* light that he needs it for a very short period: for such a short period, in fact, that he can photograph a hummingbird in flight, wings flapping 500 times per second, or a bullet emerging from the barrel of a gun. The image recorded in a matter of microseconds, the wings and bullet appear motionless. The electronic flash lamp's basic circuit is shown in Fig. 102.

The market for pictures of hummingbirds and bullets in flight being far from brisk these days, commercial (and also amateur) photogs prefer a longer flash. The many different *speedlights* on the market today range in flash duration from 1/200th to 1/10,000th of a second. Length of flash determines exposure time, even when the flash is synchronized with the shutter. Although the first units were designed for the 110-volt a.c. house circuit, there are now dozens of portables on the market which operate on either dry cells or a small storage battery (some can also be plugged in to 110 volts a.c.) and cost anywhere from $30 to $370. One of the a.c. units sells for $600.

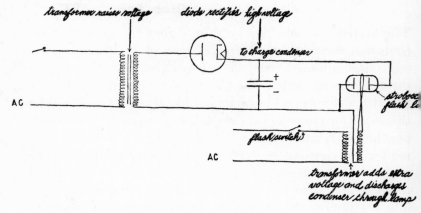

FIG. 102. Basic electronic flash circuit for photographers. A certain minimum voltage is necessary to fire the lamp by ionizing its argon gas, causing the flash. The transformer raises the 110-volt a.c. input, charging the big condenser to *almost* the required voltage. When the switch is closed, the secondary of the small, auxiliary transformer provides enough extra voltage, through the single turn around the lamp, to fire it.

Let's leave gas-filled lamps for a moment to consider the most ubiquitous electronic device, next to the radio—the phonograph. The phonograph is often combined with the radio, using the latter's audio amplifier and speaker. Electronically speaking, only the *pickup* need be added.

The pickup converts mechanical energy (from the needle's movement) to electrical energy. The oldest type is electromagnetic. The needle is attached to a small coil, either directly or by a lever arrangement. The coil "floats" in the magnetic field of a permanent magnet; its back-and-forth movements across the field's lines of force generate voltages in it that mirror the needle's vibrations. This is the *magnetic* or *dynamic* pickup.

There is just one other commonly used type of phonograph pickup, the *crystal*. Though its fidelity is inferior to the magnetic's, it is more widely used because of its relative cheapness; it generates enough voltage to use with a single amplifier tube.

The subject of crystals and electricity is a large one. It had its beginning in Paris back in 1880, when the Curie brothers, Jacques and Pierre, carried out a series of experiments that must have looked pretty silly at the time. They piled weights on top of pieces of white quartz connected to a meter; and strangely enough the meter would often register a small flow of current. They called this current piezo (pie-EE-zoe) electricity (*piezein* in Greek means to press).

The best crystals for generating electricity are a beautiful, white, translucent quartz, obtainable in quantity only from crude pit mines in Brazil. (Arkansas and California produce some.) Thin wafers cut from this quartz are used throughout the electronics industry. The wafer generates a voltage when it is forced to vibrate, which has the effect of squeezing or pressing. The wafer will vibrate only at its natural frequency, however, which is determined by the way it is cut and by its dimensions. For each type of cut, the natural frequency is mainly determined by thickness; the thinner the crystal the higher the frequency. A one-megacycle crystal has about the thickness of a silver half dollar.

The crystal wafer can be set in vibration by mechanical force or by applying an oscillating potential to it. In either case, the applied *frequency* must be the same as the crystal's. For this reason, the crystals are valuable for filtering out unwanted frequencies in a receiver, or for controlling the initial oscillator of a radio or television transmitter (Fig. 103). The crystal is said to prevent the transmitter's signal from *drifting*. Our government's standard clocks are crystal controlled.

Crystal phonograph pickups are synthetic, being crystallized out of a supersaturated solution of Rochelle salt, which is also found in baking powder and Seidlitz powders. These crystals generate a *band* of frequencies. Two of them, made into a kind of double-decker sandwich, are called a *cell,* and if you deform this cell by applying stress, it will generate a voltage. Fig. 104 indicates how this is done by bending, as

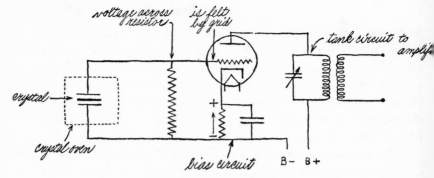

voltage across resistor

is felt by grid

tank circuit to amplif

crystal

crystal oven

bias circuit

B-   B+

FIG. 103.   Crystal-controlled oscillator.

in a microphone (A), and by twisting, as in a phonograph pickup (B). Conversely, applying a signal voltage to this type of cell will cause physical distortion at the same frequency; in a crystal loudspeaker the twisting crystal is connected by a driving lever to the diaphragm, which produces the sound waves. Crystal microphones and speakers are widely used in hearing aids.

A more recent type of piezoelectric pickup, made of the ceramic material barium titanate, has fast been growing in popularity. Over half of the 50 or more models of commercial phonographs, put out by about 20 manufacturers and selling all the way from $100 to $1,600, use this *ceramic* cartridge. It generates a good voltage, between .5 and 4 volts,

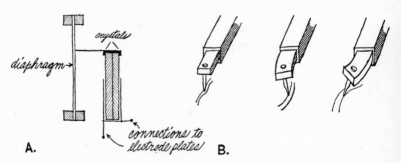

diaphragm

crystals

connections to electrode plates

A.

B.

FIG. 104.   Rochelle-salt crystal generates voltages in (A) crystal microphone pickup. (B) crystal phonograph.

only slightly less than the crystal. Unlike the latter, it isn't subject to temperature and humidity deterioration. A satisfactorily flat frequency curve from 30 to 10,000 cycles is claimed for the top-quality makes of both types. One of the best ceramics is the Electro-Voice Ultra-Linear, which costs more than most magnetics. Others are the Shure, Webster, American, and Astatic.

The magnetics are of two types. The dynamic, in which the voltage is generated in a coil moved by the stylus, as explained above. The Fairchild, Recoton, and Electro-Sonic (ELS) are examples. The other magnetic has one or more stationary coils. Voltage is generated in the coils by moving iron attached to the stylus. The moving iron of GE's very popular variable-reluctance cartridge is a cantilever, pivoted in the center. The cantilever is magnetized by a small permanent magnet (alnico V) over which it moves. One end holds the stylus, the other end vibrates between the iron cores of a pair of coils. The vibration generates the required voltage in the coils. The relationship between mechanical movement of the stylus and the voltage is practically linear, provided the cantilever doesn't move very far, which isn't necessary. Frequency response is almost flat from 30 to 15,000 cycles. Output is around 10 millivolts.

A more expensive variable-reluctance pickup, the Pickering, generates around 50 millivolts. Its stylus is attached to the steel core of a tiny coil. As the magnetized steel moves from side to side, it generates a voltage in the coil.

A third pickup of this type is the Audak, whose construction is similar to GE's. It has a high output and is relatively heavy, requiring an Audak arm to balance it.

Because the two coils of GE's cartridge are wound in opposite directions, any voltages *induced* in them, in contrast to the voltages *generated* by the movement of the cantilever, are opposed and so tend to cancel. This discourages 60-cycle power-supply hum. Irregularities on the bottom of the record grooves cause needle scratch. But as the up-and-down movement of the stylus doesn't generate a voltage (only the side-to-side movement), the cartridge rejects this noise. All magnetics now operate without this vertical response.

In cutting a record, the bass notes (under 1,000 cycles) would move the stylus too far from side to side, wasting space, if they weren't *attenuated*. The treble notes (above 1,000 cycles) would move the stylus too short a distance, leaving the music close to the noise level, if they weren't *boosted*. All magnetic pickups require an *equalizing network* to compensate for this "distortion." The network reduces the already low voltage they generate, which makes necessary a *preamplifier* ahead of the main amplifier.

The hi-fi phonograph cartridge had reached near perfection when, at the 1957 convention of the Audio Engineering Society, the Westrex demonstration of its 45/45 *stereophonic* record sent the engineers back to their drafting boards. Soon stereo cartridges were ready for testing, and by mid-1958 both discs and cartridges were on the market.

Stereo adds a new dimension to recorded sound. In the concert hall, your *two* ears enable you to separate the orchestra music through the difference in arrival times. Close your eyes and you still hear the strings from one direction, the bass from another. Old-style recorded music eliminates this sense of space because the entire orchestra is funneled through a *single* "ear," the microphone. As a result, the reproduction sounds as if it were coming out of a hole.

Stereo uses two mikes for two sound channels, one mike on each side of the orchestra. Much of the sound is picked up by both mikes equally, but each mike *favors* the sound from its own side of the orchestra. And when the two recordings are reproduced through separate amplifiers and speakers, with the two speakers suitably positioned, the listener has the illusion of sitting in the concert hall.

The original method for recording sound on disc had the

cutting stylus moving up and down, cutting a *vertical* (hill and dale) modulation in the groove. The later, improved, method uses a lateral (side to side) cut. Several systems have been devised for *combining* both the vertical and the lateral cuts in the same groove for stereo. The Westrex system uses both movements together by cutting one channel in each wall of a V-shaped groove, 45 degrees from the vertical. But how can a single stylus follow both modulations? The modulations are so *mixed* that the stylus tip has only a single path to follow. However, the stylus is connected to *two* pickup units, electromagnetic or crystal, each with its separate amplifier and speaker. A stylus movement perpendicular to one wall of the groove energizes one pickup, the same opposite movement energizes the other one. In-between motion energizes both in varying degree.

Now we come to electronics' gift to the blindfolded lady with the scales: the lie detector.

Severe emotional strain can cause blood pressure to rise, heart beat and respiration to increase, perspiration to collect in the palms of the hands, etc. The lie detector is merely a machine that measures this kind of physical reaction. One type operates on the theory that our emotions change the resistance of the skin. Electrodes are attached to the wrists, and variations in current flow marked on a moving paper tape as the suspect is questioned. The questions build slowly to a climax, for it is not considered good practice to *start out* with "Where did you hide the gun?" Operator skill may mean the difference between success and failure of the test. The fear that accompanies a feeling of guilt decreases the dermal resistance, causing a rise in current flow. Blood pressure and heart beat are recorded simultaneously.

Though courts of law seldom admit the evidence of the lie detector as conclusive, the police prefer it to the rubber hose —at least they should—and department stores, banks, insurance companies, and other business firms have found it useful in solving mysteries that feature the disappearance of such items as jewelry, fur coats, and old bank notes. Certain government agencies also employ the device. The Oak Ridge plant, unique among atomic-energy establishments, has used it consistently for testing employees in critical positions related to security. Perhaps it is significant that none of the atomic-bomb cases involving disloyalty have originated there.

Soon after broadcasting came in, the electron caused a second mild cataclysm in our lives when it put words into the mouths of moviedom's shadows. Edison's first "talkies" used phonograph records, followed by De Forest's steel tape, but ideal results were not obtained until the sound was photographed and placed right on the film next to the pictures.

Photographing sound would present quite a problem if we tried to do it direct; but all we want is the sound *frequencies*, and it's a simple matter if we first convert them to *electrical* frequencies by means of a microphone, and then send them to a glow lamp; for the glow lamp's fluctuating light can be focused on a moving film—where the sound frequencies end up as a strip of variations in light and dark. The closer together the variations the higher the frequency. The strip is called the *sound track.*

As the film unwinds in the theater projection booth, the sound track passes in front of a light that shines through it onto a phototube. The phototube reconverts the light fluctuations to current variations, a copy of the same variations generated on the movie lot by the microphone, days or years before. After amplification, this audio frequency current goes to a big loudspeaker system back of the screen; and if it's Brigitte Bardot you're watching, her *spoken* lines also fill the theater to overflowing.

The glow lamp is a little too simple for best results.

Movietone's system sends the mike current to a light valve placed between a steady light and the moving film; the varying current opens and closes the valve, exposing the film to a continuous series of parallel lines. Photophone also uses a steady light, which is reflected to the moving film by a small mirror controlled electromagnetically. Fig. 101 illustrates the basic idea.

Sound waves can also be "frozen" for future reproduction on an iron wire. Valdemar Poulsen of Denmark, inventor of the wireless arc, did it first in 1898. But, as in so many other electrical devices, quality had to wait upon the refinement possible with electronic tubes. The diagram of Fig. 105 explains how the modern tape recorder works. For a plastic *tape,* dusted with particles of iron oxide for magnetization, has long since replaced the iron wire. Tape is more easily spliced for editing. And tape quality has steadily improved since the first *Magnetophon* tape machine was brought home from Germany following World War II.

A magnetic material is not as quickly yielding to the rising and falling magnetizing force as, for example, a stream of electrons to a varying grid voltage; there is some lag, called *hysteresis.* Though tape always worked well enough with the audio frequencies, the magnetization didn't respond nearly fast enough for the much higher frequencies of television which, when a picture with much detail is televised, may be as high as 4 mc. The TV programs had to be recorded on film, an expensive and not very satisfactory process. Quality difference between a live show and one filmed from the screen of a kinescope is obvious.

Both the Bing Crosby Enterprises Laboratory in Hollywood and the David Sarnoff Research Center at Princeton, N.J. (RCA), wrestled with the problem of video tape for almost a decade. Both staged periodic demonstrations for the press, RCA radiating the most optimism. In December 1953, at a

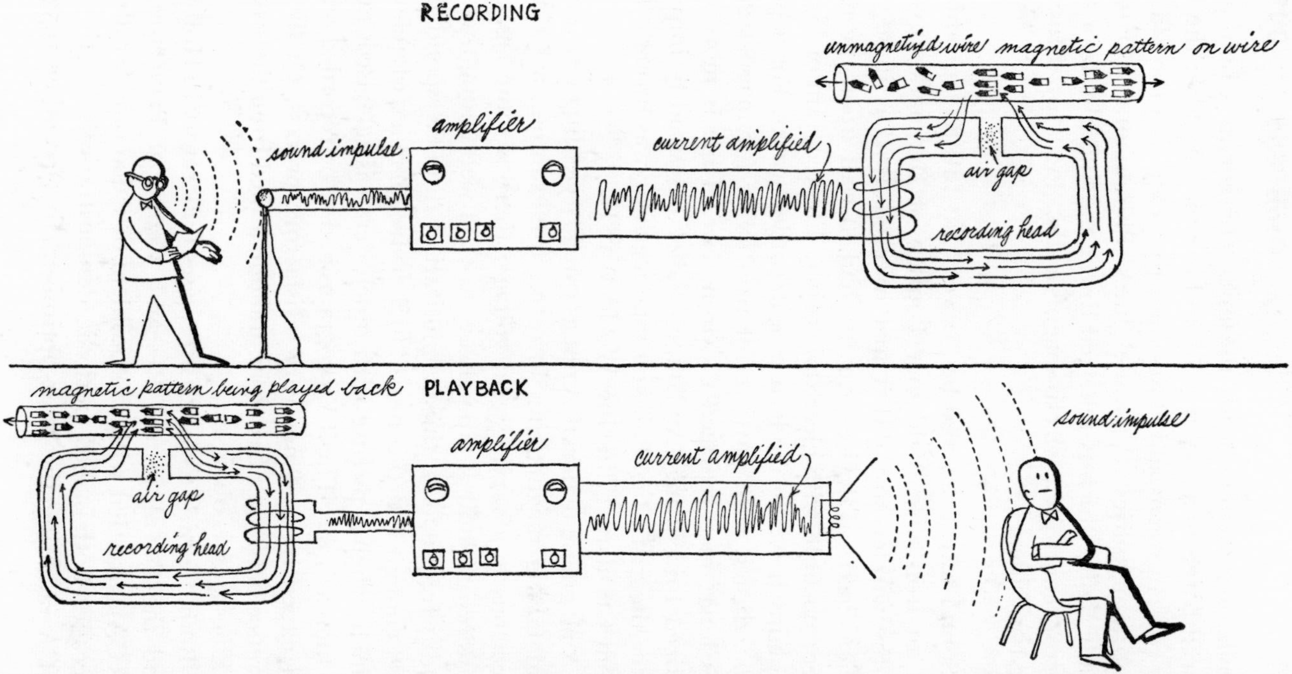

RECORDING

unmagnetised magnetic pattern on wire

air gap

recording head

current amplified

amplifier

sound impulse

PLAYBACK

magnetic pattern being played back

air gap

recording head

amplifier

current amplified

sound impulse

Fig. 105. How the wire or tape recorder works.

demonstration of both color and black-and-white video tape, General Sarnoff called it the first major step into an era of "electronic photography." Advantages over film, he said, include better quality, greater economy, and the fact that it can be played back immediately. The sum of these advantages should create a revolution in TV production. Programs can be taped at a time convenient for the staff, as far ahead of show time as desired. Fewer studios will be required under this system. Programs can be released to the network at times most advantageous for the various time zones across the country. The concluding part of a sports event need not be interrupted for another event; the latter can be taped and released a few minutes later.

One way to combat hysteresis—the lag of magnetization behind the magnetizing current changes—at the high video frequencies is to run the tape fast. The RCA machine used up a 17-inch-diameter reel for just 4 minutes of program. But the big prize went to Crosby. In mid-1956 the three TV networks announced the purchase of magnetic video tape recorders from the Ampex Corporation of Redwood City, California. Ampex is Crosby's manufacturing branch. Early in 1957 the machines were in extensive use for delayed broadcasts by all the networks.

The Ampex machine provides a full hour of television programs on a 14-inch reel of 2-inch tape. The principle is the same as in the audio recorder of Fig. 105, except that there are four recording heads instead of one. The four heads are built into a drum which rotates at right angles to the tape. The instant one head leaves the tape, another one makes contact. Thus, one head is always recording. The relative movements of head and tape cause the magnetic pattern to be recorded transversely on the tape. If you should take these transverse lines and place them end to end, they would reach much farther than the tape itself. In other words, if they were recorded as in Fig. 105, with a single head, tape speed would have to be much too fast, even for the best tape.

Ampex is coming out with a color video tape machine for playback on another machine.

Magnetic tape is used to feed problems into the big electronic calculating machines, popularly known as electronic "brains." Actually, what they really do is count. They can not only add, but they can also multiply, subtract, and divide. (Multiplication is repeated addition, subtraction is addition in reverse, and division is the reverse of multiplication.) The machine uses built-in tables, automatically controls its order of operation, and stores intermediate results on tape or drum (electromagnetically), or on the screen of a CR tube (electrostatically). The storage property, called "memory," has had much to do with the popular idea that the machine can think. However, it took man to build it, and until the day when it locks the scientist in the laboratory and runs off with his wife, I think we can safely call it the inferior partner.

The most complex mathematical problems confronting the scientist and engineer boil down to simple addition. The *digital* computer, described above, can handle thousands of additions per second. It can do work in a matter of minutes that would require years of labor with paper and pencil.

How do vacuum tubes count? They do it by starting and stopping. They use binary numbers, consisting of 1's and zeros. Any number can be represented by a sequence of 1's and zeros. For example, 00001 can represent 1; 00010, 2; 00011, 3; 00101, 5; etc. For the zero, the tubes don't conduct, for the digit they do. In this way they can add just as readily as a man with an abacus, though immeasurably faster.

Another type, the *analogue* computer, operates a little differently. As its name implies, it produces analogies—between numbers and some kind of a quantity. The slide rule operates on this principle. It multiplies two numbers by placing two lengths, two distances, end to end. For quantities, the analogue computer can use resistances, currents, or voltages. The basic principle is illustrated by the FM altimeter's counter described in Chapter 26. Here we have the distance between the plane and ground analogous to the size of a current flow. The current passes through a meter in a tube's plate circuit. The amount of current is proportional to the voltage on the tube's grid, which comes from a resistor connected across a condenser. The resistor's voltage is determined by the number of pulses per second charging the condenser. The number of these pulses per second is governed by the height of the plane. (Called *integration,* because the voltage across the condenser at any instant is an *integral* of the charging rate.) Resistor and condenser are connected opposite to those shown ahead of tubes 4 and 5, Fig. 55A.

The International Business Machines Corporation, which built the first big calculator (at Harvard), makes a half-million-dollar machine for rental to business and industry. The rate: around $18,000 per month. The company also makes smaller machines, down to a calculating card puncher which rents for around $500 per month, though to date it has resisted the temptation to turn out a handy little portable job for replacing the horse player's pencil.

Vacuum tubes get hot, need lots of power for filaments (which burn out), and thousands of them make a heavy, bulky machine. Perhaps the first "miniaturized" version was the Bell Labs' TRADIC, for Transistor-Digital-Computer. Today, transistorized computers are a must for both military planes and missiles. They are used mainly with navigation systems. What is this tiny transistor, not much bigger than a ninety-dollar diamond, that's been impudently pushing aside the mighty vacuum tube lately?

When De Forest's audion, back in 1906, not only proved a better detector than a chunk of galena or carborundum, but could amplify and oscillate also, it killed the crystal detector deader than the hairy elephant. Or so we thought at the time. But it seems the burial was a little hasty, for the crystal has lately been resurrected and now threatens to turn the tables on the tube and relegate *it* to the limbo that shelters such items as the Leyden jar condenser, the spark transmitter, and the Newcomen engine. Less than five years ago, a group at the Bell laboratories, under William Shockley, while engaged in pure research, stumbled onto a *germanium* crystal that not only is a better detector than galena or silicon, but can be made to amplify and oscillate like a tube.

The Bell group was soon experimenting with what it christened the *transistor* (because it transfers a voltage across a resistor): a pinhead of germanium soldered to a metal plate and tickled with two hair-thin wires, or cat's whiskers, about two-thousandths of an inch apart—all housed in a metal cylinder only five-eighths of an inch long and three-sixteenths of an inch in diameter (Fig. 106).

Germanium, whose atomic number is 32, looks like tin or lead, and costs almost as much as gold. Germanium dioxide is extracted from the dust in the stacks of zinc smelters and from the ashes and soot of large coal consumers. Germanium is also mined. In common with silicon, germanium in its impure state is a semiconductor, which means that it is both a poor insulator and a bad conductor. But it is also something infinitely more valuable than either one.

The germanium dioxide is first reduced and purified, and selected impurities are added while it is in the molten state. The impurities, in very small quantities, have opposite effects. Arsenic or antimony produces what is called *n*-type germanium, the *n* for negative. This type has a small surplus of electrons with freedom of movement. Indium, boron, aluminum, and gallium produce the *p*-type germanium, the *p* for positive. In this type, the impurities remove electrons from the germanium atoms, leaving *holes*, which are positive charges, or act like positive charges. We shall discuss these holes later. Both *n*- and *p*-type germanium will conduct electricity, to a limited extent. But the important fact is that the free electrons, and the holes, can be *controlled* in a manner similar to the way in which the electrons from the hot cathode in a tube are controlled.

A tiny rod of germanium, half *n* type and half *p* type, is called an *n-p junction*. Electrons will flow from the *n* type into the *p* type quite readily, but there is considerable resistance to an electron flow in the opposite direction, from *p* type to *n* type. This makes the *n-p* junction a rectifier. Both germanium and silicon *n-p* junction diodes are valuable devices in many branches of electronics.

The original "cat's whisker," or point-contact transistor, shown in Fig. 106, was *formed* by passing heavy reverse currents into the crystal. The currents converted the crystal near each point contact into a *p*-type germanium. The rest of the crystal, between the two points, remained *n* type. The result was two *p-n* junctions joined together. A *p-n-p* chain proved to be more than a rectifier, just as the Fleming valve did when De Forest added the grid.

One of the point contacts is called the *emitter,* the other one the *collector* (Fig. 106). If the positive collector is given

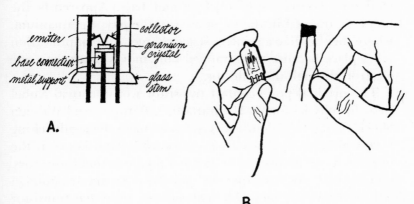

A.

B.

FIG. 106. (A) Point-Contact transistor. (B) Size compared with miniature tube.

a negative voltage, with respect to the *base* of the crystal, only a very small current will flow between it and the base. However, the situation changes if the positive emitter is biased positively with respect to the base. This connection, positive on *p* type, negative on *n* type, is the correct one for current flow through a rectifier. Now the emitter current *governs* the collector current; any change in the emitter current increases the minute current flow between collector and base. Furthermore, the collector-power change is much larger than the emitter-power change. *Amplification!*

How does the voltage between emitter and base exert its "leverage" on the collector current? The picture the scientists give us is not one you'd care to hang on the living-room wall. They speak of moving electrons, which is fair enough, but they also give us "flowing holes." Let's look into them.

The positive potential on the *p*-type emitter draws electrons from the *n*-type base, leaving holes. The positive holes migrate toward the negative potential on the collector. (How does one move a hole? One doesn't. One digs a new one. The positive emitter voltage *must* "dig" the holes by removing electrons.) The holes in the *p*-type collector step up the electron flow between the collector and base. Apparently the holes are trapped in the impurities in the *p*-type germanium, where they act like a positive space charge. And amplification takes place because each trapped hole moves more than one electron through the collector.

The original point-contact transistor won the 1956 Nobel Prize for physics for W. H. Brattain, J. Bardeen, and William Shockley at Bell. Transistors are now made by sandwiching a very thin section of either *n* type or *p* type between the opposite type, to form *p-n-p* or *n-p-n* type *junction transistors*. The former operates like the point-contact model, though with greater efficiency. The collector of the *n-p-n* transistor is biased positively with respect to the base. Small currents both of electrons and "holes" pass between the collector and the base. However, in this case the emitter emits electrons instead of holes, which are moved through the p-type base into the positively biased n-type collector. The "holes" move in the opposite direction. The n-p-n transistor can be aptly compared with the triode. The base, in controlling electron movement, is like the tube's grid; and the collector, with its amplified current flow, is analogous to the plate or anode.

Like the audion, the first transistor suffered from severe limitations. It could amplify, but with very low voltage gain; it could oscillate, but only at very low frequencies; it was noisy; it produced very little power; and it stopped operating if the weather turned hot. But at the same time it possessed two virtues denied the tube: pygmy proportions and minute power requirements. Some of the latest junction transistors, enclosed in plastic, are only 3/16ths of an inch in diameter. The transistor has no power-consuming cathode to heat. These two virtues promised an enormous advantage over the tube, in such applications as hearing aids, computers, portable radio, and TV apparatus, all airborne electronic gear, and the telemetering devices in man-made satellites. In addition, the transistor was free from microphonics (noise or howling caused by the mechanical movement of a tube's elements), had good mechanical strength, and promised lower unit cost.

Since its introduction in 1948, the transistor has fast been overcoming its initial handicaps, until today it finds hundreds of useful applications. Manufacturers now make all-transistor hearing aids which, together with batteries, weigh no more than an ounce. Some are worn inside the ear.

Amplification factor and power output have been increased to the point where a power transistor with high gain is now available for the power tube in auto and home radios. The noise factor has been reduced to the point where transistors now perform even better than tubes in the preamplifier of hi-fi installations. Some now retail for as little as $1.50, against

$8 wholesale for some of the first ones. However, cost is still a factor in restricting their use.

Power has been increased by using gallium mixed with indium in the p-type emitter. Oscillating and amplifying frequencies have been raised by reducing the thickness of the base. The new, diffused-base transistor has attained frequencies as high as 500 mc. (This is the alpha cut-off frequency, when current amplification falls to .7 of its low frequency value.) These p-n-p transistors can be used as amplifiers in v.h.f. TV receivers.

Forward scattering, the new method of very high frequency communication via the ionosphere, not only holds promise for a global TV network, but also for moving mail and printed matter across the oceans. The material must first be photographed on movie film. The film provides a video frequency—using the flying-spot method of scanning. The video frequency modulates the higher, carrier frequency. In the receiver, another flying-spot scanner restores the material to film again. Called *Ultrafax,* it's telephoto in fast motion. The complete text of *Gone with the Wind* has been transmitted from film to film in two minutes and 21 seconds by this method. I don't think that Marconi, who waited patiently for days with his little headphone, coherer and kite antenna for the feeble three-dot signal from the other side of the Atlantic, would be astonished by all this if he were still around. Marconi was not only among the first to have faith in the practical usefulness of the waves of Faraday, Maxwell, and Hertz, but he lived long enough to meet the electron. He also had some success in transmitting the very highs for distances well beyond the line of sight.

While the engineer-inventor has been employing present knowledge of the electron to create all sorts of revolutions in our lives, the scientist has been whittling away at it with his mathematical theory until it has lost its standing as a *ma-terial* particle, a standing based upon the fact that its mass and charge have both been measured; *now* he tells us that the electron acts too strangely in its journey around the nucleus to be mentioned in the same breath with the planet's journey around the sun; for it is impossible to determine both the electron's velocity and its position at the same time. This makes it impossible to predict its future. The scientist would rather we looked at the electron in quantities only, as we do the molecules of a gas.

Electrons, in their controlled use in man-made machines, and in their function in the living organism, seem to be energy itself. And what if energy is only the physicist's synonym for man's *élan vital,* his very life force? In any case, we should be prepared if, at some future date, the scientist should present us with an electronic machine for tuning in thought waves, enabling us to listen to each other's brains. Already Dr. W. Ross Ashby, a British scientist now at Princeton, has announced a design for an *intelligence amplifier.* If radio waves can be amplified, he says, why shouldn't it be possible to amplify intellectual power? And because matter-energy is never destroyed, the next logical step should be one that broaches the veil separating us from the past: a receiver that tunes in the thoughts of those long since dead. Thales and Aristotle, for example; Democritus, Peregrinus, Ohm, Volta, Ampère, Shakespeare, Paul Revere's horse. Would we gain anything from such post-mortem eavesdropping? I wonder. Would it be of any use, for example, to learn just what was passing through Sir Walter Raleigh's head the instant before he lost it to the executioner's blade? Probably nothing nearly so good as the thought he left us in writing.*

As the lady was just saying, "What *will* they think of *next!*"

---

* Cowards (may) fear to die; but courage stout
Rather than live in snuff, will be put out.

—On the snuff of a candle
one night before he died.

30

SATELLITE AND MISSILE ELECTRONICS

FIRST to fire a rocket in anger were the Chinese, seven centuries ago. Old hands with fire-crackers, they had recently discovered the secret of adding saltpeter (potassium nitrate) to the sulphur and charcoal. The discovery came just in time for them to devise an incendiary missile for use against the invading Mongols, who were besieging the Chinese city of Kai-Fung-Fu. The saltpeter provided the oxygen for fast burning of the sulphur and charcoal.

The Arabs introduced the "Chinese arrow" to the Western World, where it also became a weapon of war. In the sixteenth century the Westerners adapted the quick-burning powder to a more effective weapon, the matchlock musket, thereby creating a revolution in warfare. Now the wheel of history has come full turn. Modern chemistry, metallurgy, and electronics, together with the discovery of fission and fusion, have made the rocket or ballistic missile into the most devastating weapon in all history, capable even of wiping out the better part of our civilization. On the more pleasant side, the developers of this ultimate weapon are confident their new technology will soon enable them to build ships for cruising among the planets. Just as a start, the first project calls for sending adventurers off to the moon. And if we can only find passengers who are convinced the moon is okay to live, but they wouldn't want to visit there, it won't be long now, for the big problem is how to honor a return-trip ticket.

Last to fire a rocket in anger were also the Chinese. Recently the Nationalists successfully launched air-to-air Sidewinder missiles against the Russian fighter planes of their Communist brethren, who were bombarding the Nationalist-held offshore islands of Matsu and Quemoy.

Our best-known World War II rocket was the antitank bazooka. But the real potential of this type of weapon was first dramatized by the German V-2. The V-1, of course, was not a rocket, it was a pilotless airplane, a drone, a *cruising* missile like our 600 m.p.h. Snark of today. The V-2 was the first long-range trajectory missile or rocket. It was forty-seven feet long and weighed thirteen tons fully loaded. The fuel was alcohol, and liquid oxygen provided faster burning than the Chinese rocket's saltpeter.

When components of the German V-2 began arriving at the White Sands Proving Ground in New Mexico, shortly after the war, a group from the California Institute of Technology was already there, preparing for test firings of the WAC Corporal. (This missile was first called the Private. Why it became a WAC when promoted has never been satisfactorily explained.) Professor Robert F. Goddard, America's one outstanding rocket pioneer, who died in August 1945, had previously launched some rockets in the area. All three of these projects were planned for research of the upper atmosphere, heretofore carried out with balloons.

The moon has never seemed too far away. And when the

Montgolfier brothers of France invented the hot-air balloon in 1783, many were confident that passenger service would soon be established. One year later, Dr. John Jeffries, a Bostonian living in London, took up a hydrogen balloon carrying barometer, thermometer, compass, hygrometer, electroscope, and half a dozen bottles of distilled water. (What, no opera hat and champagne bucket!) The bottles were emptied at different altitudes, then sealed, to obtain air samples.

In 1875, three Frenchmen set a world's record of 29,000 feet in a balloon called the *Zenith,* though two of them perished in the thin, cold air and the third never regained his health. After this the scientists started sending their instruments up in the gondola unattended, which presented the problem of recovering the recording devices. After the advent of radio, in the early 1900s, it was only natural that *telemetry* should be tried. (*Tele,* from the Greek, means "far off"; *meter* means "measure.")

Telemetry was invented by a Dutch instrument maker named Olland in 1877. He used a clock with sweep second hand. When the second hand was straight up it made contact, closing the battery circuit and transmitting a short pulse to the receiving station. This was the *reference pulse.* When the sweep second hand passed the minute hand it transmitted a longer pulse; when it passed the hour hand there was a longer pulse still. Both minute and hour hands were disconnected from the works for connection to a sensing device, such as a weathervane or rain gauge.

With the rain gauge the minute hand could be geared to the float. As rainfall caused the float to rise, it moved the minute hand away from the straight-up position. Thus the amount of rainfall was correlated with the time interval between reference pulse and the minute hand's longer pulse.

First to telemeter from a balloon was a Russian professor, Pyotr A. Moltchanoff, in 1925. He modulated the radio wave with the pulses from a modified version of Olland's clock.

Later Dr. Vaisala, a Finnish scientist, improved upon this by frequency modulating the carrier with voltages from the sensing devices. This was one of the earliest applications of FM, later adapted to FM broadcasting by Major Armstrong.

In radio, an audio frequency (30–15,000 cycles) either amplitude or frequency modulates the carrier wave. TV's much wider video frequency band, from a few cycles per second to three megacycles, amplitude modulates the carrier. With telemetry, however, the radio frequency carrier is usually modulated not by one but by a number of different frequencies.

In the chapter on color television we learned that this could be done by modulating a subcarrier, which in turn modulated the carrier. This is called *frequency multiplexing*. FM stations will soon be using it for broadcasting two or more signals on the same channel. Two signals are enough for stereophonic sound.

Frequency multiplexing has become standard in testing aircraft and missiles. The Government has standardized 18 subcarrier frequencies for modulating a carrier frequency in the 215–235 mc. band. This permits 18 different categories of information to be radioed to the ground simultaneously. And by using one of the subcarriers to carry bits of information in sequence, the total can be raised to 77.

The 18 subcarrier oscillators generate frequencies between 400 and 70,000 cycles. Each subcarrier is frequency modulated not more than $7\frac{1}{2}$ percent on each side of the center frequency. Such restrictions are necessary to prevent cross-modulation. All the modulated subcarriers are first combined, and the resultant complex frequency is then used to phase modulate a radio frequency in the 215 to 235 mc. range.

In the receiver, after the necessary amount of radio frequency amplification, the subcarriers are separated from the carrier by bandpass filters, such as are used in the crossover network of a multispeaker hi-fi system. Then comes a discriminator, as in any FM set, one for each of the separated subcarriers, to convert the frequency change to a voltage change. Each changing voltage, of course, was generated by one of the functions in aircraft or missile. As it must be seen to be studied, the type of electro-mechanical device pictured in Fig. 101 preserves it either on film or on paper tape. The received signal is also taped, just in case.

The function in which the engineers are interested is sensed by means of a *transducer*. Any device that converts one form of energy into another, such as loudspeaker or microphone, is a transducer. The phonograph pickup is a good example for us here because, like many of the transducers aloft, it converts mechanical movement—the vibration of the needle—into electrical energy.

Vibration of any part of the vehicle, gas pressure, acceleration, the movement of the rudder can all be converted to a voltage for modulating subcarrier frequencies. One method is to connect the mechanical movement in some way to a slug of magnetic material suspended in the core of a coil whose inductance governs the subcarrier oscillator frequency. Moving the slug further into the coil increases the inductance and lowers the frequency. Pulling it out has the opposite effect. Another method is to use the movement to vary a resistor, called a *potentiometer*. The potentiometer is in the circuit of a subcarrier oscillator whose frequency changes with a resistance change. Perhaps the most widely used method is one that varies the resistance of a potentiometer with battery. The resultant voltage change controls the oscillator frequency through a reactance tube. (Modulation of the FM radio transmitter is accomplished through a reactance tube.) Fig. 107 shows the block diagram of a function linked to one of the transmitter's voltage-modulated oscillators.

Russia's first Sputnik (October 4, 1957) was two feet in diameter and weighed 184 pounds. Sputniks II and III tipped

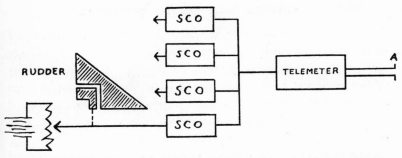

Fig. 107. Block diagram showing voltage control of one of the subcarrier oscillators.

the scales at 1,120 and 2,925 pounds, respectively. With no problems of space or weight, the telemetering gear could be built from standard parts, powered by storage batteries. (Frequencies 20 and 40 mc.) Explorer I, exploded into orbit on January 31, 1958, weighed only 31 pounds. The apparatus described above was too heavy for this little sphere. Fortunately little power is needed, which makes satellite miniaturization relatively simple.

On March 17, 1958, after a number of failures, a successful push-up put Navy's 3.25-pound Vanguard I into orbit. Nine days later the Army Ballistic Missile Agency hung another 31 pounder, Explorer III, in the heavens. (Explorer II was a failure.) And on July 26, the same agency successfully orbited 38-pound Explorer IV.

Our first four satellites were all equipped with two transmitters each, frequency 108 mc. In all but Explorer I, one of the transmitters was powered by solar batteries. The instruments aboard measured cosmic-ray intensity, density of micrometeorites, and temperatures inside and outside the vehicle.

Typical of our satellite telemetry apparatus is one designed for Vanguard I. It consists of seven plug-in *modules* that look like plastic pancakes. All are 5½ inches in diameter, varying in thickness from ¾ to 2½ inches. Stacked one on top of the other they make a package almost the same shape and size as a 2-pound coffee tin.

Each pancake module is a complete unit, such as a crystal-controlled, 100-milliwatt radio transmitter, the telemetering circuits, or a battery pack. The miniaturization is made possible through the use of printed circuits, transistors, tiny coils, etc. And if these modules seem small, the Army Signal Corps has in development, through RCA and others, what are called *micro-modules, one tenth* their size. A wafer only .3 inch square and .01 inch thick will hold diode, coil, transistor, several resistors and capacitors for some specific circuit function.

Modulation of the carrier wave is by *bursts* or *pulses*. Like Olland's original system, time between pulses means something. So does the width of the pulses and pulse frequency. The signal is taped and photographed from the screen of an oscilloscope for study.

Satellite temperature readings may be obtained through a *thermistor,* which is a resistor whose value varies with temperature. The resistance of metals increases as they get hotter. On the other hand, the resistance of a semiconductor, such as silver sulphide, decreases quite rapidly with a rise in temperature. A small bead of semiconducting material, together with a small battery, may therefore be used to translate temperature change into a voltage change.

One of the hazards for the space traveler could be the meteorites and micrometeorites (the former about the size of a pea, on the average, and the latter a sort of interplanetary dust), which move at velocities up to 25,000 m.p.h. They may be detected either by a tiny crystal microphone in the skin of the satellite or by some kind of erosion gauge such as a small glass plate covered with a thin conducting film whose resistance decreases as it is erased by the impact of the particles. Our satellites have registered very few collisions.

Two electronic devices for measuring radiation, including nature's most powerful radiation, the mysterious cosmic rays from outer space, are the scintillation counter and the Geiger counter. In the former the rays strike a crystal phosphor trans-

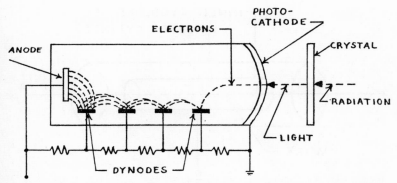

Fig. 108. Basic structure of photomultiplier tube, showing multiplication through secondary electron emission.

parent screen, producing a quick flash of light. A photocathode converts the light into an electron pulse, so weak that a *photomultiplier* must be used (Fig. 108).

The much better known Geiger counter, if not quite so sensitive, is less complex. The particle of radiation is converted to a pulse in a gas-filled glass tube between two high-potential electrodes (Fig. 109). A positive voltage is applied to the wire, a negative voltage to the surrounding cylinder. The fast-moving particle ionizes a molecule of gas, and the electrons freed by the collision are attracted to the positive wire. They usually bang into other gas molecules, freeing more electrons that add to the intensity of the pulse. After amplification the pulse modulates the radio's carrier. In the conventional Geiger counter, output goes to a meter, earphone, or speaker.

Explorers I and III and Sputnik II have revealed a band of dangerously intense cosmic radiation. Explorer IV accurately counted the particles by means of four miniature ionization chambers, two of them wrapped in a lead shield to help determine their penetrating power. Telemeter reports reveal that the radiation doubles every 60 miles above 250 miles. How far up the high intensity persists was not known until the launching of the Pioneer.

On October 11, 1958, just one year and a week after Sputnik I, the world outside the Iron Curtain was electrified by

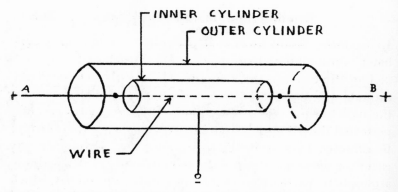

FIG. 109. Basic structure of ionization chamber used in Geiger counter.

the successful launching of this 85-pound space probe from Cape Canaveral. Although it was plainly marked "To the Moon's Gravitational Field," the odds were ten to one against its flying straight enough to come within the required 50,000 miles from the moon at the proper time for possible orbiting. However, as it turned out, the aiming didn't matter, because the thrust was only enough to take it 77,000 miles into space. A final, radio-controlled retro-rocket, for putting the vehicle into orbit, didn't function, probably because of battery failure in the extreme cold, and it plunged earthward, its melted-down remains coming to rest in the South Pacific sector of Davy Jones's locker.

The Pioneer's 30 pounds of sensing devices and telemetry gear were housed in a disc-shaped fiberglas shell, 29 inches in diameter, with a single dipole antenna mounted on top. A *magnetometer,* for measuring the moon's magnetic field if any exists, as well as the earth's, revealed that the latter's field resembles that of a bar magnet, which was no surprise. (The magnetometer is essentially a coil that generates a voltage as it moves through the field.)

However, not until the Pioneer III launching, Dec. 6, 1958, did we learn there are two belts of high-intensity radiation, consisting of protons and electrons trapped in the earth's magnetic field; one peaks at 2,000 miles out, the other at

10,000 miles, fading away at 40,000 miles. There is an "escape hatch" through both belts over each of the poles.

The Pioneer carried a simple TV camera, whose photo-cathode was sensitive only to the infrared rays, for televising the dark (to us) side of the moon. CBS-Hytron has recently perfected the *TV-Eye,* a high-quality camera small enough to be powered by a satellite's solar cells. The astronomers are eager for telescopic shots of the stars from above our masking atmosphere, particularly of the sun's higher ultraviolet, which drastically affects the ionosphere. Pictures of the earth's cloud cover should prove invaluable to the meteorologist for his forecasts. A satellite now being built is equipped with lead-sulphide cells for telemetering the amount of light reflected from the cloud cover.

A Russian scientist has even revealed plans for a satellite moving with the speed of the earth, 22,000 miles up, containing receiver and 2-kw. TV transmitter for relaying Soviet programs to most of the world's peoples between the two 82nd parallels. Suggested name: the Goblin.

Recent newspaper and magazine stories have wrapped a passel of mystery around a "little black box" which, installed in plane, missile, ship, or sub, pilots it to its precise destination untouched by human hands. Apparently the stars, for navigation purposes, will soon be strictly for the birds. (Recent experiments in two European planetariums reveal that the birds still use this ancient method of navigation during their migrations. Only bats have radar.) But if the reader has even a smattering of elementary physics, the mystery can be readily dissolved in a few basic principles. The problems solved by the engineers in achieving the fantastic accuracy required by these boxes were concerned mostly with getting rid of the bugs that developed, an extermination job that has taken around a decade.

The two, totally different, systems of self-navigation are *inertial guidance* and *Doppler.*

Inertial guidance means just what it says: a method of navigation that uses inertia for guidance. It's the same inertia that pushes you back against the seat when you suddenly accelerate your car. Inertial guidance determines the acceleration from the amount of this inertial effect.

Both systems can be compared with conventional dead reckoning. If an airplane navigator knows his precise course, and the exact distance traveled, a ruler laid on a Mercator chart will tell him where he is. The problem of determining precise course and distance traveled with only compass and air-speed indicator is largely aggravated by errors caused by winds. Both systems detour this problem by measuring *ground speed* instead of air speed.

The device that senses the acceleration in the inertial-guidance system is the *accelerometer*. Basically, it is a pendulum. Hang a pendulum in a plane, and so long as the craft is absolutely stable, flying at constant speed, the pendulum will point straight down toward the center of the earth. But any kind of acceleration, because of the pendulum's inertia, will move it off the center position.

An ordinary pendulum, under normal conditions, would swing around like the lantern in the cabin of the *Santa Maria*. But suppose we provide a table that is level at all times—a stable table—upon which to mount the pendulum. Then the table would absorb all the angular movements resulting from rolling and pitching. Such a table can be had by mounting it in gimbals, like a ship's compass, and attaching to it three gyroscopes. Nearly everyone is familiar with the operation of the gyro. Its spinning wheel, which holds the direction of its axis of rotation, makes possible not only the automatic pilot but such standard nonelectronic flying instruments as the turn-and-bank indicator, heading indicator, and drift meter.

Any sensed movement of the table generates a voltage which, after amplification, feeds one of three *servomotors* that help the gyros keep it stable. (The servomotor is part of an electromechanical system in which a small amount of electricity controls one large enough to do the work. A voltage taken from the operation is constantly compared with the controlling voltage, and any difference, called the *error,* is amplified and fed back to correct it.)

We mount the accelerometer pendulum on the stable table. Then we set our course, lining up the table with our destination. (A second accelerometer is positioned at right angles to the first. In some systems three are used.) The accelerometer then senses only *changes* in vehicular motion, and not gravity or other disturbing accelerations. This is possible because it's an 84-minute pendulum and is, in effect, as long as the radius of the earth. The old-fashioned clock's three-foot pendulum swings back and forth once each second. The 84-minute pendulum is obtained electronically through damping obtained from feedback. It translates acceleration into a voltage by moving a coil through a magnetic field, just as the dynamic mike or phono pickup does. During take-off, for example, a voltage is built up proportional to the amount of acceleration. This voltage, plus any later acceleration voltages, and minus any deceleration voltages, is "stored" and used to calculate the distance traveled as time passes. This is called *integration.*

A simple method of integration is to charge a capacitor through a resistor, the capacitor's voltage controlling the plate current of a tube. But this method is not accurate enough here. One practical way to do it involves a motor generator. A small motor runs continuously. Its speed, however, is controlled by the amplified output of the accelerometer, which is fed to a field winding. The motor turns a generator, which feeds a voltage back to the same field winding. The feedback voltage keeps the motor turning at whatever speed is determined by accelerometer output. Thus the vehicle's speed is correlated with the number of revolutions per second of a motor's shaft. A computer that keeps track of the revolutions can give both ground speed and distance traveled, like your car's speedometer. Integrated signals from a second accelerometer for guidance, and a third for elevation, also go to the computer, whose output is compared with the course the missile must follow to land on target. The corrections then go to devices operating the controls. Guidance only functions for the first five minutes or so after firing.

Inertial guidance, first installed in the Navajo missile about eight years ago, is now used with the long-range missiles Titan (ICBM), Thor (IRBM), Jupiter (IRBM), and Polaris (IRBM). The Vanguard satellite project has an inertial guidance system, and it is used with the 200-mile Sergeant and Redstone missiles.

The only missile to employ Doppler for guidance is the ICBM Atlas, in conjunction with radio command. At the present time, only Doppler is practicable for commercial and private aircraft, though it is not practicable for ships. Doppler systems are now selling for around $20,000, against the IG system's probable $200,000.

Doppler is a radar system of navigation that capitalizes upon a discovery made in 1842 by the Austrian scientist Christian Doppler in connection with light waves from the stars. He found that the apparent frequency of a wave train was changed, or shifted, as the result of the relative motion between source and observer. The example most often given with sound waves is that of the whistle from a passing locomotive. As the train approaches an observer, the whistle's pitch (its frequency) seems to rise, and as it moves away its pitch seems to fall. It is as though the fundamental frequency, shown on paper, was collapsed or pulled apart like an accordion.

Two beams are usually used, each aimed a little to one side and either ahead of the aircraft or behind it (Fig. 110). As the difference frequency caused by the Doppler shift is in the audio range, one signal might go to each of a pair of headphones worn by the pilot, like the old radio ranges, and any

FIG. 110. Twin Doppler beams aimed aft.

difference in frequency would tell him he was off course. Fortunately, electronic circuits can be used with display devices to much greater advantage.

Five different companies now have 13 Doppler autonavigation models in various stages of production, weighing from 85 to 200 pounds each. Weight is determined mostly by the variety of information displayed. Added computers can obtain enough information from the Doppler shift to show not only ground speed and drift angle but also position in latitude and longitude, ground track and deviation from desired course, distance traveled along the ground, and distance from destination. Only a little more sophistication need be added for a red light to flash when the stewardess approaches the cockpit, or the pilot's basal metabolism drops below the danger point.

Stripped-down models are available that meter only ground speed and drift angle. Two continuous waves are radiated from one half of a double antenna with a modified parabolic reflector, back of a flush-mounted *radome*. (A radome is the protective housing of a dielectric that is transparent to the electromagnetic wave.) The reflector is divided in the center to separate the transmitting from the receiving dipole. Both military and commercial Dopplers are now using the

8,800-mc. band, though the latter may soon be shifted to 13,000 mc.

Each of the two receivers uses superhet techniques to produce the audio frequency, equal to the difference between the transmitted and received frequencies. The difference usually varies from one to 18 kilocycles per second, depending upon the velocity of the vehicle, the transmitted frequency, and the angle with the ground.

Because the transmitted beam is not pencil sharp, spreading out on the surface, the returned frequency covers a narrow band. A center frequency is obtained by bandpass filters. Small changes between the two difference frequencies caused by roll and pitch, being of relatively high frequency, can also be easily filtered out.

Drift increases the frequency on one side of the vehicle, decreases it on the other. So the amount of drift is proportional to the difference between the two frequencies. To obtain ground speed, along the direction of aircraft heading, the two frequencies are added (vectorially). These two output signals go to indicators in the cockpit, and they can also actuate an automatic navigation computer.

Radar is used for homing by both the air-to-air Falcon and the Sparrow 3. The launching aircraft fixes a beam on the target and a receiver in the missile picks up the echo for guidance. With what is called beam guidance, the missile rides a beam from the launching plane or from the ground, somewhat as an aircraft with auto pilot rides an ILS beam. Beam guidance is used by air-to-air Sparrow 1, and by surface-to-air Terriers 1 and 2. Infrared guidance is used by the Sidewinder, an offspring called the Diamondback, and by a third air-to-air missile, the GAR-2A model of the Falcon.

The 155-pound infrared Sidewinder, first of the ultramodern missiles to be tested in combat, has a range of upwards of two miles. Two infrared sensing devices, one on each side of the missile, contain lead-sulphide cells held at an extremely low temperature. These heat-sensitive cells convert the infra-red radiation from the target plane's engine into low-level electrical signals which, after amplification, go to an automatic pilot that controls the rear fins. The circuits are confidential, though there are a number of ways to correlate a change in voltage caused by straying off course with the direction of straying, so the pilot "knows" which fins will get it back on target.

Our surface-to-air ground-defense missiles, such as the Bomarc and Nike Hercules, now guarding many of our cities, as well as military bases both at home and abroad, rely chiefly upon ground-control command (GCC) for guidance. An acquisition radar first picks up the target, then turns it over to a tracking radar whose signals are automatically fed to a computer. From the computer comes the necessary information for aiming and firing the missile so it will explode in the vicinity of the target. The Bomarc also carries a last-second radar homing device and proximity fuse.

In development is an antimissile missile, the Nike Zeus, which won't be operational until sometime in the early 1960s. The big problem is guidance. There's no rest for the scientists and engineers.

Chapter index. See also general index.

SUGGESTED READING

There are dozens of good books on all phases of electronics, for those who would pursue its study. Following are some of my own choices.

MATHEMATICS
>   *Basic Math for Radio and Electronics,* F. M. Colebrook and J. W. Head. Philosophical Library.

ALTERNATING CURRENT
>   *Alternating Current Fundamentals,* Joseph J. DeFrance, B.S., E.E. Prentice-Hall.

THE CATHODE RAY TUBE
>   *The Cathode Ray Tube at Work,* John F. Rider. John F. Rider Publishing Co. Written for the radio and TV service man.

RADIO SERVICING
>   *Elements of Radio,* Abraham Marcus and William Marcus. Prentice-Hall. A good introduction to practical radio.
>
>   *Radio Servicing: Theory and Practice,* Abraham Marcus. Prentice-Hall. A more advanced text on servicing.

TELEVISION SERVICING
>   *Television Simplified,* Milton S. Kiver. Van Nostrand. Good, clear explanation of all the circuits of the TV receiver. Be sure and get the latest edition.
>
>   *TV, It's a Cinch,* E. Aisberg. Gernsback Library, Inc. For the radio technician.

FM

F-M Simplified, Milton S. Kiver. Van Nostrand. Simple explanation of FM transmission and reception.

INDUSTRIAL ELECTRONICS

Industrial Electronics, Andrew W. Kramer. Pitman Publishing Co. Little math, not too technical.

Electronics in Industry, George M. Chute. McGraw-Hill. A practical book.

ELECTRONIC NAVIGATION

Radar and Electronic Navigation, G. J. Sonnenberg. Van Nostrand. Theory and practice.

RADIO ENGINEERING

Electronic and Radio Engineering, Frederick Emmons Terman, Sc.D. (Stanford). 4th edition, 1957. McGraw-Hill. Long a standard text.

TELEVISION ENGINEERING

Practical Television Engineering, Scott Helt. Rinehart. A very good introduction to the subject.

HIGH FIDELITY

High Fidelity: A Practical Guide, Charles Fowler. McGraw-Hill. Best book on the subject for the layman. Readable and complete.

TRANSISTORS

Transistor Circuits, Rufus P. Turner. Gernsback Library, Inc.

ELECTRONIC COMPUTERS

Electronic Computers, T. E. Ivall. Philosophical Library.

INDEX *(See also special index following Chapter 30.)*

374 | Index

Audio frequency. *See* Frequency

Audion, 164–179, 190, 214; invention, 167; operation, 168–173, Fig. 50; as oscillator, 173; patent on, 167; in regenerative circuit, 173; sold to telephone co., 165, 176; ultra-audion, 173, 174

Australia, TV system, 253

Automatic brightness control, television, 249

Automatic frequency control (AFC), television, 248

Automatic gain control (AGC), 249, 252

Automatic volume control (AVC), radio, 219

Automation, 312

Avogadro's Law, 9

Ayer, N. W., Advertising Agency, 175

B

Babcock, C. D., names audion, 167

Bacon, Roger, compass theory, 76

Baffle, 209, 210

Baird, J. L., TV inventor, 222, 276

Bakewell, F. C., telephoto system, 332

Ballantine, Stuart, invents negative feed-back, 202

Bardeen, J., Nobel prize winner, 350

Base, transistor, 350

Battery (electrochemical), and condenser, 38; crown of cups, 54; dry cell, 55; experimental cell, 54 (Fig. 13), 56; invention of, 50–57, Fig. 12; pila or pile, 50, 53; storage, 57

Beat note, 197

Becquerel, Antoine Henri, discovers radioactivity, 22

Belgium, TV system, 253

Bell, Alexander Graham, harmonic telegraph, 112; telephone, 112–115; telephone patent, Fig. 32

Bell Aircraft, 302

Bell Laboratories, develops TRADIC, 347; transistor, 348

Bellum, Inger, 81

Bendix, light amplifier, 268

Berger, Hans, 329

Bernard, Sarah, 88

Beta rhythm, brain wave, 329

Betatron, 314, 325

Bias, grid, 171, 186; AVC, 219; C battery, 171, Fig. 50A; circuit, 189, Fig. 103; picture tube, TV, 237; tape recorder, 343

Big Jim, Navy transmitter, 192

Binary numbers, 346

Bing Crosby Enterprises, 345

Binns, Jack, first SOS, 148

Bismark, Otto, chef, S.S. *America*, 310

Bohr, Niels, nuclear physicist, 20, 24

Bologna (Italy), 142, 143, 204

Booster, TV. *See* Antenna

Boulder Dam, 96

Bourseul, Charles, telephone idea, 111

Boyle, Robert, 36; defines elements, 6

Boy Scouts, 70

Boy's Book of Invention, The, 194

Brain tumor, lesions, abscesses, concussions, 329

Brain wave, 329, 330

Branly, Edouard, coherer, 144–146

Brant Rock (Mass.), 152

Brattain, W. H., Nobel prize winner, 350

Braun, Ferdinand, CR tube, 223

Brazil, 337

Breit, Gregory, radar inventor, 292

Brigham Young University, 229

Brightness control, TV, 237

Brightness signal (Color TV), 279

Broadcasting, 149, 156, 157; first, 175

Browne, Sir Thomas, 75

Brush, Charles Francis, invents storage battery, 57

Brushes, generator, 93, 94, 95

Bureau of Standards, U.S., 288

Bursitis, 327

Button, microphone, 116

Buzz bombs, 292

C

C battery, 168, 169, 170, 171

CAA. *See* Civil Aeronautics Administration

Caesium-silver compound, 225, 226

Cal Tech, 158

Calculator, electronic, 346, 347

Cambridge University, 12, 21, 26, 134

Camera tube, TV, CBS-Hytron (color), 273; iconoscope, 223–228, 230, 231, Fig. 65; image dissector, 230, 231; image orthicon, 231–233, Fig. 67; miniature, 234; orthicon, 231; RCA color, 273, 274

Campbell-Swinton, A.A., scientist, 233

Cancer, 331

Capacitor. *See* Condenser

Capehart Farnsworth Corp., 230

Carbon tetrachloride, 268

Carlsbad Caverns, 65